D1243850

On the History of Lunacy:
the 19th century and after

Edward H. Hare, MA, MD, FRCP

On the History of Lunacy:

the 19th century and after

Edward H. Hare

GABBAY
1998

Copyright in this format © 1998 Estate of E.H. Hare
Foreword © Dr John Crammer

First published in Great Britain 1998 by
Gabbay, 47 Alleyn Road, Dulwich, London SE21 8AD, UK

Designed and typeset by Judith Bastin on an Apple Macintosh in Quark Xpress
Printed and bound by Antony Rowe Ltd,
Bumper's Farm, Chippenham, Wiltshire

ISBN 0 9532699 0 6

Contents

Biographical Note

EDWARD H. HARE, MA, MD, FRCP (1917–1996) was physician in psychological medicine at the Bethlem Royal and Maudsley Hospitals, and the associated Institute of Psychiatry of the University of London, from 1957 until his death in 1996. He practised as a full-time member of the National Health Service, but in addition carried out much original research with many publications in epidemiology, pharmacology, and the history of medicine. He was Editor of the *British Journal of Psychiatry* (1973–1977) and Honarary Fellow of the Royal College of Psychiatrists from 1978.

A scholar of Gonville and Caius College, Cambridge, his clinical training was at University College Hospital, London. He began study of the social epidemiology of mental illness while a junior doctor in Bristol, and this work culminated in 1965 in a monograph (with C. K. Shaw) on 'Mental Health on a new Housing Estate'. For a time he then examined the effectiveness of new drugs in the treatment of anxiety, insomnia, depression and schizophrenia. He returned to epidemiology with statistical analysis of the incidence of different mental disorders in relation to sufferers' ages at onset, years and seasons of birth, position in family, immigrant status and so on.

Meanwhile he began a series of historical researches, chiefly on changes in mental illnesses across the 19th century, and the social and conceptual responses thereto. The most important of these papers are brought together and reprinted in this book. Their findings are relevant to Government organization of medical and paramedical services, to the Public Health, and to the practice of medicine by opinion rather than science. They are an enduring contribution to epidemiology and to history, and a stimulus to new thought.

Acknowledgements

We are grateful to the following copyright holders for permission to reprint:

Oxford University Press for 'Old Familiar Faces' (here 'Some physical problems in asylums') which appeared in two parts in *Psychiatric Developments* 1985; **4**: 245–255 and 383–392 published by them.

Elsevier Science Inc. for 'The changing content of psychiatric illness' in *Journal of Psychosomatic Research* 1974; **18**: 283–289.

British Journal of Psychiatry for 'The origin and spread of dementia paralytica' in *Journal of Mental Science* 1959; **105**: 594–626; 'Masturbatory insanity: The history of an idea' in *Journal of Mental Science* 1962; **108**: 1–25. 'The two manias, a study of the evolution of the modern concept of mania' in *British Journal of Psychiatry* 1981; **138**: 89–99. 'Was insanity on the increase?' in *British Journal of Psychiatry* 1983; **142**: 439–455. 'Schizophrenia as a recent disease' in *British Journal of Psychiatry* 1988; **153**: 521–531. 'The history of nervous disorders, 1600–1840 and a comparison with modern views' in *British Journal of Psychiatry* 1991; **159**: 37–45.

Publications of E.H. Hare

The papers have been grouped under nine broad subject headings: Historical, Clinical and Metabolic, Neurological, Pharmacotherapy and Physical, Social psychiatry, Epidemiological/demographic, Chapters in Books, articles for non-specialists, Editorial work. The list is complete, however Book Reviews, Letters to the Editor, and papers given to conferences, but not in print, have been omitted.

HISTORICAL

The Origin and Spread of Dementia Paralytica. *J Ment Sci* 1959; **105**: 594.

Masturbatory Insanity: The History of an Idea. *J Ment Sci* 1962; **108**: 1.

Michael Faraday's Loss of Memory. *Proc R Soc Med* 1974; **67**: 617–618.

The changing content of psychiatric illness. *J Psychosom Res* 1974; **18**: 283–289.

Michael Faraday's Loss of Memory. *Proc R Inst Gt Brit* 1976; **49**: 33–52.

Medical astrology and its relation to modern psychiatry. *Proc R Soc Med* 1977; **70**: 105–110.

A comparison of reports in State Trials and the Annual Register. In: West DJ and Walk A (eds). *Daniel McNaughton: His Trial and the Aftermath*. Gaskell Books: Ashford, 1977, pp 82–86.

Psychiatry in the 1870's – Kilvert's Mad Folk (Walk A and Hare EH). *Bull R Coll Psychiat* 1979; October: 150–153.

The two manias: A study of the evolution of the modern concept of mania. *Br J Psychiatry* 1981; **138**: 89–99.

Was insanity on the increase? (The Maudsley Lecture). *BMJ* 1983; **142**: 439–455.

Commentary on a chapter by DH Tuke. In: Thompson C (ed.). *The Origins of Modern Psychiatry*. Cassell: London, 1987, pp 50–60.

Commentary on Ellard's paper 'Did schizophrenia exist before the 18th century'. *Austr NZ J Psychiat* 1987.

Schizophrenia before 1800? The case of the Revd George Trosse. *Psychol Med* 1988; **18**: 279–285.

The History of 'Nervous Disorders' from 1600 to 1840 and a Comparison with Modern Views. *Br J Psychiatry* 1991; **159**: 37–45.

CLINICAL AND METABOLIC

Acute Porphyria presenting with Mental Symptoms. *J Ment Sci* 1953; **99**: 144.

Variations in the Iodine Avidity of the Normal Human Thyroid as measured by the 24-hour 131-I uptake (Hare EH and Haigh CP). *Clin Sci* 1955; **14**: 441.

A short note on pseudo-hallucinations. *Br J Psychiatry* 1973; **122**: 469–476.

Hypomania. *Bethlem and Maudsley Gazette* Summer 1976; pp 3–5.

Old familiar faces: Some aspects of the asylum era in Great Britain, Part I. *Psychiat Dev* 1985; **3**: 245–255.

Old familiar faces: Some aspects of the asylum era in Great Britain, Part II. *Psychiat Dev* 1985; **4**: 383–392.

NEUROLOGICAL

Personal Observations on the Spectral March of Migraine. *J Neurol Sci* 1966; **3**: 259–264.

Spina Bifida and Family Stress (Hare EH, Laurence KM, Payne H and Rawnsley K). *BMJ* 1966; **ii**: 757–760.

Spina Bifida and the Family. *Maternal and Child Care* 1966; **2**: 287–289.

The Parents of the Child with Spina Bifida Cystica (Hare EH and Laurence KM). *Pediatr Digest* 1969; February: 26–35.

The duration of the fortification spectrum in migraine. In: Cumings JN (ed.). *Background to Migraine*. 5th Migraine Symposium, September 1972. Heinemann: London, 1973, pp 93–98.

PHARMACOTHERAPY AND PHYSICAL

The Results in 178 cases of Prefrontal Leucotomy at the Bristol Mental Hospitals. *Bristol Med-Chir J* 1953; **69**: 134.

The Effect of Mephenesin in Neurotic Anxiety: a controlled trial. *J Ment Sci* 1955; **101**: 172.

The Comparative Efficacy of Hypnotics. *Br J Prev Soc Med* 1955; **9**: 140.

Reserpine in Anxiety States (Hare EH, Seager CP and Leitch A). *Lancet* 1956; **i**: 545.

'Ritalin' and Chlorpromazine in Chronic Schizophrenia: a controlled clinical trial (Salisbury BJ and Hare EH). *J Ment Sci* 1957; **103**: 830.

Psychotic Reactions due to Antituberculous Drugs. *Tubercle* 1958; **39**: 90.

Unusual Reaction to Clorpromazine. *BMJ* 1958; **i**: 1462.

Thalidomide: Clinical Trial of a New Hypnotic Drug (Hare EH, Salter CE and Lodge Patch IC). *J Clin Exp Psychopath* 1959; **20**: 243.

Comparative Hypnotic Efficacy of 'Phenaglate' (Eilenberg MD, Lodge Patch IC and Hare EH). *J Ment Sci* 1960; **106**: 675.

Ethinamate and Methyprylone as Hypnotics: A Comparative Trial (Lodge Patch IC, Eilenberg MD and Hare EH). *J Ment Sci* 1960; **106**: 1455.

Phenelzine and Dexamphetamine in Depressive Illness (Hare EH, Dominian J and Sharpe L). *BMJ* 1962; **i**: 9.

Imipramine and 'Drinamyl' in Depressive Illness: A Comparative Trial (Hare EH, McCance C and McCormick WO). *BMJ* 1964; **i**: 818–820.

Do Psychiatric Out-patients Take Their Drugs? (Willcox DRC, Gillan RU and Hare EH). *BMJ* 1965; **ii**: 790–792.

Are drugs of use in depression? (Anglo-German Psychiatric Conference, Edinburgh, May 1964). *Anglo-German Med Rev* 1965; **2**: 727–732.

Drugs in Anxiety and Depression. *Clin Med* 1966; **73**: 57–58.

Do Psychiatric In-patients Take Their Pills? (Hare EH and Willcox DRC). *Br J Psychiatry* 1967; **113**: 1435–1440.

Prophylactic lithium in affective disorders (Coppen A, Noguera R, Bailey J, Burns BH, Swani MS, Hare EH, Gardner R and Maggs R). *Lancet* 1971; **ii**: 275–279.

SOCIAL PSYCHIATRY

The Ecology of Mental Disease. *J Ment Sci* 1952; **98**: 579.

The Attitude of the Psychiatric Patient to his Hospital Experiences. *Medical Press* 1953; **229**: 323.

Mental Illness and Social Class in Bristol. *Br J Prev Soc Med* 1955; **9**: 191–195.

Mental Illness and Social Conditions in Bristol. *J Ment Sci* 1956; **102**: 349.

Family Setting and the Urban Distribution of Schizophrenia. *J Ment Sci* 1956; **102**: 753.

Psychiatric Problems in New Communities. *Ment Health* 1964; **23**: 58–60.

Mental Health on a New Housing Estate (Hare EH and Shaw GK). Oxford University Press, Maudsley monographs No 12: London, 1965.

The Maudsley Personality Inventory (Short Form). Distribution of Scores and Test-Retest Reliability in an Urban Population (Shaw GK and Hare EH). *Br J Psychiatry* 1965; **111**: 226–235.

Effect of severe stress on the Maudsley Personality Inventory score in normal subjects (Hare EH, Payne H, Laurence KM and Rawnsley K). *Br J Soc Clin Psychol* 1972; **11**: 353–358.

A Study in Family Health: (1) Health in relation to Family Size (Hare EH and Shaw GK). *Br J Psychiatry* 1965; **111**: 461–466.

A Study in Family Health: (2) A Comparison of the Health of Fathers, Mothers and Children (Hare EH and Shaw GK). *Br J Psychiatry* 1965; **111**: 467–472.

EPIDEMIOLOGICAL/DEMOGRAPHIC

The Epidemiology of Mental Illness. *J R Soc Health* 1959; **79**: 361.

Each of the following. Hare EH (ed.). The Bethlem Royal Hospital and the Maudsley Hospital, London.
    Third Triennial Statistical Report (1955–1957), 1959.
    Fourth Triennial Statistical Report (1958–1960), 1962.
    Fifth Triennial Statistical Report (1961–1963), 1965.
    Sixth Triennial Statistical Report (1964–1966), 1968.
    Seventh Triennial Statistical Report (1967–1969), 1971.

Mental Disorder and Season of Birth: comparison of psychoses with neurosis (Hare EH and Price JS). *Br J Psychiatry* 1969; **115**: 533–540.

Birth Order Studies: some sources of bias (Price JS and Hare EH). *Br J Psychiatry* 1969; **115**: 633–646.

Birth Order   and Family Size: bias caused by changes in birth rate (Hare EH and Price JS). *Br J Psychiatry* 1969; **115**: 647–658.

Birth rank in schizophrenia: with a consideration of the bias due to changes in birth-rate (Hare EH and Price JS). *Br J Psychiatry* 1970; **116**: 409–420.

Birth rank and schizophrenia (Hare EH, Price JS and Slater ETO). *Nature* 1970; **228**: 1223–1224.

Birth order and month of birth in schizophrenia (in Russian). *Medicine* 1971; **5**: 39–42.

The age-distribution of schizophrenia and neurosis: findings in a national sample (Hare EH, Price JS and Slater ETO). *Br J Psychiatry* 1971; **119**: 445–448.

Marriage and fertility of psychiatric patients compared with national data (Slater ETO, Hare EH and Price JS). *Soc Biol* 1971; **18** (Suppl.): S60–S73.

Marital status of first admissions to psychiatric beds in England and Wales in 1965 and 1966 (Price JS, Slater ETO and Hare EH). *Soc Biol* 1971; **18** (Suppl.): S74–S94.

Schizophrenia and season of birth (Hare EH, Price JS and Slater ETO). *Br J Psychiatry* 1972; **120**: 124–125.

Fertility in obsessional neurosis (Hare EH, Price JS and Slater ETO). *Br J Psychiatry* 1972; **121**: 197–206.

Parental social class in psychiatric patients (Hare EH, Price JS and Slater ETO). *Br J Psychiatry* 1972; **121**: 515–524.

Mental disorder and season of birth (Hare EH, Price JS and Slater ETO). *Nature* 1973; **241**: 480.

Neurotic and psychotic forms of depressive illness: evidence from age-incidence in a national sample (Spicer CG, Hare EH and Slater ETO). *Br J Psychiatry* 1973; **123**: 535–541.

Mental disorder and season of birth: a national sample compared with the general population (Hare EH, Price JS and Slater ETO). *Br J Psychiatry* 1974; **124**: 81–86.

Birth order and birth rate bias: findings in a representative sample of the adult population of Great Britain (Hare EH and Price JS). *J Biosoc Sci* 1974; **6**: 139–150.

A note on the distribution of family sizes in the adult population of Great Britain 1972. *J Biosoc Sci* 1974; **6**: 343–346.

Manic-depressive psychosis and season of birth. *Acta Psychiat Scand* 1975; **52**: 69–79.

Season of birth in schizophrenia and neurosis. *Am J Psychiat* 1975; **132**: 1168–1171.

The season of birth of siblings of psychiatric patients. *Br J Psychiatry* 1976; **129**: 49–54.

Variations in the seasonal distribution of births of psychotic patients in England and Wales. *Br J Psychiatry* 1978; **132**: 155–158.

Seasonal variation in admissions of psychiatric patients and its relation to seasonal variation in their births (Hare EH and Walter SD). *J Epidemiol Comm Health* 1978; **32**: 47–52.

Age at paternity in England and Wales 1901–1960 (Hare EH and Moran PAP). *J Biosoc Sci* 1978; **10**: 423–427.

Incidence de la saison au moment de la naissance dans la schizophrénie. *Médecine et Hygiène* 1978; **36**: 2394–2398.

Parental age and birth order in homosexual patients: A replication of Slater's study (Hare EH and Moran PAP). *Br J Psychiatry* 1979; **134**: 178–182.

Raised parental age in psychiatric patients: Evidence for the constitutional hypothesis (Hare EH and Moran PAP). *Br J Psychiatry* 1979; **134**: 169–177.

Schizophrenia and season of birth (Hare EH, Bulusu L and Adelstein A). *Population Trends* 1979; **19**: 9–11.

Schizophrenia as an infectious disease. *Br J Psychiatry* 1979; **135**: 468–473.

Sex ratio of siblings of psychiatric patients (Hare EH and Lyster WB). *Biol Psychiat* 1980; **15**: 495–498.

Seasonal variations in psychiatric illness. *Trends Neurosci* 1980; **3**: 295–296.

The changing seasonality of infant deaths in England and Wales 1912–1978 and its relation to seasonal temperature (Hare EH, Moran PAP and MacFarlane A). *J Epidemiol Comm Health* 1981; **35**: 77–82.

A relation between seasonal temperature and the birth rate of schizophrenic patients (Hare EH and Moran PAP). *Acta Psychiat Scand* 1981; **63**: 396–405.

Age prevalence and the season of birth effect in Schizophrenia: a response to Lewis and Griffin (Schur E and Hare EH). *Psychol Bull* 1983; **93**: 373–377.

Aspects of the epidemiology of schizophrenia. *Br J Psychiatry* 1986; **149**: 554–561.

Schizophrenia as a recent disease. *Br J Psychiatry* 1988; **153**: 521–531.

Epidemiological Evidence that Maternal Influenza Contributes to the Aetiology of Schizophrenia: An analysis of Scottish, English and Danish Data (Adams W, Kendell RE, Hare EH and Munk Jørgensen P). *Br J Psychiatry* 1993; **163**: 522–534.

The relationship of schizophrenic birth to 16 infectious diseases (O'Callaghan E, Shah PC, Takei N, Murray G, Glover G, Hare EH and Murray RM). *Br J Psychiatry* 1994; **165**: 353–356.

CHAPTERS IN BOOKS

The Distribution of Mental Illness in the Community. In: Richter D, Tanner JM, Taylor Lord and Zangwill OL (eds). *Aspects of Psychiatric Research*. Oxford University Press, London, 1962, pp 36–65.
The Natural History of the Course of Depressive Illness. In: Meyrick RL (ed.). *A Conference on Depression*. South London Faculty of the College of General Practitioners: London, 1962.
The Epidemiology of Schizophrenia. In: Coppen A and Walk A (eds). *Recent Developments in Schizophrenia: A Symposium*. Headley Bros (*Br J Psychiatry* Special Publication No 1): Ashford, 1967, pp 9–24.
The Relation between Social Psychiatry and Psychotherapy. In: Foulkes SH and Stewart Prince G (eds). *Psychiatry in a Changing Society*. Tavistock Publications: London, 1969, pp 3–16.
Social anxiety and the role of medicine. In: Roth M and Cowie V (eds). *Psychiatry, Genetics and Pathology: A Tribute to Eliot Slater*. Gaskell Press: London, 1979, pp 125–136.
Epidemiology of Schizophrenia. In: Wing JK (ed.). *Handbook of Psychiatry, Vol 3: Psychoses of Uncertain aetiology*. Cambridge University Press: Cambridge, 1982, pp 44–48.
Epidemiological evidence for a viral factor in the aetiology of the functional psychoses. In: Morozov PV (ed.). *Advances in Biological Psychiatry, Vol 12: Research on the Viral Hypothesis of Mental Disorder*. Karger: Basel, 1983, pp 52–75.
The Changing Nature of Mental Illness and its Significance. In: Calhoun JB (ed.). *Environment and Population: Problems of Adaptation*. Praeger: New York, 1983, pp 279–283.
The etiology of the functional psychoses: evidence from seasonality and other epidemiological studies. In: Miura T (ed.). *Seasonal Effects on Reproduction, Infection and Psychoses, Vol 5 Progress in Biometeorology*. SPB Academic Publishing: The Hague, 1987, pp 185–194.
The epidemiology of schizophrenia and effective psychosis. *Br Med Bull* 1987; **43**: 514–530.
Temporal factors and trends, including birth seasonality and the viral hypothesis. In: Tsuang MT and Simpson JC (eds). *Handbook of Schizophrenia, Vol 3: Nosology, Epidemiology and Genetics*. Elsevier: Amsterdam, 1988, pp 345–377.

ARTICLES FOR NON-SPECIALISTS

Preventing Mental Illness. *Woman Health Officer* 1956; **29**: 37.
Research into Problems of Mental Illness in relation to the Community. *Nursing Times* 1957; **53**: 105.
Drugs and Behaviour (essay review). *Sci Progress* 1957; **45**: 328.
Problems of Mental Illness in relation to the Community. *Public Health* 1958; **71**: 448.
Suicide. *Family Doctor* 1958; **8**: 425.
The Mental Health Act 1959: its implications for the General Practitioner. *Curr Med Drugs* 1961; **2**: 20–26.
Mental Health in New Housing Estates. *New Society* 1965; **125**: 13.
Do New Towns breed Mental Illness. *Can Ment Health* 1965; **13**: 5–9.
Mental Health in New Towns: what next? *J Psychosom Res* 1966; **10**: 53–58.
Do new Housing Estates endanger mental health? *Nursing Mirror*: 21 April 1967; viii.
Schizophrenia: (1) Manifestations, diagnosis and cause. *Update Plus* 1971; **1**: 59–62.
Schizophrenia: (2) The history and principles of community care. *Update Plus* 1971; **1**: 157–161.
The diagnosis and management of depressive illness: history of the word depression. *Update* 1973; **6**: 263–270.
Social class and schizophrenia. *Nursing Mirror* 1973; 37–38.
Creativity and mental illness. *BMJ* 1987; **ii**: 1589.

EDITORIAL WORK

Psychiatric Epidemiology. The Proceedings of the International Symposium held at Aberdeen University, 22–25 July 1969. Hare EH and Wing JK (eds). Oxford University Press: London, 1970, p. 379.
Memorandum on Publication Time of articles in the Journal (News and Notes, Aug 5–7). *Br J Psychiatry* 1975; **125**.
Surviving inflation? Some recent financial problems of a specialist medical journal. In: Balaban M (ed.). *Scientific Information Transfer: The Editor's Role*. D Reidel Publishing Co: Dordrecht, 1978, pp 405–413.

Foreword

Mental and behavioural abnormalities in human beings have been recognised since ancient times. For many centuries four main types were distinguished: the excited, restless, irritable, easily aggressive (Mania); the inactive, unresponsive, gloomy, even suicidal (Melancholia); the failing memory with foolish actions (Dementia) and the delusional with auditory and visual experiences not vouchsafed to others (Phrenitis). There were various speculative ideas about such cases – that they were due to possession by devils, or to divine inspiration, or to an impeded flow of humours to and from the brain, or to the influence of the stars, or an effect of the phases of the moon ('lunacy' in this narrow sense dates from the 16th century). Each explanation suggested a particular form of help – prayer, or diet, or drugs, or pilgrimage, or horoscope – from priest, astrologer or medico.

But whatever the beliefs about causes, many of those afflicted posed practical problems of care and restraint to their families, their neighbours, their society. They neglected to eat or keep clean, they might wander away and turn up among strangers or be totally lost, threaten people, destroy property, fail to do any work or only pursue mysterious activities. They became incomprehensible, unpredictable in behaviour, insusceptible to rational argument and unable to maintain social relationships. Because of their self-absorption, ignoring or defying some of the conventional behaviours of their community, they were seen as a threat to it and provoked fears of what they might do – arson, suicide, homicide, blasphemy, financial destruction, and so on.

Care and restraint were a family matter. The rich could afford locked rooms at home and servants to control the afflicted relative until such time as he or she recovered (which in a proportion of cases happened spontaneously). The poor had to manage by shutting up the mad on straw in an empty outhouse, or tying them to the leg of a table. Wanderers, whose family was unknown, were imprisoned. The restrained were liable to physical illnesses of various kinds and early death, which relieved the family of a heavy burden. For centuries, England never had a population above 5 million. Child mortality was high and few adults could expect to live beyond 40 years. Towns were very small and most people lived in very small scattered rural communities with emptiness around, and mental illness could easily be hidden. But in the 18th century, things began to change, more children to survive, and people to live longer. Agriculture improved, with better feeding, early industrialisation and more travel by regular coach, turnpike and canal, and towns began to grow and gain facilities (infirmary, assembly rooms, hotel, big houses) at the expense of the countryside. Add to this the growth of foreign trade and empire (N. America, India) and it is easy to see there was a growth in personal wealth. People who went mad while employed as resident domestic staff in a big house or hotel, or who lived cheek by jowl in terraces of small urban houses could hardly be hidden from neighbours or remain welcome where they resided, which increased problems of care and restraint. The opening of private madhouses by lay people, and sometimes by doctors, where for a profitable fee, mentally ill people would be taken in, guarded and cared for out of the way, proved a popular business for the well-to-do, but was also used for employees of the East India Company and for officers and men of the Navy and Army who had been repatriated because of mental illness. The poor, numerically a majority, could not afford the fees, but occasionally a parish might pay from vestry funds for one of them to stay in a madhouse as an alternative to offering outdoor relief, i.e. financial aid, to the family of a disabled person to help them survive.

From the first, this trade in lunacy prospered, free of all regulation and control. But there began to be repeated complaints that people who were not mad were being shut up in madhouses at the behest of relatives or business partners, to get them out of the way while their funds were misappropriated. There were also complaints of cruelty and neglect of inmates, and failure to summon a doctor if an inmate fell physically ill. Morbidity and mortality often seemed suspiciously high. Successive enquiries and Parliamentary debates then led to slowly increasing control. Madhouses had to be licensed and inspected from time to time, regular records kept, patients only accepted after authorisation by a magistrate. Procedures were however not tight enough, and prisons began meanwhile, to complain at having to accept the mad, sometimes on an indefinite basis.

Finally in 1808, Parliament passed the County Asylums Act, which invented a new public facility, a non-profit-making institution of care to be built and run by local magistrates. Each county was encouraged (but not compelled) to have a new specially designed building to take local lunatics freely, without any fee. The capital cost was to be raised locally from a local tax or rate imposed by the magistrates, the running cost per patient charged on a weekly basis to the family if they could pay or, in the majority of cases, to the parish from which the patient came. A committee of the magistrates would employ a steward, nurses and attendants to care for the inmates in a humane way, and inspect the place regularly; they would have no financial interest in it. Lunatics would only be admitted (and discharged) by the magistrates, who had to be convinced by what the family, the vicar and the overseer of the poor said, later supported by the testimony of a doctor or doctors (i.e. certification). This made admission to the asylum compulsory (on both patient and asylum) and involved some loss of civil rights. Lunacy lost its connection with the moon and became a legal category of persons under compulsory care. This is English history, of course: in other countries (France, Germany) matters were somewhat different.

Many counties were averse to spending money in this way, and construction was slow, so that ultimately (in 1845) asylum creation was made compulsory, all the more because the extent of madness in the population was much larger than had been realised and appeared to be on the increase. Many of those admitted to asylums were found to be suffering also from physical illness, sometimes through self-neglect or from fights or suicidal attempts. From 1828 therefore, it was made obligatory to have a full-time resident medical officer on the staff of any institution with 100 beds or more. This was a general practitioner (surgeon-apothecary), to recognize and treat physical ills, and to supervise the diet and climate believed necessary for health.

In time it came to be realised that the closeness of institutional life predisposed to the spread of pulmonary tuberculosis, dysentery, cholera and nutritional deficiencies, which meant more medical work. (In a different field, Florence Nightingale wrote papers showing that peace-time soldiers living in army barracks had much worse health than men of the same age living outside). In time also, with the growth in size of the asylum and its staff, it became necessary to have a manager responsible to the magistrates for the day to day running, and eventually after various experiments the doctor also became the manager, a physician superintendent.

Bringing hundreds of lunatics to one place and seeing them almost daily, inevitably led to a growth in knowledge of mental illnesses, though this was incomplete since the doctor did no work outside his asylum, did not control admissions and saw no cases among the uncertifiable. He became a sort of admin. specialist, an alienist perhaps, but not a psychiatrist or general physician. He could see there were different distinct patterns of illness, some needing separate management in his asylum. Some patients got better quickly, some slowly, some not at all: those who got better could go home, and some of them might be well for a year or more and then break down again, others stay well. Of the permanent inmates, some deteriorated and died, some calmed down but remained disabled, others were calm with episodic disturbances, some had fits, others never. Each patient kept to one of these patterns of illness, as if it were a distinct disease, and so allowed prediction of what would happen in the case, but since the cause was unknown and there was no physical pathology, the same pattern of disease might simply be the result of a similar constitution. Women who broke down after childbirth, men who were mentally ill after head injury, stroke or excessive indulgence in alcohol showed one or another of the same patterns of illness as those with no such background. There was nothing to stop a lunatic staying at home, provided he did not annoy society and his family cared for him. Or he could go to a licensed house if someone paid. If he had neither family nor money, he could go to the workhouse and only if he was troublesome there, for example annoying other residents, would he be sent on to the asylum. In this way, folk over 60 years of age whose relatives were all dead, and in a few cases orphan children, came to live out their days in the asylum, and there were also patients well enough to go home but who were somewhat disabled and needing some care but whose families refused to have them back. The asylum was used to offer care to a wide range of socially or mentally disabled people.

The magistrates were the local government of the time. In 1890 they were replaced by elected municipal and county councillors. This means that each locality largely went its own way and standards came to vary very much from one asylum to another, depending on some influential local figure perhaps and on the local ignorance and prejudice about the mad. Sometimes the institution would improve; at other times, and more often, it would deteriorate. The trouble was basically money. Local pride might dictate a fine new building at the start: spacious, clean and well furnished, with adequate sanitation. But it never seemed big enough, and the Committee would be happy to overcrowd it with more and more cases without adding to the size of bathrooms, laundry or kitchens, or number of nurses. They allowed the place to become dirty and the furnishings and clothing impoverished and inadequate, while they tried to cut the cost of food. It was as if they came to resent spending on such low grade and useless human beings, or blamed them for their illness as the result of idleness or a vicious life. It is not surprising if there was low morale and sometimes cruelty and poor medical practice, secrecy, public unconcern or exaggerated fear of the mad, and a belief, enshrined in the Lunacy Act 1890, that madness was incurable and a threat to Society, and the only solution was to weed out the mad, exclude them from the community and make sure they were locked out.

But if the asylums which had begun so hopefully had by 1900 run into a dreadful isolated dead end, elsewhere medicine had advanced triumphantly. Detailed clinical observation of heart, lungs, other organs and the nervous system, with the technology of the clinical thermometer, ophthalmoscope, stethoscope, and the study of blood, urine and sputum, combined with the abnormalities of anatomy discovered at postmortem to produce explanations of disease referable to individual organs or parts thereof and to suggest lines of alleviation or effective treatment. Some behavioural symptoms came to be related to thyroid disease or brain tumour, but there were other cases where refusal to eat, or insomnia or depression with gastrointestinal symptoms, or various pains and fears or anxieties could not be related to any pathological or biochemical disturbance, at least by the methods of those times. They became the province of the neurologist, and their study by Charcot and Janet, Freud and Jung, opened the subject of dynamic psychology – mechanisms in human behaviour, which could be manipulated in therapy. The successful psychological treatment of 'Shell Shock' in the 1914–1918 war was a major demonstration of the value of psychotherapy. The war had a big effect on public attitudes to lunacy and mental illness when people saw the way healthy young men became psychiatric casualties, and there began to be public disclosures of what the inside of asylums had become. Between them neurology and experimental psychology, dynamic psychology, biochemistry and morbid anatomy and other biological science, joined with the hard won knowledge of lunacy, and nervous disorders from clinical medicine, to create psychiatry as a new science. The new public view of such illness was expressed in the Royal Commission on Lunacy and Mental Disorder, reporting in 1926.

It declared that treatment for all who desired it, provided in any suitable hospital or clinic or at home, and not the protection of Society by the closed world of the asylum, should be the aim of medical and nursing services, who should be properly trained to carry out this task, with the least possible use of compulsion, legal formality, or locking up, and patients offered the same standard of domestic comfort as in an ordinary hotel. The Mental Treatment Act (1930) and the Mental Health Act (1959) gave effect to this new view. Lunacy was dead; asylums were translated into mental hospitals, and then into psychiatric hospitals which became part of the National Health Service. With new concepts of care and practice, the asylum was to be demolished.

This rapid scan of a century and a half's changing public attitudes to mental disorder may give a false impression of simplicity to what proves to be a complex affair. Few people have any first-hand experience of mental illness, except perhaps their own or that of a close relative. Such knowledge is felt to be unpleasant and suffers a taboo. The words used to describe it are tainted with inappropriate emotions. A doctor says "I can't tell him he's got schizophrenia, its a death sentence" – so he tells him nothing. (But it is not a death sentence, and one can explain the disabilities without using the dread word). A relative says "Of course, I know he's not mad, its just his nerves" (which expresses nothing except the speaker's fear of 'madness', whatever he thinks that is). "Its called mental illness so it must be in the mind and treated mentally, not with these drugs". "Nervous breakdowns are due to overwork or sexual difficulties". Public knowledge is littered with erroneous information and old exploded theories. It is not so long ago that masturbation was seriously affirmed to give rise to blindness or cause insanity, an idea that went on in public belief long after it had died out of medicine, no doubt because it was associated with moral disapproval. Dr Hare (this volume, p. 146) shows from the extensive 19th century literature on the subject how the belief grew up, based on inaccurate and incomplete observation, and an inadequate scientific methodology.

Dr Hare approached medical history, and the history of pre-psychiatry, as an epidemiologist and statistician. He was interested in the history through the ages of illnesses, rather than the history of medical schools, great physicians, power struggles or medical philosophy. He was not a student of individual cases but of groups, which meant that he could bypass the possibly complex and confusing influence of individual psychology on individual psychosis. He thought the individual who showed mental symptoms was a biologically damaged person who responded abnormally to normal physical or emotional stresses, and the psychiatric problem was to define the damage and learn its cause, with the possibility of preventing it in the future. What made a specific vulnerability? On the other hand, what determined the community's response to the biologically damaged person, in terms of beliefs, emotions, crowd responses and government actions, was a matter for social psychology and history.

For his first major historical study (this volume, p. 36) he chose 'Dementia paralytica' (GPI or general paralysis of the insane), which was an important part of the work of a 19th century asylum. Out of his six Croonian lectures to the Royal College of Physicians of London in 1849 'On some of the Forms of Insanity' Conolly, internationally known physician to the lunatic asylum at Hanwell (800 beds, West London) devoted two to GPI and made it clear no-one knew the cause of this trouble or how to cure it. Hanwell always had up to 30 GPI patients at any one time, mostly men, who lived up to four years from admission, but slowly deteriorated in memory, speech, movement and then died. He hazards as causes of the illness bereavement, domestic unhappiness, excessive drinking and remarks that "men of active and well-exercised minds are more disposed to this than to any other form of mental malady". Among the cases he quotes, one will do to illustrate the illness. A country solicitor age 50, temperate, moral, exemplary in conduct and looking healthy, worked habitually from about 5am to 10pm daily. He became grandiloquent, claimed to be very wealthy, gave his doctor a cheque for £1000, said he was the Duke of Lincolnshire, but also Sheriff of Dover in right of his wife, who was queen of the Queen's bedchamber.

This illness, so important in the 19th century, has disappeared. It was due to infection with the spirochaete which causes syphilis, spread only by sexual intercourse. But it was a late delayed effect, 10 or 20 years after the original infection, with no sign that the organism was still there waiting to attack the brain. Syphilis had been widespread in Europe since about 1500, but Hare from study of the very large literature since the late 18th century concludes that GPI was a new phenomenon in 1800, when it began to be described, first in Paris and northern France, then slowly spreading through Europe. Today the spirochaete can be killed with an artificial fever, or better with penicillin. But the demise of GPI may also be partly due to changes in human immunity, and in sexual practice, in particular the wider use of effective condoms.

Hare was sensitive to the idea that illnesses were not static but could suddenly begin, wax and wane, and sometimes recur, irrespective of human intervention. In 'The two manias' (this volume, p. 72) he explores the idea that mania changed its character in the course of a century. Schizophrenia may have done likewise. In 'Was insanity on the increase?' (this volume, p. 88) he proposes that the increase in asylum patients through the 19th century was a true increase in frequency of illness and not just a growing awareness of the convenience of using asylums, and that this resulted from an increase in dementia praecox or schizophrenia. Furthermore, this increase came to an end about 1900, and since then the number of new cases annually may have been slowly declining. There is much anecdotal evidence that the range and severity of symptoms have declined too: is this just a matter of different handling or a less repressive social response? Schizophrenia can be compared with GPI. Perhaps it is a long-delayed outcome of some biological insult to the individual before or after birth – by infection, trauma, toxin or malnutrition.

Hare's picture of mental illness is one where the illness is the result of an impairment or disability in the individual, something in the constitution which makes for a specific vulnerability so that there is an unusual response to some acute environmental situations. This impairment may be a limited physical disturbance of brain function, or some learned experience imprinted in the brain in the past, particularly with emotion recollected in distress. But whether this unusual response is regarded by the community as illness, or crime, or eccentricity, or of no account is a matter of social history, in the way of local history, since national cultures vary across space as well as time. By looking at group illness rather than individual illness he opens the way to correlations between recognized illness and religious and political belief, sexual life, poverty, education and other components of daily life. By taking a historical view he raises new questions about the causes of psychoses, about the effects of genetic mutations and cultural environmental changes.

J. L. C.

1

The changing content
of psychiatric illness

I should like to draw your attention to the mutability of disease. Diseases keep changing and sometimes we know why this happens and sometimes we don't. We know, for example, that epidemics of 'flu vary in severity because of mutations in the influenza virus. We know, or think we know, why carcinoma of the lung has become more prevalent. When a killing disease rapidly increases in prevalence we struggle hard to find the cause. But when the mortality of a disease slowly diminishes we are apt to be less interested, and this is perhaps because we too readily suppose that medical science is conquering it. Over the last century there has been a well documented decrease in mortality from various infectious diseases (Figure 1); and because most of that decrease occurred during a period when medical treatment and prophylaxis seems unlikely to have played an important part, and because, at least in the case of tuberculosis, there has been no evident change in the virulence of the infecting organism, the decrease has reasonably been attributed to an increased resistance of the population to disease, and this in turn was probably due largely to improved nutrition and smaller families (McKeown, 1965 and Powles, 1973). Thus diseases may change in response to changes in the physical environment.

Diseases may also change because of cultural and social changes. This is well recognized for the manifestations of the neuroses, particularly hysteria. Such changes can be explained along the lines that there are changing fashions in the socially acceptable modes of expressing mental distress or discontent, and patients have to keep up with the fashion in this as in other respects. But of course it is not only patients who have to keep up with fashion. Everyone is influenced by the social pressures of custom, fashion and advertisement, at least almost everyone: there may be exceptions, like the man who said he drank Guinness, not because it was advertised but because it was good for him. There is evidence to indicate that if a diagnosis is in doubt, and it very often is in psychiatry, doctors will be biased towards diagnosing conditions for which a fashionable form of treatment is available. At the Phipps Clinic, Baltimore, there was a sudden increase during 1957 and 1958 in the proportion of cases diagnosed schizophrenia, and a corresponding decrease in the proportion diagnosed affective disorder: ten years later the reverse occurred. These changes have been reasonably attributed to the introduction of phenothiazines in the earlier of these periods, and of lithium in the later (Baldessarini, 1970). A similar change in the diagnosis of neurotic conditions has occurred at the Maudsley Hospital over the past 15 years (Figure 2 and Figure 3); the increase in the proportion of neurotic cases diagnosed depression coincided with the introduction of

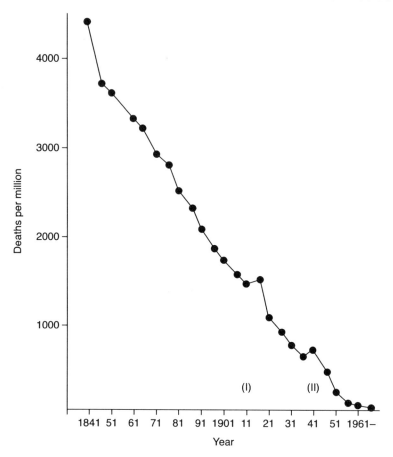

Figure 1. Death rate from tuberculosis, England and Wales (quinquennial averages). (I) and (II) world wars.

drugs specifically promoted as of use in depressive states, and the more recent increase in the proportion diagnosed phobic coincided with the development of behaviour therapy for this condition. I mention these instances to show the difficulty in following diseases over the years; diagnostic criteria change and it is sometimes hard to say how far the criteria change because the diseases change or *vice versa*.

The influence of culture and fashion on the manifestations and diagnosis of neurotic conditions offers scope for much detailed historical study (see Murphy (1973), for an exotic example); but I will turn to consider some changes that have occurred in the manifestations of the functional psychoses over the past few decades.

One of the most obvious changes is the decreased severity of mania. This is reflected in the common use of the term 'hypomania'. There is no reason to doubt that this term is used because psychiatrists, like laymen, still retain a mental image of mania as 'raving madness' with the patient in a state of furious excitement. Severe cases of that sort are very rare now and when they occur are usually associated with

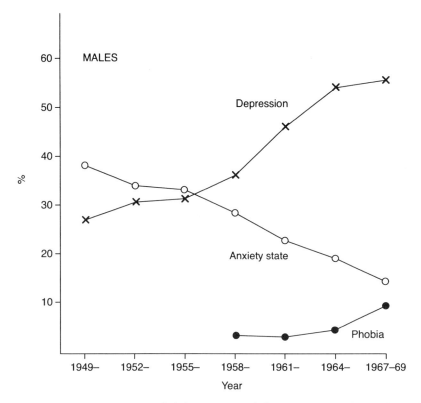

Figure 2. Depression, anxiety state and phobia as percent of all neuroses. First male attenders at the Bethlem-Maudsley Hospital.

physical illness. In 1844 Graham Bell, in America, described 'acute delirious mania', but by 1892 Clouston no longer believed that condition to exist and stated that even acute mania had become "not at all so common"; and today the term 'mania' has been largely abandoned as a clinical diagnosis. It might at first sight seem curious that we use the term hypomania for what we take to be mild mania but do not use any equivalent term for mild depression, but it could be said that we have simply dropped the old term 'melancholia' because we less commonly see the severe cases of agitated depression which that term implied. Why should this amelioration have occurred in mania? There are a number of likely reasons but I do not think we should exclude the possibility that a general increase in the health of adults and their constitutional resistance to disease may have played an important part.

If we now consider schizophrenia, the most striking change since 1914 has been in its improved prognosis. This has been well documented in Britain and is confirmed by reports from Scandinavia; but it is so marked as to be obvious to any psychiatrist who has been in clinical practice for 20 years or more. The improved prognosis is another way of saying that schizophrenia has become a clinically milder disease. There are other indicators of this. Thus from a study of the old case records, Klaf

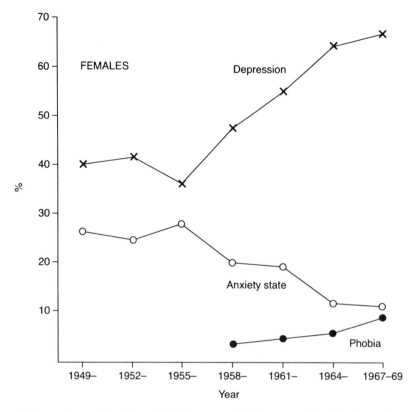

Figure 3. Depression, anxiety state and phobia as percent of all neuroses. First female attenders at the Bethlem-Maudsley Hospital.

and Hamilton (1961) found that among patients admitted to Bethlem Hospital during the 1850's with what we would now call schizophrenia, more than half (57%) were acutely disturbed on admission; whereas at Bethlem during the 1950's, a century later, less than a tenth (9%) were so described. Acute catatonic excitement, the type of schizophrenia which was associated with the greatest degree of motor disturbance, is now rarely if ever seen in this country, though I can remember many cases when I first began working in mental hospitals in 1947. We may note too what may be called the rise and fall of schizophreniform psychosis. In the 1930's it became apparent that many patients diagnosed schizophrenic recovered more than they ought to have done according to the Kraepelinian teaching. The explanation brought forward by Langfeldt was that such cases were not true schizophrenias, and this set in train the supposed distinction between process (or nuclear) schizophrenia and the schizophreniform disorders. But nowadays, at least in Britain, nobody seems to make this distinction and the term schizophreniform psychosis is applied instead to the symptomatic schizophrenias. It rather looks as if 'process schizophrenia' has disappeared. Another way in which schizophrenia seems to have become milder is in the relative infrequency of severe personality disintegration, the dementia part of dementia praecox: the burnt-out cases of the old back wards occur only rarely now and we hardly see the catatonic posturings, the bizarre mannerisms, the florid Messianic fantasies, the word salads, that all psychiatrists of my generation will remember.

If these changes mean that schizophrenia has become a milder disease in this country, then we must wonder why this has happened. The usual explanation, of course, is that patients now come for treatment at an earlier stage of their disease and that treatment – and in particular social management, has greatly improved. But when we remember the evidence that diseases have changed in nature and severity for reasons which are not at all obvious (see Hare (1959, 1972) for the case of general paralysis), we should consider the possibility that the same may apply in the case of schizophrenia and that medical treatment may have played only a relatively small part. There is still argument whether the improved prognosis of schizophrenia began before or after the introduction of phenothiazine drugs in about 1957; but my own experience leaves me in no doubt that the improvement came first. Rees was able to unlock almost all the wards at Warlingham Park Hospital by 1952, and in 1956 we had to abandon coma insulin therapy there – and this was before we knew about the controlled trial of Ackner et al. (1957), simply because there were no longer being admitted enough cases of acute schizophrenia in young healthy males to keep the insulin ward going. We may therefore consider applying to the case of schizophrenia the hypothesis which I have already suggested may apply in the case of mania: that an important factor in the amelioration has been the increased good health of the population.

If a disease is ameliorating due to what might be called 'natural causes', we might expect several associated events to be occurring. The most obvious of these is a decline in incidence. It is difficult to get satisfactory evidence here because of the uncertainty of diagnosis, the possibility that diagnostic habits are changing, and the fact that with improved psychiatric services more cases are likely to come to notice (for as Odegard has said, there is always a reservoir of cases in the community ready to be admitted to hospital as soon as beds become available). But there is in fact quite a bit of evidence to suggest a declining incidence of schizophrenia in industrialized countries. Even in 1940, Dayton could write that some set of influences were apparently changing and reducing the pressure on the types of personality that develop schizophrenia: he had noted a decreasing incidence of schizophrenia in Massachusetts between 1917 and 1933 and an increase in paranoia. Perhaps the best index we have is the hospital admissions in Norway where over many years the population has been fairly stable and the hospital services at a consistently high level. Between 1926 and 1965, Odegard found a fairly steady decrease in the incidence of schizophrenia but an increase in the incidence of paranoia (see also Sylvänne, 1952; Larson and Sjögren, 1954; Ey, 1959; Achté, 1961; Retterstöl, 1970 and Watt, 1973).

Another change commonly observed in diseases which are becoming milder is an increasing age of onset. This should be relatively simple to examine, at least in terms of age at first diagnosis. We may first notice that during the 19th century, dementia praecox was considered to be typically a disease of adolescence, the praecox part of dementia praecox, but that today the mean age of onset is nearly 30. We may also note that, in so far as we believe there is a relation between schizophrenia and the paranoid psychoses, the evidence for a decreasing incidence of schizophrenia and a concomitant increase in paranoia can be taken as reflecting an increase in the age of onset of the schizophrenia syndrome. More direct evidence comes from the Registrar General's Supplements on Mental Health in England and Wales (1964). Here the first admission rate in both sexes showed little or no increase between 1952 and 1960 for age groups under 35, but a marked increase for those aged 35 and over, and particularly for those aged over 45. Of course, such figures, like any other statistics, may be interpreted in different ways: the increased rate in older groups might simply indicate a relatively greater readiness of admission to hospital at those ages.

Finally, if schizophrenia is becoming a milder disease from causes unassociated with the provision of psychiatric care and treatment, we might expect to see a change in its natural history and clinical manifestation. It is, I think, well recognized that the type of course characterized by acute onset and severe deterioration after the acute phase has subsided, is now rare in this country, though Eugen Bleuler in 1911 considered this to be the course in one quarter of all cases. In a further quarter of cases, Bleuler considered the course to be one of exacerbations with remissions, each remission causing a further degree of personality deterioration. But again, this does not seem to happen much now. What happens most commonly now is an acute attack with a good remission; recurrences occur but are not commonly associated with any marked impairment of the general personality. Moreover, at least in my experience at Bethlem Hospital, the recurrences of schizophrenia are apt increasingly to have an affective component so that, after two or three recurrences, the attack may seem an almost pure manic depressive condition and the original diagnosis is then brought into doubt. This curious, but to my mind unmistakable, trend in the course of schizophrenic disease has been noted in the United States by Ziskind et al. (1971) in an article entitled, 'Can schizophrenia change into affective psychosis?' Ziskind suggested the phenomenon might be the consequence of phenothiazine medication but an explanation in terms of amelioration of the disease seems equally worth considering. We may notice here an increasing tendency to diagnose schizo-affective disorder. The subject has been studied by Kendell and Gourlay (1970) who reached the alarming conclusion, alarming, that is, to the traditionalists, that there was nothing in their findings to support the view of schizophrenia and affective psychosis being clinically different entities. This problem might be resolved if we took the view that nowadays the recurrence of schizophrenic illness need not necessarily lead to the recurrence of frank clinical manifestations of that disease but might at a milder level cause a disturbance or distress of mind sufficient to precipitate an affective illness.

I have put forward a hypothesis which, admittedly in a rather general way, will account for much of the changing nature of the functional psychoses in this country, and perhaps in other industrialized countries, from around 1914 or so. Does it lead to predictions about further changes in these psychoses, of a sort which can be put to the test? Assuming that the general standard of living continues to increase, or at least does not decline, we might predict that the changes which I have described as representing an amelioration will continue. If so, then those changes which are at present somewhat a matter of conjecture, the diminishing incidence of schizophrenia, the increasing mean age of onset, the increasing association of schizophrenia with affective symptoms, should become sufficiently pronounced to be clearly demonstrable by clinical and epidemiological techniques. Moreover, if schizophrenia has been ameliorating and continues to do so, we may expect that its severer forms will increasingly give place to the milder and broader disorders of the schizophrenia spectrum; and that would mean that the clinical distinction between schizophrenia on the one hand, and affective psychosis, neurosis and personality disorder on the other, would become increasingly blurred in the same way as the Kraepelinian distinction between the sub-types of schizophrenia seems to have become blurred in our own day.

In putting forward this hypothesis for your consideration, I do not of course in any way mean to detract from the very real and very important advances that have been made in the care and treatment of patients with psychiatric disorder. But I do want to suggest to you that psychiatric disorders are changing all the time, that we ought to be carefully monitoring these changes, and that we should at least keep in mind the possibility that part of these changes, and perhaps a considerable part, are due to secular processes of a sort which have too often been considered as only peripheral to the conventional concerns of medicine.

References

Achté KA. (1961) Der Verlauf der Schizophrenien und der schizophreniformen Psychosen. *Acta Psychiat Neurol Scand* **155** (Suppl).

Ackner B, Harris A and Oldham AJ. (1957) Insulin treatment of schizophrenia. A controlled study. *Lancet* **1**: 607.

Baldessarini RJ. (1970) Frequency of diagnosis of schizophrenia and affective disorder from 1944–1968. *Am J Psychiat* **127**: 759.

Clouston TS. (1892) *Clinical Lectures on Mental Diseases* (3rd edn). Churchill: London, p. 154.

Dayton NA. (1940) *New Facts on Mental Disorders*. Thomas: Springfield, p. 351.

Ey H. (1959) Unity and diversity in schizophrenia: clinical and logical analysis of the concept of schizophrenia. *Am J Psychiat* **115**: 706.

Hare EH. (1959) The origin and spread of dementia paralytica. *J Ment Sci* **105**: 594–626. [See this volume, p. 36]

Hare EH. (1972) Conquest of general paralysis. *BMJ* **3**: 418.

Kendell RE and Gourlay J. (1970) The clinical distinction between the affective psychoses and schizophrenia. *Br J Psychiat* **117**: 261.

Klaf FS and Hamilton JG. (1961) Schizophrenia – a hundred years ago and today. *J Ment Sci* **107**: pp 819–827.

Larson T and Sjögren T. (1954) A methodological, psychiatric and statistical study of a large Swedish rural population. *Acta Psychiat Neurol Scand* **89** (Suppl): 159.

McKeown T. (1965) *Medicine in Modern Society*. Allen & Unwin: London.

Murphy HB. (1973) History and evolution of syndromes: the striking case of latah and amok. In: Hammer H, Salzinger K and Sutton S (eds). *Psychopathology*. Wiley: New York.

Odegard O. (1971) Hospitalized psychosis in Norway: time trends 1921–1965. *Soc Psychiat* **6**: 53.

Powles J. (1973) On the limitations of modern medicine. *Sci, Med & Man* **1**: 1.

Registrar General. (1964) *Statistical Review of England and Wales for the Year 1960, Supplement on Mental Health*. HMSO: London.

Retterstöl N. (1970) *Prognosis in Paranoid Psychoses.* Thomas: Chicago.
Syvänne S. (1952) Incidence of schizophrenia in Helsinki in 1929–1938 and 1946–50. *Acta Psychiat Neurol Scand* **80** (Suppl): 53.
Watt CAH. (1973) Review of schizophrenics in a rural practice over 26 years. *BMJ* **1**: 465.
Ziskind E, Somerfeld E and Jena R. (1971) Can schizophrenia change to affective psychosis? *Am J Psychiat* **128**: 331.

2

The history of 'nervous disorders' from 1600 to 1840, and a comparison with modern views

In the 18th century the main varieties of nervous illness – hypochondria, hysteria, the spleen, the vapours and dyspepsia – became included under the general term 'nervous disorders'. When no physical disorder of the nerves could be detected in such conditions, the hypothesis of nervous disorder was replaced by the more vague concept of 'nervous temperament'. The fact that there is still no evidence of pathological change in such cases continues to expose physicians to the alternative hypothesis of a purely psychological cause. The modern era in our understanding of the nervous system may be said to date from 1843 when Du Bois Reymond showed the electrical nature of nervous conduction. The publication of Jorden's Briefe Discourse *in 1603 may be taken to represent the start of a discrete period (1600 to 1840) in the history of neurotic illness.*

The group of disorders known in the 18th and 19th centuries as 'nervous disorders' – which includes hypochondria, hysteria, and dyspepsia – had long posed a problem for the medical profession. They were very common and produced much minor ill-health. Their symptoms were responsible for many medical consultations, but no rational treatment was possible, as there was no general agreement about their causes.

An essential feature of 'nervous disorders' was (and still is, if the term is to be used) that, although they were characterised by bodily symptoms, no signs of local disease could be found in the bodily organs. Thus, it remained uncertain how far the symptoms were caused by a bodily disease which could not be detected (in the existing state of the medical art) and how far they were purely psychological (or spiritual) in origin. During the 20 centuries from Hippocrates to Vesalius, two quite different explanations of the disorders persisted side by side. The medical explanation was that they were bodily disorders caused by an imbalance of humours, the seat of the disorder being the uterus in hysteria and the liver or spleen in hypochondria. The religious (and the popular) explanation was that they were spiritual diseases caused by evil spirits taking possession of the sufferer's mind, and with the growth of belief in witchcraft, this idea came to include the belief that possession could be induced by witchcraft.

A fuller version of this paper is published as Appendix III of *Benjamin's Son* by P. H. Schurr (1991), published by Royal Society of Medicine Services, London.

The 17th century saw the downfall of both these aetiological hypotheses. Progress in science during the preceding century had already undermined the old humoral doctrine, for which there was little or no physiological evidence; and Harvey's demonstration of the circulation of the blood (1628) overthrew Galen's teaching on that subject and so laid his other teachings open to criticism. At the same time, the freedom of thought released by the Reformation was weakening the belief in evil spirits and witchcraft. However, the belief in witchcraft as a cause of possession did not yield easily to reason: for although there was no objective evidence for witchcraft, there was also none against it. A person accused of witchcraft in a court of law could never prove her innocence; the accusation could only be refuted by showing that the symptoms of the 'possessed' were being simulated or could more reasonably be explained in terms of a bodily disorder.

Natural causes in the body

A landmark in this new era was the publication in 1603 of Edward Jorden's *Briefe Discourse of a Disease called the Suffocation of the Mother*. In the previous year, Jorden had been one of several members of the Royal College of Physicians giving evidence at the trial of a woman accused of witchcraft. He (and one other member) concluded that the woman was not a witch but was sick. The curt judicial rejection of his opinion stung him into writing his book where he took issue (p. 3) with those who "are apt to make everything a supernatural work which they do not understand" and where he maintained that the symptoms commonly taken to be the effect of witchcraft have "their natural causes in the body".[1]

Jorden accepted the traditional view that hysteria was a disorder of the uterus (the 'mother') but he was concerned to explain how a disorder in one organ could lead to such varied symptoms as fainting fits, tremblings, palpitations, dyspnoea and feelings of suffocation. The traditional explanation was that the other organs acted in 'consent' or 'sympathy' with the affected part, and Jorden described three particular ways in which this might happen. These were: by direct contact ('vicinitie'); by diffusion of "an offensive vapour or humour"; and "by similitude of substance or function", as, for example, the similitude which "all nervous parts have with the brain". The spread of disease by direct contact is a readily acceptable idea – Jorden gives the example of disturbed bladder function due to prolapse of the uterus. But his other two suggestions were to preoccupy physicians and physiologists during the next two centuries.

Sympathy

The doctrine of sympathy dates at least from Galen's time (the 2nd century AD), but it is of no real value unless accompanied by an attempt to explain how the sympathy

---

[1] At this time King James I was still a firm believer in witchcraft. His notorious *Demonology* had been published in 1597. But his opinions were to change, and he "grew first diffident of, and then flatly to deny, the workings of witches and devils as but falsehoods and delusions" (Walker, 1981). Yet the belief that possession could be induced by witchcraft remained common in Britain throughout the 17th century – it was accepted by Thomas Willis (Tourney, 1972).

is brought about. Galen, who held that hypochondria and hysteria were disorders arising from sympathy, explained this in terms of vapours ascending from the stomach or uterus to the head (Whytt, 1767), and he also compared the attraction between other organs and the uterus to the attraction between iron and a magnet (Rowley, 1793). Some such explanation was certainly needed if an attempt was to be made to understand how symptoms arose: for how was it, asked Rowley (1793, p. 391), that a scratch on the hand or foot could lead to "that horrid, fatal disease, the locked jaw?" The view that sympathy could be explained by humours or vapours persisted through much of the 17th century – Harvey (1651) accepted it for hysteria. But it was the nervous system which soon seemed to have the stronger claim. Laurentius, in about 1600, had suggested that the sympathy between the uterus and the breasts during pregnancy was transmitted partly through the vena azygos and partly through the intercostal nerves (Whytt, 1767); and Thomas Willis, whose ana-tomical studies commanded wide respect, speculated that it was in the nervous sys-tem that "the hidden causes of disease and their symptoms, which commonly are ascribed to the incantations of witches, may be found out and clearly laid open" (Willis, 1684, p. 125). Since the seat of hypochondria and hysteria was believed to be in the abdominal organs, the conveyors of sympathy would most naturally seem to be the abdominal chain of nerves. This led Winslow (1732) to propose a new name for what had been called the intercostal nerves. Because of "their frequent associ-ation with almost all the other principal nerves in the body", he thought they would better be called "the great sympathetic nerves" (Vol. II, p. 164).

A belief in the importance of the nervous system as the principal mediator of sympathy had become generally accepted by the end of the 17th century. But when further study showed there might be no evidence of disease in the spleen or uterus in cases of hypochondria or hysteria, the conclusion was that the seat of the disorder must be in the nerves themselves rather than in the organs. It was this conclusion which (we may presume) led to the concept of 'nervous disorders', a term which (in Britain at least) came into common use after 1733 when Cheyne's book *The English Malady: or a Treatise of Nervous Diseases of All Kinds* . . . was published. Thereafter, sympathy was less often invoked.

The doctrine of sympathy was the earliest attempt to explain what seemed, within the confines of the body, to be 'action at a distance'. It was believed, for in-stance, that a wound would be healed by applying a secret remedy to a cloth stained with its blood or to the weapon which caused the wound. The concept of 'action at a distance' also extended to the use of medicinal plants whose leaves resembled the shape of the organ believed to be affected. As an explanation of 'nervous disorders', 'sympathy' was replaced by hypotheses based on the new discoveries in physiology and anatomy. Today, its vestiges remain in medical terminology – the sympathetic nervous system, sympathetic ophthalmia – but the idea, the name, hovers in the background of medicine, ready to be invoked when an old synthesis is breaking down or a new one seems to be emerging. Copland (1824) and Philip (1825) briefly recalled it when all the newer explanations of nervous disorders were seen to have failed. A modern instance, perhaps, was Sherrington's concept of integration as the essential function of the nervous system, a concept in its turn superseded by the discovery of the reticular activating system (Walshe, 1958).

Jorden's claim that hysteria had its "natural causes in the body" can only be made good when the natural causes have been found. Until then, the somatic hypothesis is no stronger than psychological hypotheses such as those of evil spirits, magnetism or psychoanalysis. The judge who rejected Jorden's opinion in 1602 did so because if neither natural cause nor remedy could be found then the disorder had to be supernatural (Bradwell, 1603). However this does not allow for the cause being natural but unknown.

The persistent (and persistently unrewarded) belief of physicians in a somatic cause of nervous disorders – and of the functional psychoses too – must reflect either an intuitive feeling derived from wide experience of disease or a professional claim that such conditions be considered to fall within the province of medicine. Whatever the reason, the attempt by physicians to find a somatic cause led to much speculation, though little real progress, throughout the 17th and 18th centuries.

The vapours

Until the 'nervous' hypothesis of hysteria and hypochondria finally gained ascendancy in the 1730s, the older idea of these disorders being caused by vapours or disordered humours in the spleen was widely accepted. As Cheyne put it in 1733 (p. 194), "every symptom not already classed under some particular limited distemper is called by the general name of spleen or vapours". The concept of 'vapour' was closely related to that of 'humour' but from the early 17th century it became the preferred term, probably because a vapour, unlike a humour, could be identified with a real substance, the 'wind' which was apt to be generated in excess during digestive disorders. In the mid-17th century, de la Boe regarded hysteria as due to vapours arising from the digestive tract (Mettler, 1947); and Purcell (1707), in his *Treatise of Vapours*, explained many of the symptoms as the result of wind from the stomach and intestines causing pressure on the nerves there. Purcell described the initial symptoms of the vapours as a heaviness in the breast and a grumbling in the belly. The patients then "belch up, and sometimes vomit, sower, sharp, insipid or bitter humours . . . They have difficulty in breathing and think they feel something that comes up into their throat which is ready to choke them; they struggle; they cry out and make odd or inarticulate sounds or mutterings . . . they perceive a swimming in their heads; a dimness comes over their eyes; they turn pale; are scarce able to stand; their pulse is weak; they shut their eyes, fall down and remain senseless for some time." Blackmore (1725, p. 41), in his *Treatise of the Spleen and Vapours*, assigned their prime cause to laxity of fibres in one of the abdominal organs allowing "peccant juices" to percolate through to the blood and adulterate the animal spirits formed in the brain.

In popular speech, the word 'vapours' persisted long after the medical theories based on it had been discarded. Samuel Johnson, in his *Dictionary* of 1755, described the vapours as "diseases caused by flatulence or by diseased nerves"; and the term remained sufficiently common during the 19th century to demand an entry in Tuke's

Dictionary of Psychological Medicine (1892) where it is described as "a popular term for hypochondriasis and hysteria".

The spleen

"The primitive doctors", wrote Blackmore in 1725 (p. 100), "imagined that all hypochondriacal symptoms were derived from a collection of black dregs and lees separated from the blood and lodged in the spleen; whence, as they supposed, noxious reeks and cloudy evaporations were always ascending to the superior regions". This Galenical view was still taken by Willis in 1667 (Mandeville, 1730), but from the early 18th century the part played by the spleen was being disputed on both anatomical and physiological grounds. Thus Blackmore said that primitive belief was now exploded because "there are no passages or proper conveyances by which these steams and exhalations may mount"; he noted that in dogs the spleen could be excised without ill effect, proving it was not a vital organ. Moreover, those who accepted the contemporary teaching of 'the spleen' and vapours being caused by laxity of the (muscle) fibres, said the spleen could not be the seat of these disorders because it contains no muscles.

Such arguments were no doubt the reason why medical writers soon ceased to mention 'the spleen' as a distinct disorder. But, as with the vapours, a term introduced to describe a causal theory and abandoned when the theory was shown to be untenable, lived on much longer in popular speech. In most medical writings of the 18th century the symptoms attributed to the spleen were those we now tend to associate with hypochondria and low spirits. Robinson (1729) lists eight groups of symptoms of the spleen in man. The symptoms include poor appetite, low spirits, belching, regurgitation, murmurings of the bowel (like 'caterwauling conflicts'), weakness and trembling of the legs, costiveness, slimy stools, thumping inside the skull, sweats, groundless fears of death, poor memory, fits of despair and disturbed sleep ("he starts in his sleep, and often awakes from his slumbers terribly affrighted with the horrors of his dreams"). The popular usage had a wider connotation – a fact which is noteworthy in the light of present-day theories. In dictionaries of the English language, 'spleen' has commonly included ideas of anger and cheerfulness as well as of melancholy. Thus in Dr Johnson's *Dictionary*, spleen may mean not only melancholy and hypochondriacal vapours but spite, ill-humour, a fit of anger, or immoderate merriment; and the organ itself "is supposed the seat of anger, melancholy and mirth". The *Oxford English Dictionary* (1971) gives essentially the same meaning. Two reasons may be suggested why medical writers had a restricted meaning for 'the spleen'. Anger or merriment would not ordinarily lead to a medical consultation; and it would not be easy to explain how a single physical cause could lead to such seemingly incompatible mental effects as melancholy and mirth. No discussion of the spleen in this period would be complete without reference to the well-written book on the subject by William Stukeley (1723). Stukeley took the view that one of the functions of the spleen was to purify the black humour conveyed to it by the splenic vein from the intestines.

But just as black bile creates anger and melancholy, so the spleen when purged of it is rendered "chearful and alert" (p. 2). Like Malphigi, Stukeley confessed himself perfectly ignorant of "nature's intention of forming the curious organ of the spleen" (p. 2). But that fact, he says, will not stop him from speculating about its functions "because the greatness of our profession permits everyone a free way of thinking".

Dyspepsia

As a medical term, the English word dyspepsia dates from 1657 but the belief that hypochondriacal disorders were related to indigestion is very old and was held by Aetius and Paul of Aegina (Gully, 1837). This belief was still fashionable during the 17th and 18th centuries. Thus Baglivi, in his *Practice of Physick* (1704, p. 186), said that "those who sicken upon disorder of the mind use chiefly to be seized with the diseases of the stomach". According to Purcell, the principal cause of vapours is indigestion, the turning of ailments into "crudities" by "vicious concoction". "By what I know from observation", says the physician in Mandeville's *Treatise* (p. 94), "it is demonstrable to me that the cause of hypochondriac and hysteric diseases is in the stomach". Buchan's popular *Domestic Medicine* (1769) asserts that "all nervous patients, without exception, are affected with wind or flatulences in the stomach and bowels", while Cullen, in the 1770s, defined hypochondria as "indigestion with langour, sadness and fear, from uncertain causes" (Johnson, 1827, p. 44).

These authors did not (as far as I can see) use the term 'dyspepsia'. The common use of that term dates only from the early 19th century. It was evidently coming into favour when Philip was writing his *Treatise on Indigestion* (1825), for he says he has preferred the use of 'indigestion' to 'dyspepsia' because the latter has been taken to mean a much less varied disease. Johnson (1827, part II, p. 41) asserted the primacy of the stomach as a cause of nervousness and hypochondria, but considered both 'indigestion' and 'dyspepsia' to be unsatisfactory terms, for in such cases (he believed) the digestive system was "morbidly sensitive" rather than disordered. This shift in opinion – from stomach disorder to some morbid abdominal state – is seen in Gully's book on nervousness (1837, p. 261) where he says that while it is true that "the starting point of the symptoms is invariably in the abdomen", the cause is not disorder of the digestive system but a morbid irritation of the ganglionic system of nerves. Interest in stomach disorder as a cause of hypochondria probably faded from lack of pathological evidence and also, perhaps, from a change in dietary habits rendering the abdominal symptoms less prominent in the clinical picture. But in the 1830s, a close relationship between dyspepsia, hypochondria and hysteria was still commonly maintained.

Hypochondria and hysteria

By the 1730s British physicians had come to accept that the spleen and the vapours were simply outdated terms for hypochondria and hysteria. But there was much debate about how far these were distinct disorders. The debate arose (we might now think) partly because of the dead-weight of tradition, partly because of the difficulty in delineating the characteristic symptoms, and partly because the symptoms seemed so variable. He gave three reasons why hysteria could not be caused by the uterus: hysteria may occur in virgins where the uterus is too small to be able to cause 'suffocation'; the uterus is bound down by ligaments and so could not rise up into the chest; and insofar as the uterus can move, this causes no sensation. As long as the uterus was considered the seat of hysteria, this was necessarily a female disorder. But both Willis (1681) and Sydenham (1749) asserted that it could occur in men; Willis's anatomical arguments strengthened that view. Trotter (1807, p. 188) says hysteria is characterised by "uneasy flutterings about the breast, with the sense of a ball rising to the throat"; the patient then becomes giddy and falls down, "often in violent agitations and convulsions, with loud screams and looks expressive of horror". The essential similarity between hysteria and hypochondria was maintained by Sydenham (1749), Blackmore (1725) and Browne (1729), and denied by Hoffman (see Sydenham, 1749), Whytt (1767), de Sauvages (see Veith, 1965) and Cullen (1810). There was no consensus here, and a student was likely to accept the opinion of his teachers.

There were two main reasons for thinking the disorders different. Hypochondria was typically a chronic, continuous state occurring mainly in persons over 45, while hysteria commonly took the form of isolated episodes, mainly in those under 35 (Cullen, 1810). Moreover, hysteria was particularly associated with 'fits'. Willis considered that hysteria "is chiefly and primarily convulsive" (1684, p. 76); Hoffman (Sydenham, 1749, p. 368) said hysteria often seized women so suddenly that they "fall down directly without sense or motion"; Cheyne (1733) classed hysterical fits with epileptic fits and fits of yawning; and Cullen (1810) put hysteria with tetanus and epilepsy in his third group of nervous disorders, the 'spasmi'. The convulsive aspects of hysteria seem to have become less striking, and whatever the reason for this, the effect would have been to leave the symptoms more like those of hypochondria.

There was another difference between hysteria and hypochondria which, though little remarked at the time, is of interest for present-day ideas. Blackmore (1725, p. 154) observed that melancholy "is so nearly related to the spleen that it is called by some, hypochondriac melancholy" (many notes on hypochondriacal melancholy are given by Jackson (1986)); while in the type of hysteria characterised by tremblings and palpitations, there is "sometimes an immoderate gaity of temper'. Robinson (1729), who did not see any distinction between the spleen and the vapours, says these disorders are liable to degenerate into madness – melancholy if the constitution was phlegmatic, mania if it was bilious. A hundred and fifty years later the same idea was expressed by Savage (1892) who wrote that "just as hysteria passes insensibly into mania, so hypochondriasis passes insensibly into forms of melancholia". The idea of excitability, particularly of sexual excitability, has been persistent in the history of hysteria. Cullen (1810, p. 153) said that hysteria "occurs especially in females who are liable to nymphomania" and his classification included the species *Hysterica libidinosa*. "We must protest", wrote Charcot on hysteria in Tuke's *Dictionary* (1892), "against the opinion universally adopted by the public that all hysterical women have a tendency to lubricity, almost bordering on nymphomania".

There was also the contrary view of hysterical females as sexually frigid. Harvey (see Hunter and Macalpine, 1963) had advised marriage as a cure for a hysterical woman, but Mandeville (1730) thought such advice might prove unfair to the prospective husband. I have found no observations on the sexual propensities of hysterical males.

Nervous disorders

The gradual consensus of opinion in the early decades of the 18th century – that there was no essential difference between the spleen, the vapours, hypochondria and hysteria – allowed the simplifying postulate that they could all be subsumed under the general term 'nervous disorders'. Although there was at first uncertainty how inclusive this term should be – Sydenham in 1681 (1749, p. 383) had included the green-sickness (a type of anaemia) of young women as "doubtless a species of hysteric disorder" – it became restricted to disorders where no pathological abnormality could be found and which therefore, on the assumption that their cause lay in the body rather than the soul, were presumed due to a disorder of the nervous system. But their clinical identity remained confused and it was the opinion of many that the term nervous disorder was a rag-bag for conditions not classifiable elsewhere ("a common subterfuge for mere ignorance of the nature of distempers", said Cheyne (1733, p. 194)).

Medical writers before the 19th century rarely discussed the prevalence of the disorders they described. But when the nervous disorders became a single diagnostic group, their high prevalence was very evident. Sydenham (1749) thought that hysterical disorders (in which he included hypochondria) made up one-sixth of the diseases to which mankind was prone. Blackmore (1725, p. 367) said they were as common as fevers and that one-third of people "are destroyed or made miserable by them" (p. iv). "Scarce known to our ancestors", said Cheyne (p. 1), they are "computed to make almost one-third of the complaints of the people of condition in England". Trotter (1807, p. xvii), observing that "nervous disorders make up about two-thirds of the whole with which civilised society is infested", concluded that since Cheyne's time they must have been spreading to the inferior orders of society. And, as has commonly been the case when a disorder of unknown cause appears to be increasing in civilised countries, the effects of luxury, idleness, debauchery and town life were blamed.

The high prevalence of nervous disorders no doubt increased the urgency to find their bodily causes. If the cause lay in the peripheral nerves, then it was most likely to be a disorder of nervous conduction. Since Galen's time, nervous conduction had been explained in terms of animal spirits. These were thought to be formed in the brain by refinement of vital spirits brought there by the blood, and then distributed from the cerebral ventricles via the spinal cord to channels in the nerves.[2] This

---

[2] Vesalius accepted that animal spirits were distributed through the nerves "as through hollow channels" or "as light passes through the air" (Foster, 1901, p. 257), but he differed from Galen in holding that animal spirits were formed in the brain not only from the blood but also from air drawn up from the nose through holes in the cribriform plate (p. 256) – a misconception corrected by Lower (1672).

doctrine was accepted by Descartes (Mettler, 1947); and Willis (1681) did not doubt that hysterical symptoms "arise often from that the animal spirits . . . are infected with some taint". Purcell followed the mechanical explanations of Descartes and Willis when he attributed the vapours to pressure on the stomach nerves (from wind) causing reflux of animal spirits to the brain, whence they rebounded ("by the law of the angles of incidence and reflection") to cause unnatural stimulation of the stomach muscles.

The attempt to explain nervous conduction (and so nervous disorder) by flow of a liquid or gas failed only because the theory was realistic enough to allow its falsification by experiment. There were many objections to it,[3] but no satisfactory alternative could be found and there followed a period – roughly from the 1740s to the 1830s – when the cause of nervous disorders was still attributed to the nervous system but attention shifted from particular parts or functions to the more general idea of constitution or temperament. In this setting, the hypothesis of Lobstein (1823) that nervous disorders were due to disease of the sympathetic ganglia was a perfectly reasonable one. But it was to be the last outlier in the long range of attempts to find a localised cause.[4] By the time nervous conduction was shown to be associated with electric currents – in 1843 by Du Bois-Raymond (Brazier, 1958) – the hope of finding a specific cause of nervous disorders had largely been abandoned.

The nervous temperament

Most writers on nervous disorders mention temperament or constitution as a predisposing factor. Thus Sydenham (1749, p. 376) considered the antecedent cause of hysteria to lie in "the temperament of the body . . . given us by nature"; and like Baglivi (1696, p. 179), he attributed the greater incidence of hysteria in females to their having been "made more delicate". According to Blackmore (1725, p. 42) the predisposition to the spleen and vapours lay in "the original formation of the nerves . . . which in these patients are woven by nature of too delicate and tender threads"; and this is echoed by Browne (1729). The importance of constitution was more decidedly stressed by Whytt (1767, p. 95): "nervous disorders are chiefly those

---

[3] Objections are listed by Mandeville (1730, p. 135), Cheyne (1733, p. 80), James (1745) and Whytt (1767, p. 6). If the contraction of a muscle was due to the sudden influx of animal spirits from the nerves, its volume should increase; but Glisson in 1677 showed the volume decreased (Mettler, 1947, p. 121). If a contracted muscle was cut under water, bubbles of gas should be released; but Borelli in 1680 disproved this (Brazier, 1958). Channels for the flow of spirits in the nerves should be visible, but even with Leeuwenhoek's lenses none could be seen; and if a nerve was tied and the proximal end milked, there should be a swelling: or if it was cut, fluid should ooze or bubble out; but this did not happen (James, 1745). And, as Stenson knew (Foster, 1901, p. 284), muscles could contract even when detached from their nerves. Haller had been a strong supporter of the animal spirits as flowing through tubes in the nerves (1779, p. 220), but "had candidly given up the opinion" on finding it unconfirmed by his experiments on living animals (Whytt, 1767, p. 68).

[4] Lobstein's hypothesis was reasonable because it was testable. It was accepted, although not confirmed, by Gully (1837), but does not seem to have received support from further pathological studies. Freud's somatic theory of anxiety neurosis – that it was due to pressure built up in the seminal vesicles from lack of sexual activity – was less easily testable. He soon dropped it in favour of a purely psychological theory.

complaints which proceed, in a great measure, from a weak or unnatural constitution of the nerves". 'Weak nerves' might result either from a defect in constitution
or from those diseases or irregular modes of life which "weaken the whole body,
especially the nerves" (p. 109).

The gradually increasing emphasis on the importance of temperament culmi-
nates in Trotter's *View of the Nervous Temperament* (1807). Here, the peripheral nervous system is no longer discussed as a cause of nervous disorders. The bodily
causes are to be looked for within the more vague concept of temperament. The
predisposition to nervous disorders is the nervous temperament, and this might be
inherited from nervous parents or acquired from such circumstances as malnourish-
ment in infancy, fevers, head injuries, the injudicious use of drugs, or poisons.
Nervous disorders will develop if there is further debilitation of the nervous system
by a wrong life-style – overeating, alcoholism, insufficient exercise, etc. Trotter describes the mental characteristics of nervous persons (i.e., those with the nervous
temperament). These are mainly of a negative kind – "extravagant ideas, super-
stition, reverie" (p. 223); but may also be socially valuable – high sensibility, creative
eccentricity.

Difficulties in the study of nervous disorders

Trotter's concept of nervous disorder as the effect of environmental insult on constitutional disposition may be seen as an end-point in the attempts by medical men,
during the 200 years since Jorden's work, to bring order into a very confusing subject. If we reflect on the reasons why progress in the subject was so limited during
this period, we may discern a series of inter-related difficulties.

The principal difficulty lay in delimiting the group of symptoms by which nervous disorders were to be recognised. There was little consistency in the clinical pictures – as Trotter (p. xv) said, "they vary in every constitution and assume in the
same person at different times an inconstant assembly of symptoms". Symptoms
and signs were commonly hard to describe in words and this made it hard for
physicians to agree on the meaning of the medical terms.

Because of the problems of delineation, the differential diagnosis of nervous disorder – from serious organic disease to whims, fancies and conceits – was apt to
be difficult. With the progress of clinical medicine and pathology a number of conditions originally included in the nervous group (such as epilepsies, chorea and
migraine) became excluded, but these would have constituted only a small part. The
distinction between nervous disorder and temperamental peculiarity was not only
more subtle but involved the question whether nervous disorders were 'real' medical conditions requiring appropriate medicinal treatment. Robinson (1729, part II,
chap. 2) devoted a chapter to the reality of the spleen and vapours, and to the
"dangerous consequences that attend their neglect". Blackmore (1725), noting that
hysterical symptoms may imitate many diseases – epileptic fits, paralytic numbness,
asthma, rheumatism, putrid fevers – pointed to the danger of saying (p. 111), "Oh!
this is nothing but vapours". And Heberden (1802, p. 235) was in no doubt that

nervous disorders arose "from as real a cause as any other distemper". But the justification of such opinions lay in a demonstrable pathological lesion linked with the symptoms, or at least in a plausible hypothesis to explain the symptoms in pathological terms. The search for a lesion was doomed to failure – we still have not found one. Of the hypotheses, the most useful was that of disturbed animal spirits because it led to new findings based on investigations designed to test it. Scientific knowledge was generally insufficient to allow testable hypotheses, and as scientific rigour developed, the far-fetched analogies of the 17th century easily became the target of ridicule.

The failure to find a satisfying medical explanation of nervous disorders meant that there was no sound basis for rational therapy. This led to a distrust of 'hypothetical doctors'. To the busy practitioner, the purpose of medicine was to cure diseases: the search for knowledge was irrelevant (Mettler, 1947). The sceptical Stensen, who dismissed the idea of animal spirits and nervous fluid as mere words meaning nothing, said that rational treatments based on such ideas were in most cases erroneous (Foster, 1901, p. 285). Wise doctors like Harvey and Willis dropped their theories when treating patients (Veith, 1965).

The inability to demonstrate that nervous disorders were bodily in origin had two further consequences. The first was the confusing use of equivocal terms. Although the concept of animal spirits was very different from that of evil spirits, the word 'spirits' carried the double burden of a physical and a mental meaning: and this confusion led many into supposing that low spirits (in the mental sense) could be raised by strengthening the spirits (in the animal sense). The management of disorders caused by irregular motions of the animal spirits, said Sydenham (1681, para. 96, 116), included chalybeate ("whereby the drooping spirits are roused and revived") and riding on horseback ("for strengthening and cheering the spirits"); and Baglivi (1704, p. 77), observing that many diseases of the mind arise from the "weight of care that hangs upon everyone's shoulders", concluded that "the oppressed and almost sunk spirits ought to be rous'd up and exhilarated" (p. 180). For Descartes, animal spirits occupied an intermediate position between mind and matter (Riese, 1958) and this became a common view.[5] But with the fall of the animal spirit theory, the mind–body problem became as opaque as ever. "Our ignorance of the connection and sympathies of body and mind", said Heberden (1802, p. 225) that is, nervous disorder, "makes a great difficulty in the history of all distempers and particularly of this".

The second consequence was that if nervous disorders were not disorders of the body then they must be disorders of the mind. This allowed them to be explained in purely psychological terms. But if that were so, then medicaments and regime were irrelevant: if improvement occurred, that would be due to the natural course of the disorder, and if it did not occur then the sufferer must accept his symptoms

[5] The physician in Mandeville's dialogue (1730, p. 165) remarks that the spirits are the *internuncii* between the immaterial thinking substance and those parts which are influenced by thinking. Alexander Monro (1753, p. 354) said, "We have not, and perhaps cannot have, any idea of the manner in how mind and body act upon each other," but if there is an interaction then this must be by the nervous fluid.

as philosophically as he could (Brain, 1963).[6] Of course, it was easy for physicians to criticise animism – Vicq d'Azyr said of Stahl that he had invented an imaginary soul to resolve those phenomena which could not yet be explained by the laws of physics and chemistry (Brazier, 1958) – but that did not prove the bodily cause of nervous disorders or help the practitioner in his treatment of a nervous patient.

Nervous disorders today

The efforts of medical men during the period 1600–1840 to understand the nature of nervous disorders can be better appreciated if we consider what we know about them today. The term 'neurosis' was introduced by Cullen (1810) to include a wide range of disorders of the nervous system, but from the latter part of the 19th century its use became restricted to the functional complaints earlier subsumed under nervous disorders. In common usage during the first half of the 20th century, neurosis has now fallen from favour, and neither the term itself nor any correspondingly inclusive term finds a place in the influential classification of the American Psychiatric Association (the DSM–III system; 1980). Today, both neurosis and nervous disorder are popular rather than medical terms.

But the conditions themselves persist; patients still consult doctors for symptoms which cannot be attributed to any recognised disorder of demonstrable pathology. The principal change has been in the nature of the symptoms. Hypochondriasis and hysteria are rarely diagnosed today. In the DSM–III classification, hypochondriasis is a disorder of older persons and characterised by the patient's irrational fears of having some serious disease. The functional symptoms of what was called hysteria in the 17th century are now grouped under minor headings (conversion disorder, somatisation disorder, histrionic personality). The symptom of anxiety did not figure largely in 18th-century descriptions of nervous disorders but is now the characteristic of a major group, the anxiety disorders. The low spirits and despondency so commonly noted in the 18th century as symptoms of hypochondria now find a place within 'affective disorders': the group which includes depressive and manic psychoses, and cyclothymic and dysthymic disorder.

From the clinical point of view there have been obvious changes in symptomatology. Dyspepsia is now rarely taken to be an indication of nervous troubles. The symptoms which used to be most typical of hysteria – the fits, the fainting, the sense of suffocation (globus hystericus) and the voiding of much pale urine (for example, Sydenham, 1749; Blackmore, 1725) – are now quite uncommon in industrialised

---

[6] Sydenham firmly believed that hysteria was to be cured by medicines – he used a series of remedies "until the patient responded" (Dewhurst, 1966, p. 53). For a physician to promise his patient a natural remission in the course of time was, he considered, something suggested by "malice of prejudiced persons" (p. 84). Could he have had in mind Gideon Harvey, physician to Charles II? In his *Art of Curing Diseases by Expectation* (1689), Harvey not only made the subversive remark that in serious diseases "more owe their deaths to physicians than are pretendedly cured by them" (p. 4), but pertinently asked how it was that poor people, unable to afford the fees of a doctor or apothecary, nevertheless commonly recovered from "slight disorders" (p. 3). The need for the patient to minister to himself in nervous disorder was stressed by Heberden – "much more is in his power than he is aware of, or can certainly be brought to believe" (1802, p. 235).

countries. It remains an open question how far such changes relate to changes in the social acceptability of different kinds of illness behaviour or to changes in diet, dress, general health, and environmental effects on constitution.

The essential symptoms of hypochondria, however, seem to have persisted largely unchanged, and in the old descriptions it is not difficult to recognise modern ideas of affective disorder and particularly of cyclothymia and dysthymia. It was well recognised in the 18th century that hypochondria might progress to melancholic or maniacal madness; and it is accepted by psychiatrists today that these two forms of psychosis are not only closely related, but typically occur in persons with constitutional cyclothymia (that is, swings of mood largely unrelated to external events). The old idea that the spleen was the site of melancholy and of merriment is now reconciled in the view that the cyclothymic person has phases of depression and elation (elation becoming hypomania if sufficiently marked). The old concept of hysteria probably contained an element of cyclothymia – Heberden's (1802) "fits and excitability", and Cullen's (1810) "liability to nymphomania" (p. 15) – for sexual excitability is characteristic of hypomania in females.

The continued failure during the 19th century to find any bodily cause of nervous disorders left the way open for new psychological theories, the most acclaimed of which was psychoanalysis. In Britain and America, from 1920, to about 1960, the aetiology of the neuroses was confidently attributed to unconscious mental conflicts. When medical confidence in these theories declined, environmental factors were again examined. Controlled studies have not, on the whole, supported the opinion that poor living standards or dissatisfaction with social conditions are important causes of neurotic illness, and the concept of constitutional vulnerability has again attracted attention.

If a person's constitution can be damaged by environmental insults in early childhood, we might suppose, from the great improvements in child health, that this factor would be much smaller now than in Trotter's time. Trotter's estimate, in 1807, that nervous disorders formed two-thirds of all disorders, might be compared with the prevalence rate of 10–15% found in a modern study (Shepherd *et al*, 1966) among general practitioners in London. But the comparison is hazardous, and it is the genetic aspect of constitution which at present seems most relevant. There is good evidence, especially from studies of twins and adopted children, that genetic factors are important in minor psychiatric disorders. The recent tentative location of genetic sites associated with manic-depressive psychoses gives hope that such sites may also exist, and be found, for the cyclothymic and dysthymic traits. That would at last be convincing evidence for a bodily cause in one class of nervous disorder, though it would still be only a step towards rational treatment and prevention.

References

American Psychiatric Association. (1980) *Diagnostic and Statistical Manual of Mental Disorders* (3rd edn) (DSM–III). APA: Washington, DC.

Baglivi G. (1704) *The Practice of Physick* (transl from the original Latin of 1696). Bell: London.

Blackmore R. (1725) *A Treatise of the Spleen and Vapours*. Pemberton: London.

Brain WR. (1963) The concept of hysteria in the time of William Harvey. *Proc Roy Soc Med* **56**: 317–324.

Brazier MAB. (1958) The evolution of concepts relating to the electrical activity of the nervous system. 1600 to 1800. In: *The History and Philosophy of Knowledge of the Brain and its Functions*. Blackwell: Oxford, pp 191–222.

Browne R. (1729) *Medicina Musica . . . to which is annex'd a New Essay on the Nature and Cure of the Spleen and Vapours*. Cooke: London.

Buchan W. (1792) *Domestic Medicine: or a Treatise of the Prevention and Cure of Diseases by Regimen and Simple Medicines* (13th edn, 1st edn 1769). Strahan: London.

Cheyne G. (1733) *The English Malady: or a Treatise of Nervous Diseases of All Kinds, as Spleen, Vapours, Lowness of Spirits, Hypochondriacal and Hysterical Distempers, etc*. Strahan & Leake: London.

Copland J. (1824) *Annotation to The Elements of Physiology by Richerand, A* (4th edn transl JJM De Luys, 1st edn 1801). London.

Cullen W. (1810) *First Lines of the Practice of Physic, Volume 2* (1st edn 1784). Reid and Bathgate: Edinburgh.

Dewhurst K. (1966) *Dr Thomas Sydenham (1624–1689) His Life and Original Writings*. Wellcome Historical Medical Library: London.

Foster M. (1901) *Lectures on the History of Physiology*. Cambridge University Press: Cambridge.

Gully JM. (1837) *An Exposition of the Symptoms, Essential Nature and Treatment of Neuropathy or Nervousness*. Churchill: London.

Haller A. (1779) *First Lines of Physiology* (transl W Gullen, first published 1757). Elliot: Edinburgh.

Harvey G. (1689) *The Art of Curing Diseases by Expectation*. Thackeray: London.

Harvey W. (1651) Exercitationes de generatione animalium: transl R Willis in *The Works of William Harvey* (1847). Sydenham Society, London, pp 528–529.

Heberden W. (1802) *Commentaries on the History and Cure of Diseases*. Payne: London.

Hunter R and Macalpine I. (1963) *Three Hundred Years of Psychiatry 1538–1860*. Oxford University Press: London.

James R. (1745) *A Medical Dictionary* (Vol 3). Osborne: London.

Jackson SW. (1986) *Melancholia and Depression. From Hippocratic Times to Modern Times*. Yale University Press: New Haven.

Johnson J. (1827) *An Essay on Morbid Sensibility of the Stomach and Bowels etc*. Underwood: London.

Johnson S. (1775) *Dictionary* (4th edn). London.

Jorden E. (1603) *A Briefe Discourse of a Disease called the Suffocation of the Mother* (Reprinted 1990). Windet: London.

Lobstein JF. (1823) *De Nervi Sympathetici humani fabrici, usu et morbis*. Levrault: Paris. (transl Pancoast J. (1831) as *A Treatise on the Structure, Function and Disorders of the Human Sympathetic Nerve*. Auner: Philadelphia).

Lower R. (1672) *De Catarrhis* (Reproduced in facsimile and for the first time translated from the original Latin, by R Hunter and I Macalpine, 1963). Dawson: London.

Mandeville B. (1730) *Treatise of the Hypochondriac and Hysteric Diseases* (3rd edn, 1st edn 1711). Tonson: London.

Mettler CC. (1947) *History of Medicine*. Blakiston: Philadelphia.

Monro A. (1753) *An Anatomy of the Human Bones, Nerves and Lacteal Sac and Duct*. Hamilton & Balfour: Edinburgh.

Philip APW. (1825) *A Treatise on Indigestion and its Consequences, called Nervous and Bilious Complaints* (5th edn, 1st edn 1821). Underwood: London.

Purcell J. (1707) *A Treatise of Vapours or Hysteric Fits* (2nd edn, 1st edn 1702). Newman & Cox: London.

Riese W. (1956) *A History of Neurology*. MD Publications: New York.

Riese W. (1958) Descartes's ideas of brain function. In: *The History and Philosophy of Knowledge of the Brain and its Functions*. Blackwell: Oxford, pp 115–134.

Robinson N. (1729) *A new System of the Spleen, Vapours and Hypochondriac Melancholy Wherein of the Decays of the Nerves and Lowness of Spirits are Mechanically Accounted for*. Bettesworth: London.

Rowley W. (1793) *The Rational Practice of Physic. Volume 1: A Treatise on Female and Nervous Diseases etc*. London.

Savage GH. (1892) Hypochondriases. In: Tuke DH (ed) *A Dictionary of Psychological Medicine.* Churchill: London.

Shepherd M, Cooper B, Brown AC, et al. (1966) *Psychiatric Illness in General Practice.* OUP: London.

Stukeley W. (1723) *Of the Spleen: its description & history, particularly the Vapors.* London.

Sydenham T. (1749) *The Entire Works of Dr Thomas Sydenham, newly made into English from the originals, etc* (2nd edn transl J Swann, 1st edn 1742). Cave: London.

Tourney G. (1972) The physician and witchcraft in Restoration England. *Med History* **16**: 143–155.

Trotter T. (1807) *A View of the Nervous Temperament, etc* (2nd edn). Longman: London.

Tuke DH (ed) (1892) *A Dictionary of Psychological Medicine.* Churchill: London.

Veith I. (1965) *Hysteria. The History of a Disease.* University of Chicago Press: Chicago.

Walker DP. (1981) *Unclean Spirits: Possession and Exorcism in France and England in the late 16th and early 17th centuries.* Scolar Press: London.

Walshe FMR. (1958) Some reflections upon the opening phase of the physiology of the cerebral cortex 1850–1900. In: *The History and Philosophy of Knowledge of the Brain and its Functions.* Blackwell: Oxford, pp 223–224.

Whytt R. (1767) *Observations on the Nature, Causes and Cure of those Disorders which have commonly been called Nervous, Hypochondriacal or Hysterical* (3rd edn, 1st edn 1765). Becket & Du Hondt: Edinburgh.

Willis T. (1681) The Anatomy of the Brain, being Part 5 of Five Treatises. In: *The Remaining Medical Works of . . . Dr. Thomas Willis* (transl S Pordage). Dring: London.

Willis T. (1684) Two Discourses concerning the Soul of Brutes. In: *Dr. Willis's Practice of Physick* (transl S Pordage). Dring: London.

Winslow JB. (1732) *An Anatomical Exposition of the Structure of the Human Body* (transl G Douglas). London.

3

The origin and spread of dementia paralytica

PART I

Dementia paralytica[1] is a declining disease. Deaths due to it in England and Wales were first recorded by the Registrar General in 1901 and since that year, when the number was 2272, the annual figure has fallen steadily until in 1957 it was only 68. Moreover, there is evidence (adduced below) that not more than a small part of this decline can be attributed to improvements in medical treatment. The fear that there might be a recrudescence of dementia paralytia as a result of the spread of syphilis during the second world war has not so far been realized and it seems likely that what is now, in Great Britain at all events, an obsolescent disease will soon become a rarity. Yet there are many unsolved problems in its history. We do not know, for example, why the alleged references to this striking disease were so few and so inadequate until the third decade of the 19th century. We do not know why its recognition in many countries was so tardy in spite of the clear description given by the French alienists. Nor do we know why the disease, which at the start of the 19th century seems to have been predominantly one of males, has gradually – and at different rates in different countries – become much more evenly distributed between the sexes.

The principal aim of the present essay is to recall some aspects of the history of dementia paralytica. It is a history of which psychiatrists may very properly be proud but which, perhaps, is less well known in general medicine than it

---

[1] The disease which all English-speaking physicians recognize by the term 'general paralysis of the insane' or 'GPI' has suffered from a plurality of names. Calmeil, in 1826, called it "paralysie génerale des aliénés", which was no doubt an improvement on Bayle's "arachnitis chronique" of 1822, in that it did not assume an unproved pathological cause. But later, when Baillarger and others believed they had discovered cases of general paralysis without insanity, a new name seemed necessary, and Falret in 1853 advocated "folie paralytique". However, Calmeil's term was by that time fairly entrenched and remained the favourite in spite of Salomon's quip (1862) that "he who is generally paralysed is certainly dead". Salomon suggested the alternative "general paresis" – a term which has enjoyed a considerable vogue in America. Mickle, in his authoritative English textbook on the subject (1880), gave a list of eight English and nineteen French synonyms, but his book is still entitled *General Paralysis of the Insane*. Krafft-Ebing and other German writers favoured the name 'dementia paralytica'; and in adopting this name, which I believe to be the most satisfactory one, I have had in mind not only that it over-rides the barriers of national language but also that (a) Salomon's criticism of the term "general paralysis" is unanswered, (b) the word 'insane' is a legal rather than a medical term and has since 1930 been largely expunged from English statutes, and (c) the criticism that the initial letters of dementia paralytica may be confused with those of dementia praecox is no longer a valid one. Yet during the period with which this essay is mostly concerned (that is, broadly, the 19th century), 'general paralysis of the insane' or more simply 'general paralysis' was the common English usage.

deserves.[2] A modern Oxford historian has observed that, as all history must be a selection from the facts, its presentation is often made more pointed by ordering the facts to illustrate some general theory or interpretation of the events. In the hope of adding new interest to an old tale, I have adopted this method and shall bring forward evidence to suggest: first, that dementia paralytica, from being a rare disease or even non-existent, suddenly assumed epidemic prevalence in northern France soon after the Napoleonic wars; second, that from France the new disease spread slowly across Europe and to the New World, gradually changing in its clinical manifestations; and third, that over and above the effects of treatment and prevention there has been a natural decline in its prevalence during the past fifty years. As far as they can be upheld, these points will support the well-known hypothesis that dementia paralytica is due to a special 'neurotropic' strain of the syphilitic 'virus', for they will allow us to put forward the view that a mutation giving rise to the neurotropic strain occurred in northern Europe towards the end of the 18th century; that the spread of this mutant strain explains to some extent the curious time lapse before the disease was recognized in other countries; and that, comparably with the great epidemic of syphilis in the late 15th century, the new disease slowly changed in its prevalence and clinical manifestations.[3] It must be admitted that the neurotropic hypothesis has never had a great appeal for the best authorities on the subject. Nevertheless, it has not been discredited and still provides a possible explanation of some of the historical facts about dementia paralytica which are otherwise very difficult to explain.

The clinical and pathological characteristics of dementia paralytica were first clearly delineated during the third decade of the 19th century by physicians working in the mental hospitals of Paris. These men took the view that the disease which they described had always been in existence and that it had simply escaped the notice of earlier workers. Thus, in his *Maladies du Cerveau* (1826, Introduction, p. xxiii), Bayle[4] says that chronic meningitis, which was very common in the insane and which he first described in 1822, "had never been noticed before". Georget (1820, p. 130) simply states that among demented patients "the commonest disorder of muscular power is weakness, general or partial, of voluntary movement" and makes no suggestion that there has been a recent increase in prevalence of this disorder. Calmeil (1826, p. 7) says: "The species of paralysis that I wish to describe under the title of general

---

[2] It has been strangely neglected by the historians of medicine. Neither the early history of the disease nor the name of Antoine Bayle (who is universally credited with the principal part in its delineation) are so much as mentioned in the histories of Garrison (1929), Guthrie (1945), Castiglioni (1947) or Major (1954); and there is only a passing reference in Mettler (1947). Henry, in his *History of Medical Psychology* (Zilboorg and Henry, 1941) gives a good account, but the story should have a place in the general history of medicine.

[3] The view that the 15th century outbreak of syphilis was due to a mutant strain of the spirochaete has been succinctly put in the *Lancet* (1957). See also Hirsch (1885), Mott (1908), Morris (1912), Sudhoff (1926), Whitwell (1940), Lees (1950). Some of the arguments for and against the neurotropic hypothesis of dementia paralytica are summarized by Hutton (1941) and Wilson (1941, Vol. I, Chap. 17). Curiously, however, neither of these writers makes reference to the suggestive (though limited) epidemiological evidence mentioned in support of the hypothesis by Stewart (1924). The present essay is, in one sense, an attempt to add to this epidemiological evidence.

[4] The life, character and works of Bayle and of other eminent French psychiatrists have been described by René Semelaigne (1894, 1930). The relevant parts of Bayle's inaugural thesis of 1822 on which rests his claim to have given the first clear description of dementia paralytica have been translated into English by Moore and Solomon (1934).

paralysis of the insane is far from rare; however, as far as I know, its natural history has not yet been traced in detail." By the time Esquirol wrote his *Des Maladies Mentales*, dementia paralytica had become a well-recognised condition; yet he refers (1838, vol. 2, p. 263) to the writings of Calmeil and Bayle as only confirming "the sad truth to which I drew attention in 1805" (which was, the incurability of insanity complicated by paralysis), and this observation does not suggest that Esquirol thought there was anything new in the occurrence of paralysis in the insane. This belief in the antiquity of dementia paralytica persisted through much of the 19th century. Writing what he claimed to be the first separate volume on the subject by a British author, Thomas Austin states (1859, p. 1), "General paralysis, though it had doubtless existed from the earliest period of insanity, eluded observation or at least never so fixed the attention of those who must have witnessed it, as not to be recognized and described as a distinct disease till the early part of the present century." Sankey, that sound and erudite lecturer on mental diseases to University College, London, says (1866, p. 178), "It is quite a settled point that the disease was not recognized till a comparatively recent date but distinct allusions to the symptoms may be found in authors of very ancient times"; and he later gives his opinion that the "apparent novelty" of the disease is largely due to slowness in its recognition. Writing the chapter on Progressive General Paralysis in Charcot's *Traité de Médecine*, Ballet and Blocq (1894) observed that – "The discovery of general paralysis as a distinct disease with its own characteristic lesions . . . dates from 1822 . . . Before this, general paralytics had been observed and certain peculiarities of their illness noted, but no one had thought to isolate it as a morbid entity distinct from other nosographic species recognized at the time."

Yet there is strong evidence, marshalled by Kraepelin (1913, p. 163; 1927, p. 1135), that dementia paralytica must in fact have been rare before the Parisian outbreak. We may therefore consider why the earlier writers should have taken the view that it had always been prevalent, a view not uncommonly accepted even today. Two reasons may be brought forward. In the first place, it was generally believed during the 18th century that diseases, like plant and animal species, were fixed and immutable. The works of Linnaeus had encouraged naturalists to study with increased attention the attributes of living organisms so that each could be classified into its particular species, order and genus. This stimulus soon spread to medicine and the study of *nosography*, the classification of diseases into distinct and related types, became a popular and respected specialty.[5] But in the days before Darwin and Wallace it would not have occurred to the physician that a disease (especially a chronic disease) might arise *de novo* any more than the naturalist would have expected to find a newly

---

[5] What Linnaeus had done for botany and Cuvier for zoology, Cullen of Edinburgh (1769) attempted for general medicine and his pupil, Thomas Arnold, for insanity. Arnold's *Observations on Insanity* (1786) does not appear to have exercised much influence on his contemporaries and remains a curious relic of the attempts to classify on philosophical grounds "those disorders of the *mind* which still resist the discriminatory powers of our scientific age". Philippe Pinel, a friend of Cuvier, also published a classification of mental diseases, but though his *Nosographie philosophique* (1798) proved in the end as sterile as Arnold's *Observations*, these works may serve to indicate one significant point: that during the latter part of the 18th century, mental disorders were carefully studied with a view to the classification of syndromes and we may pardonably be astonished that so striking a disease as dementia paralytica, if it had been anywhere near as prevalent as it later became, could have escaped notice.

created species. In the second place, the syphilitic origin of dementia paralytica was unsuspected or unproved during the 19th century; the principal causal factors were thought to be alcoholic and sexual excess, and those who upheld this view could scarcely have believed that the disease was a new one in history.[6]

The 19th century belief that dementia paralytica had always existed led to search for descriptions of its symptoms and signs in the writings of earlier physicians. A consequence of this search is the frequency with which Thomas Willis is quoted as having given the first description in 1672. The evidence for his claim is worth re-examining. I have been unable to discover who first drew attention to the relevant passages in the *De Anima Brutorum*, but Sankey (1864) refers to them and thereafter most writers, especially English ones, quote them as a matter of course.[7] The passages are as follows:

> "I have observed in many that when, the Brain being indisposed, they have been distemper'd with a dullness of mind and forgetfulness, and afterwards with a stupidity and foolishness, after that have fallen into a Palsie, which I oft did predict; to wit, the Morbific matter being by degrees fallen down, and at length being heaped up somewhere within the Medullar Trunk (where the Marrowy Tracts are more straitned than in the Streaked Body) to a stopping fulness. For according as the places obstructed are more or less large, so either a universal Palsie, or an half Palsie of one side, or else some partial resolutions of members happen . . .
>
> "The oppilative or stopping Particles being fallen down from the Brain and carried forward into the oblong Marrow, enter into the Nerves destinated to the Muscles of some parts of the Face, and by obstructing the ways of the Spirits in them, bring forth the Palsie in the Tongue, and sometimes a loosening of these or those Muscles of the Eyes, Eye-lids, Lips and other parts."[8]

It is, in truth, hard to see why this extract should have come to take so prominent a place in accounts of the history of dementia paralytica. A 'half palsie of one side' or

---

[6] Maudsley was the weightiest proponent of the theory of sexual excess. In the first edition of his *Physiology and Pathology of Mind* (1867, p. 360) he takes the very moderate view that the commonest cause of dementia paralytica is intemperance, alcoholic or sexual, and, acknowledging that these are nevertheless not infrequently absent, adds that then "some sort of hereditary taint is likely enough to be present". In 1873 his views are more definite and his contribution to an aetiological discussion is reported in the *Journal of Mental Science* (1873) thus: "He would by no means venture to say that sexual excess was the sole or entire cause of general paralysis . . . but of the efficiency of sexual excesses as an exciting cause he entertained no doubt"; the excesses he had in mind were not sudden outbursts of sexual activity but "that quiet steady continuance of excesses over months or years, by married people, which was apt to be thought no vice or no harm at all." By 1879 (*Pathology of Mind*, 1st edition, p. 432) his opinion on the most frequent exciting cause is – "Sexual excess I hold confidently to have that evil pre-eminence"; and in 1895 (2nd edition, p. 465): "Were it right to ascribe it to any single cause, I should fix on sexual excess and still hold the opinion despite the dissent of those inquirers who find no evidence of such excess." Although, from our later knowledge, these extracts might tempt us to reflect on the puritan strain in Maudsley and on the Victorian attitude to sex, yet, until the weight of evidence associating dementia paralytic with syphilis became overwhelming, the theory of sexual excess explained the facts as well as any other theory and better than most. At times, however, the attempt to reconcile fact and theory strains even Maudsley's ingenuity: commenting on the rarity of general paralysis in the Highlands of Scotland, "where there is of course no deficiency of women or whisky", he asserts that an open-air life and "a great deal of bodily exercise" make people less likely to be provoked into excesses and more capable of withstanding them.

[7] Mickle (1880, p. 2) assigns the chief merit of the discovery of general paralysis to "Willis, Haslam, Bayle and Calmeil, especially the first three". I doubt whether any Frenchman would agree.

[8] Most writers quote in the original Latin, but for the benefit of those whose Latin is as rusty as my own, I give the translation made by Samuel Pordage in 1684. The 'streaked body' is, of course, the corpus striatum. Willis's explanation of paralysis is based on the theory that normal functioning of the nervous system depends on the unimpeded flow of vital spirits from the brain down through supposed channels in the nerve tracts. A 'morbific' process manifested itself by the generation of 'stopping' particles (or 'oppilative' particles, from the Latin, *oppilare*, to stop up) in the brain, and these, carried down into the narrower nerve channels, tended to clog them and so impede or prevent the flow of vital spirits.

palsy of the tongue and eyes are not at all characteristic of the disease; Griesinger (1861, p. 396) for example says, "It is only in exceptional cases that we observe greater weakness in one half of the body, an inclination of the tongue to one side, obliquity of countenance . . . Strabismus and disorders of movement of the eyes generally scarcely ever occur." Much of the description would fit the case of arteriosclerotic dementia with its slowly progressive amnesia punctuated by cerebro-vascular attacks associated with paralysis. Certainly, of the illustrative case histories which Willis gives later (pp 174–6), most show either intra-cerebral haemorrhage at post-mortem or a satisfactory response to treatment. A scrutiny of the rest of the chapter shows that Willis's concept of palsie was a wide one and included simple exhaustion and weakness. "Long and immoderate sadness, a Consumption, a Scorbutic Atrophy or wasting, being long fixed in Bed, unhealthy old Age . . . at length brings on a *Palsie*" (p. 165). Again, on a different aspect, he says (p. 166), "They who are frequently and grievously obnoxious to the Colick at length become also paralytic. The cause is so frequent here, that the succession of this Disease is accounted among its *prognosticks*." This passage may suggest lead poisoning,[9] but certainly not dementia paralytica. In the case of the "young and handsome woman" who, after suffering "a most cruel and continual Colick", became "molested with a stupefaction", Willis observes again that such distempers often forerun a palsie, which indeed followed here so that "not only all her greater Members, as her arms and legs, but almost every lesser joynt or limb was almost wholly loosened that she could not move hand nor foot or the fingers or toes of either". Yet after a month or two the young lady recovered completely. From such examples we may reasonably conclude that Willis, in observing that states of 'stupidity' were sometimes followed by palsie, had in mind diseases altogether different from dementia paralytica. Moreover, if brief generalizations are going to be adduced as evidence for the existence of dementia paralytica, why pick on Willis? Other passages from much earlier writers might equally well be adduced. Thus Hippocrates (quoted by Whitwell, 1940) says, "Mental weakness associated with a shaking voice, a tongue and voice tremulous, indicates a grave form of mental disorder",[10] and Whitwell quotes similar passages from Celsus, Aretaeus, Galen and Avicenna; one from Boerhaave in 1761 seems closer to the mark than Willis's: "if in an apparently healthy young man noticeable tremor occurs about the lips or eyelids with stammer, then paralysis will follow and death from apoplexy." Such passages have been ignored (rightly enough), yet the references to Willis continue. Morton's *Medical Bibliography* (1954), for example, states simply that Willis's *De Anima Brutorum* "includes a description of general paralysis, probably the first definite

---

[9] Griesinger (1861, p. 172) wrote: "In lead poisoning the excitement passes frequently into stupor; besides, there are often cramps and paralysis: the prior existence of lead colic . . . may assist in forming the diagnosis". Meryon (1864), discussing a case of plumbism, says: "for nearly two years the characteristic colic of lead-poisoning preceded the paralysis; and such is the invariable course of the disease." In the 17th and 18th centuries, not only was industrial plumbism common but "outbreaks of lead poisoning occurred throughout Western Europe as the result of the addition of lead to wine to promote fermentation and because of its employment in the manufacture and storage of cider and in materials for cooking vessels and other household articles" (Cantarow and Trumper, 1944).

[10] Bucknill and Tuke (1858, p. 17) also refer to this passage from the *Corpus Hippocraticum*: "We might recognize here" (they say) "symptoms of incipient general paralysis."

recognition of the condition"; Garrison (1929, pp 263 and 827) makes a similar as-sertion. These continued claims on Willis's behalf are the more surprising as they are contrary to the authoritative opinion of Robertson (1923); Robertson thought it "much more likely that Willis refers to senile or arteriosclerotic dementia". The fact is that no claim for the recognition of a disease can safely be based on a brief general-ization; it must rest on detailed case-histories of which one may be sufficient but more than one is always preferable. Willis indeed gives us case-histories, but these serve only to weaken still further the claim that he described dementia paralytica.[11]

A much more likely contender for the first English account of the disease is John Haslam, apothecary to Bethlem Hospital. In 1798 the first edition of Haslam's *Observations on Insanity* was published, and his Case 15 (p. 115) is usually upheld as the most convincing pre-Parisian description of dementia paralytica. Robertson (1923) says it "presents a clinical and pathological picture so typical that no one has ever doubted the diagnosis". Now we are told that the patient, a man of 42, ad-mitted to Bethlem Hospital in 1795, "had some years before travelled with a gentle-man over a great part of Europe" and therefore, if the case was one of dementia paralytica, we can imagine that he might have acquired the disease from the same source as, on our hypothesis, led to the Paris outbreak. On the other hand, we are dealing with an isolated case and authorities are in agreement (see, for example, Krafft-Ebing, 1894, pp 75 and 78; S. A. K. Wilson, 1954, Vol. 1, p. 553) that in any single instance the differential diagnosis on clinical and gross anatomical grounds between dementia paralytica and cerebral syphilis may be impossible; indeed, the facts that in Haslam's case the first sign of illness was a sudden headache and that the mouth was "drawn aside" are perhaps more suggestive of the latter condition. Moreover Leigh (1955) has commented on the post-mortem aspects of this case that "it is im-possible to hold that he (Haslam) has given a recognizable description of the macro-scopic anatomy of general paresis". A more serious objection to the establishment of our hypothesis is the much-quoted observation of Haslam on paralytic affections of the insane. The passage below is taken from the first edition (1798, p. 120) of the *Observations on Insanity*, the sentences in brackets being those added in the second (renamed) edition (1809, p. 259).

> "Paralytic affections are a much more frequent cause of insanity than has been commonly supposed (and they are also a very common effect of madness; more maniacs die of hemiplegia and apoplexy than from any other cause). In those afflicted from this cause we are, on inquiry, enabled to trace a sudden affection, or fit, to have preceded the disease. These patients usually bear marks of such affection, independently of their insanity: the speech is impeded and the mouth drawn aside; an arm or leg is more or less deprived of its capacity of being moved by the will; and in by far the greatest number of these cases the memory is particularly affected. (Persons thus dis-ordered are in general not at all sensible of being so affected. When so feeble that they can scarcely stand they commonly say they feel perfectly strong and capable of great exertions. However pitiable these objects may be to the feeling spectator, yet it is fortunate for the condition of the

[11] That a single case may be sufficient is illustrated by another of Willis's case histories in the same chapter 'On Palsie' of the *De Anima Brutorum* (p. 167). The "prudent and honest Woman" with the "spurious Palsie" who, when she spoke too long or too eagerly, became as mute as a fish for an hour or two, must surely, as Guthrie (1903) pointed out, have suffered from myasthenia gravis.

sufferer that his pride and pretensions are exalted in proportion to the degradation of the calamity which affects him.) Very few of these cases have received any benefit in the hospital; and from enquiries I have been able to make at the private houses where they have been afterwards confined, it has appeared that they either died suddenly from apoplexy or have had repeated fits from the effects of which they have sunk into a stupid state and have gradually dwindled away."

This passage is usually taken to indicate that dementia paralytica must have been common at Bethlem Hospital as early as 1798; but I shall attempt to dispute that view.

First, Haslam's description differs in many respects from the classical descriptions of dementia paralytica. In dementia paralytica, the mental changes are usually observed before, not after, the onset of paralysis; the paralysis develops gradually, not suddenly; it is rare for a single limb or the ipsilateral limbs only to be involved; and while apoplectiform fits are common, persistent hemiplegia is rare and death in apoplexy is also rare. As the clinical signs of dementia paralytica have changed somewhat during the past century, I will support my assertions by quoting from early, but authoritative, writers. As regards the relation between the time of onset of the mental and of the paralytic symptoms, Calmeil (1826, p. 336) says that "at Charenton, paralysis almost always appears after the onset of the mental disturbance", and Prichard (1835, p. 106) says: "It results, from a great number of observations purposely made by MM. Calmeil, Esquirol and others, that general paralysis commences sometimes long after mental derangement; in other instances simultaneously with it; while in a comparatively few cases it precedes the manifestation of disorders in the mind." As regards the mode of onset of the paralysis, the disease runs its course "gradually and even slowly, the symptoms appearing and developing themselves in a regular succession" (ibid., p. 105). As regards the mouth, Calmeil (1826, p. 10) says that the mouth and face preserve their natural position, and Westphal (1868), who gives a very careful and thorough account of the motor symptoms of dementia paralytica, says, "Unilateral paralyses of the tongue or of the face either do not occur at all, or, where they have been observed, play but an unimportant part in so far as they exhibit as a rule merely transitory, suggestive and incomplete phenomena." Westphal also observes that the apoplectiform and epileptiform attacks of dementia paralytica frequently result in unilateral or bilateral paralyses but "all these paralyses have the peculiarity that they very soon, in the course of a few hours or days, either entirely or almost entirely disappear . . . In exceptional cases they remain persistent." As regards hemiplegia and apoplexy as a cause of death, Skae (1860) examined 78 patients dying of dementia paralytica but could attribute only one death to apoplexy and one other to exhaustion from a succession of epileptic fits; Calmeil (1826, p. 79) had earlier said that death seldom follows as the simple consequence of cerebral disease.

Second, Haslam's remarks could equally well be taken to apply to other diseases, notably chronic alcoholism. "Of all forms of chronic insanity", Griesinger (1861, p. 570) wrote, "drunkenness especially appears to possess much in common with general paralysis"; and indeed the similarity gave rise to the name "alcoholic pseudo-paresis". We know, too, that chronic alcoholism had become very common in England towards the end of the 18th century from the recently developed habit of dram-drinking, and its mental effects were far more common than in France, where wines rather than spirits were the national beverage. Thus Prichard (1835, p. 204) says, "Drunkenness is a much more prevailing vice in England and in Germany than in France, Italy and Spain . . . In public lunatic asylums in England, it is generally known that, in a great proportion of cases, dram-drinking is the exciting cause." In 1844, this proportion was given as 18% by the Lunacy Commissioners (Bucknill and Tuke, 1858, p. 44), though at Bethlem Hospital Sir Alexander Morison found it only 12%. However, to quote Griesinger again (1861, p. 171), "it is generally recognized that in later times the abuse of spirits in England has very much diminished". We may conclude that insanity due to alcoholism must have been very common in England in Haslam's time; moreover, the increase in prevalence had only recently occurred, so that the cause of the associated dementia and paralyses might often have been missed.

Third, the case records of Bethlem Hospital have been preserved (though somewhat incompletely) since the year 1816 and provide original and impartial evidence on the frequency with which paralysis was diagnosed by Haslam's immediate successors. I have examined these records for the three years 1816–1818 and find that, of 295 cases admitted during those years, paralysis or a 'suspicion of paralysis' is mentioned in 19 (16 male, 3 female). However, the word 'paralysis' is clearly used in the same loose sense in which Willis used it. Any weak stuporous or troublesome patient was liable to be called paralytic.[12] Thus a 60-year old ironmonger remains

---

[12] There was a rule at Bethlem that patients who developed fits or became paralytic could be discharged immediately as incurable. In the Minutes of Evidence of the Committee appointed by Parliament in 1815 to consider the better regulation of madhouses in England there occur the following curious exchanges, which suggest that a diagnosis of 'paralysis' might be no more than a mere administrative convenience. The Committee were questioning Wallet, at that time steward of Bethlem Hospital, concerning the early discharge of patients subject to fits or paralysis. Wallet replied (p. 64):

"–I remember a woman who was discharged as paralytic, who came from Hoxton; the nurses said at the time that she was the strongest patient in the house; she was returned to Miles's.

Do you know Sarah Payne? – Yes.

Was she a strong healthy-looking person? – Very much so.

Was she a violent patient? – She was.

By whose order was she sent to Hoxton? – She was discharged by the medical gentlemen as paralytic.

Had she any paralytic attack during the time she was in the Hospital? – I never heard of any attack.

Had she, in your opinion, the appearance of a person who suffered under paralysis? – I do not know that she had; I saw the difficulty they had in taking her away, in putting on a strait waistcoat; she was very strong."

The matron of Bethlem, Elizabeth Forbes, was also questioned on Sarah Payne (p. 76):

"While she was with you, had she any paralytic attack? – She was much worse when she went back than when she came; she was more violent and unhappy and distressed, always asking if she was going to be murdered and such things; Mr. Haslam thought she was paralytic.

Had she a fit? – I never knew her to have a fit.

No contraction of limbs? – No.

No want of articulation? – No, not at all; but she was always kept handcuffed lately, and chained.

She was sent out in a considerably increased state of violence than when she came in? – Yes, which Mr. Haslam attributed to paralytic (sic).

Was she very strong? – Very strong; it required three or four people to move her; she was brought to the side-room every day, but there was great difficulty in moving her, she wanted her liberty I believe."

Later still in the Inquiry, Haslam himself was questioned about Sarah Payne (p. 128):

"What became of her? – I do not know; she was discharged from the Hospital; she was paralytic.

She was discharged as paralytic? – She was in a general state of tremor. We apprehended she would soon die; she was incurable. Patients becoming sick and weak, and not being able to undergo the discipline of the house, are immediately discharged."

"motionless and silent . . . like an immovable statue" for many months, though his health and appetite are good; yet Dr Tuthill says, "from the extreme slowness of manner and dumbness of this patient, I apprehend something of a paralytick nature has already taken place". A sailor aged 22, suddenly taken ill seven months before admission, is "occasionally violent, threatens to hang himself, swears a great deal, is dull and heavy but in good health"; Dr E. T. Monro then notes that "some suspicion of paralysis is to be attached to this case and more especially as he appears to have been wounded in the head". A lace-maker of 46 becomes weak and tremulous and develops anasarca of her legs: she is reported as "dropsical or paralytick" and is later said "to be approaching a state of paralysis or to have already suffered from it". It is noteworthy that, of the 16 males described as paralytic, three were innkeepers. Four of the 19 cases are said to have had exalted or grandiose ideas and one of these was an innkeeper. Altogether, I think the diagnosis of dementia paralytica can be seriously considered only in five cases (though a further four cases, of which the notes are perfunctory, could possibly have been paretic). Of these five cases, one is under some suspicion on account of his youth (26 years), another because he was, after a year's stay in the "curable establishment", accepted as a chronic patient (which implies that he had violent or dangerous propensities). I conclude that, although the occurrence of dementia paralytica at Bethlem Hospital during this period was possible and even probable, it was certainly not common.[13]

---

[13] Of the 19 cases stated to be paralytic, the three which seem to me the most suggestive of dementia paralytica are as follows:

(1) Male, age not stated, admitted 18 July 1816.

"Disordered about 5 weeks. Was disordered 2 years ago and recovered. Talks incoherently – not mischievous. Comes from the Parish of New Windsor, played the Serpent in the Earl of Dartmouth's Band. Staffordshire Militia 2 or 3 years ago.

July 20th. A Tremor observable in this case with great incoherence of discourse. 23rd. From the evident tremor of his limbs and lips it is to be feared that Paralytick symptoms may come on in this case.

Aug. 3rd. He imagines that he is the greatest of singers and that he performs at Covent Garden Theatre every night at the present time. 15th. Remains as heretofore. 20th. Either he has already suffered some slight Paralytick attack or the probability is that he will suffer it ere long.

Sept. 10th. Remains in the same condition and is a hopeless case, I fear. 26th. Becomes worse – trembles much and stammers in his speech sometimes – is very much lost in his mind. Has very grand ideas – considers according to Dowie's account that he has four millions of money.

Oct. 30th. He continues to exhibit symptoms of some Paralytick attack which has deprived him of his intellect. He continually harps on his wealth and musical abilities. The use of Calomel keeps him in an equable state.

November. Evident symptoms of Paralysis exist in this case and the grand line of operation appears to be the prevention of any fresh accession of similar attacks. His health is pretty good at this time.

December. The imbecility of mind which accompanies or rather succeeds Paralytick symptoms was never more obvious than in this case. His answers to questions will vary every minute. He will call his wife by 3 different names and give the most incoherent account with a stammering and tremulous voice."

(No further notes.)

(2) Male, age 26, admitted 20.11.1817.

"Disorder'd six months. This is the first attack. He imagines himself a great Commander, being a Jew Lawyer.

Dec. At the latter end of this month, he faulter'd very much in his speech and was evidently partially Paralytick.

Jan. There can be no doubt that some slight degree of paralysis has occurred in this case. The stammering tongue, staring eyes, great incoherence of speech and general demeanour evince this plainly.

Feb. This patient shows repeated proofs of his having suffer'd from some attack of paralytick tendency. His spirits are ever good.   [continued on next page]

Finally, it cannot be without significance that none of Haslam's younger contemporaries credit him with the discovery or even the description of dementia paralytica, although they were certainly well acquainted with his works. Burrows, commenting somewhat sceptically on Haslam's and Esquirol's assertion of the great prevalence of paralysis among the insane, says (1829, p. 175): "In adopting the term paralysis, as it occurs in connection with insanity, we are not sufficiently precise. Paralysis, like apoplexia, comprises very different states of disease."[14] A passage in Prichard's *Treatise on Insanity* suggests that the Bristol alienist's silence on Haslam was not mere oversight. Haslam had resigned his post as apothecary to Bethlem in 1815 but Prichard, writing of general paralysis in 1835 (p. 109), says, "At Bethlem I was assured by the house-steward . . . that he has in many instances recognized the early symptoms of this disease . . . The disease, as it occurred in Bethlem, is characterized by the same symptoms as at Charenton, viz. by imperfect muffling articulation, by tottering in the gait, weakness and inaccuracy in the voluntary movements. Monomania, with pride and the illusive belief in great possessions, is

[continued from previous page]

March. He continued very cheerful during this month altho' evidently shattered in his mind and Paralytick. He has an exceedingly good appetite, and is ready to shake hands with everybody. No coherence of speech.

May. It appearing that this patient was altogether paralytick, and that his malady arose solely from this cause, no prospect appearing of rendering him any advantage, he was this day Discharged as an Improper Object.
(signed E. T. Monro)."

(3) Male, aged 40, admitted 2.7.1818.

"This man has been disordered only 4 months and married only 6 months. He has been 3 weeks at Mr. Pell's Somers Town. He has lived 8 years with Messrs. Rundell & Bridge, Ludgate Hill. He has attempted suicide and is a native of Scarborough. He has a brother who threw himself over Blackfriars Bridge. He had a most excellent character.

Aug. 22. This man has one of the most remarkable craniums Dr. Monro ever saw. There still remains a great propensity to suicide and he appears to be partially paralytick.

Sept. He has an idea that his food and everything else he takes is poisoned. He is a truly deplorable object in every respect.

Oct. A little improvement is observable in this case since the last account. He talks less and is not so much agitated in his general demeanour. He is described as cleanly in his person.

Nov. A very miserable object, decidedly liable to attacks of Paralysis. Stammers in his speech and is extremely confused in his ideas. Very zealous in defence of his master.

Dec. Troubled with a Dyarrhoea about this Period.

Jan 11. Died of Apoplexy.

Appearance observed on examining the Body, 11th Jan. 1819:

All the vessels of the Dura and Pia Mater were loaded with blood. The surface of the latter membrane was copiously moistened with a serous Effusion. The arachnoid coat was thick and opake over the convexities of the cerebral hemispheres, and the Texture of the Pia Mater generally distended with fluid. The lateral Ventricles were considerably larger than usual and contained an increased quantity of fluid; but they were not distended.
(signed Wm. Lawrence, E. T. Monro)."

[14] The terms palsy and paralysis have given rise to some confusion in the history of medicine. They have been used to cover: (a) general enfeeblement of movement arising from any cause (for example, Willis's "being long fixed in bed"); (b) all degrees of muscular weakness attributable to special disease rather than to general debility (for example, Parkinson's "shaking palsy"); and (c) complete or nearly complete loss of voluntary power (for example, Salomon's usage, where the term 'paresis' is reserved for partial loss of power). The Parisian physicians who described dementia paralytica were well aware of the semantic difficulty: Delaye in 1824 used the term "paralysie générale et incomplète" and Calmeil (1826, p. 9) adopted the shorter term "paralysie générale" only with reluctance and perhaps because (as Baillarger suggested) it was already in common use.

The term 'general' as applied to paralysis was also a source of confusion. See an inconclusive discussion in the *Journal of Mental Science* (1896).

the mental disease which has been noticed in the majority of the cases." In his Croonian lectures of 1849, Conolly not only makes no reference to Haslam but says (p. 38), "it is extraordinary that scarcely a trace, if even a trace of a description of a paralysis, so distinct and peculiar in its character, should be found until we come to the writings of physicians yet living"; but Haslam had died in 1844. Bucknill and Tuke, in their *Manual of Psychological Medicine* (1st edition, 1858) do not mention Haslam in connection with general paralysis, nor for that matter do Falret (1853), Griesinger (1861) or Krafft-Ebing (1866). Baillarger (1860) referred to Haslam's case, but did not attach much significance to it as "very many similarly precise passages have been buried for centuries without being noticed until they were dug up by historians". In 1866 Sankey (p. 178) observes, though without further comment, that "to (Esquirol) is due the credit of attracting attention more pointedly to this disease, though Esquirol himself attributes the merit to Haslam".[15] It is from this time (so far as I can determine) that Haslam's claim begins to be more definitely and generally asserted, not only by English writers (Mickle, 1880, p. 2) but by the French (Bonnet and Poincaré, 1868, p. 4) and the German (Krafft-Ebing, 1894). Yet I cannot but think that the silence of Haslam's contemporaries, who knew and admired his work and who also knew the disease, speaks more eloquently than the historical researches of later times.

   Willis and Haslam are, by common consent (at least in English-speaking countries), agreed to have the strongest of the claims put forward for a description of dementia paralytica before the Parisians. I will not, therefore, discuss the claims made for other early writers. Mönkemüller (1911), who studied the subject at the request of Kraepelin, found "only a few cases, mostly very disputable", in the records of the 18th and earlier centuries. Among the Hundred Cases published by Chiarugi in 1793, Meckel only detected "at least one undoubted case of general paralysis, perhaps even a second"; and Möbius made an interesting observation that during the 18th century no famous man died of any illness resembling dementia paralytica, although during the 19th century such instances were common, for example Schumann, Donizetti, Nietzsche and Maupassant (Kraepelin, 1927, pp 1135 *et seq.*). More noteworthy, perhaps, than the weakness of the positive evidence is the fact that so many able investigators said nothing which can be taken to indicate any acquaintance with the disease. Pinel himself, as late as 1809, when the second edition of his treatise was published, makes no special mention of dementia in association with paralysis. Yet he was acquainted with Haslam's work (which he praises) and moreover Pinel was, until 1795, Physician to Bicêtre, the Parisian hospital for incurable male

---

[15] Why, we may wonder, should Esquirol have credited Haslam with a discovery that Haslam's own countrymen denied him? Were it not out of keeping with the magnanimous character of that great Frenchman, we might be tempted to suppose a wish to attenuate the claims of the upstart Bayle, a young man who did not belong to the school of Pinel and Esquirol but had been trained in pathological anatomy by his uncle Gaspard Laurent Bayle and his uncle's friend Laennec. A more reasonable explanation, however, would be that Esquirol, who always thought of paralysis as only a complication of insanity, would have seen no reason to believe that the cases he saw in Paris and which were later delimited by Bayle and Calmeil differed in any fundamental way from other cases of paralysis in the insane already described by Haslam.

lunatics where, if anywhere at that time, dementia paralytica should have been common.[16]

This failure to describe dementia paralytica would – if the disease had been there to describe – be all the more surprising when we take into account the striking clinical syndrome which it commonly presented. Calmeil (1826, p. 326) found the peculiar delusions to be *"infiniment remarquable"*. Conolly (1849, p. 39) makes the statement that "of all modifications of mental disorder, the form which is either accompanied from the first with that variety of paralysis which has of late years been observed and described as general paralysis, or eventually supervenes upon such bodily affection, is the most remarkable". Bucknill (1857) says, "The diagnosis of general paralysis is practically of the most facile sort" and "the form of intellectual disorder, moreover, is frequently of the most remarkable kind". Maudsley (1879, p. 432) says, "The group of cases described under this head (general paralysis) unquestionably constitute the most definite and satisfactory example of a clinical variety of mental disease." The egregious characteristics to which these writers draw attention apply principally of course to the grandiose type of dementia paralytica. This type was also called the classical type, partly because most of the cases described by Bayle (1826) were of this nature and partly because it was, during most of the 19th century, the commonest type.[17]

The great conceptual advance made by Bayle in 1822 was his belief that the mental symptoms of dementia paralytica and the associated paralysis were both the direct consequence of visible pathological changes in the brain and meninges. We may ask why, if dementia paralytica was always common, such an association between insanity, paralysis and brain change was not noticed earlier. That paralysis was the result of brain change, had of course, long been known, as Willis's cases sufficiently illustrate. The post-mortem examinations made by Chiarugi (Bayle, 1826, p. 383) and Greding (Prichard, 1835, p. 210) showed that vascular engorgement, thickening of the membranes, effusions between the dura and the pia mater and increased fluid in the ventricles were all common findings in the brains of insane patients. No doubt many of these changes were due to agonal infection, prolonged debility, fits, or old head injury; but in the brains of other cases which had shown similar mental symptoms nothing abnormal was to be found. Hence the general opinion arose that post-mortem brain changes were not due

---

[16] Browne (1875) says, "It would be difficult to rest satisfied with the belief that, whatever may be the cause, general paralysis did not exist until about 50 years ago, or that it had entirely escaped the cognizance of physicians, general and special; yet it is certain that on examining the works left by Pinel and his predecessors it is impossible to discover any monographic description of this frightful affliction, now so readily detected and diagnosed, although these distinguished men had, for long periods, access to all the experience afforded in Asylums for the Insane." But the Scottish Commissioner in Lunacy cannot have it both ways; either the disease did not exist or it existed but was not recognized.

[17] Between January, 1815 and July, 1823, Bayle (1826, p. 568) collected 189 cases of "chronic meningitis" (i.e. dementia paralytica) among 847 male admissions, and 25 among 606 female admissions to Charenton. His excellent case histories are monotonously similar in their clinical features and no series like them had ever been described before. His patients govern the universe, have 40 million tons of gold, own marble palaces, or build a new paradise. It was, as Bayle says (p. 547), "toujours le même, d'idées dominantes de richesse, de grandeur, de puissance".

to the mental disorder but to its complications – paralysis, phthisis, scurvy, etc. Pinel, according to Prichard (1835, p. 212), "seemed to give up hope of elucidating the pathology of mental derangement by necroscopical research", and this may have been a good reason for his belief (Pinel, 1809, p. 142) that "the primitive seat of insanity is generally in the region of the stomach and intestines and it is from that centre that the disorder of intelligence propagates itself". Esquirol, at least in his earlier years, was of the same opinion and in his article on Dementia in the *Dictionnaire des Sciences Médicales*, 1814, says, "The opening of the body teaches us nothing with regard to (the seat of dementia) and all the organic alterations of the brain belong less to insanity than to its complications. I possess many observations on anatomical pathology which, compared with the history of the illness, prove that madness existed before any organic lesion of the brain and that when the organic lesion took place it showed itself by convulsions or paralyses which are present as complications." Such a view is understandable if organic causes of mental disorder were rare or associated only with simple dementia; but if dementia paralytica had always been common one might have expected that the constant association between its mental and physical signs and its obvious pathological brain changes would have been noticed by the many able investigators who looked for such associations before 1822.

The evidence thus far may be summarized as follows: (1) no very satisfactory or unequivocal accounts of a disease corresponding to dementia paralytica had been given before those of the Parisian alienists in the early 19th century; (2) yet by 1823, Bayle found that a fifth of all male admissions to Charenton conformed to his description of "l'aliénation mentale avec paralysie incomplete par suite de meningitis chronique", while Esquirol (1838, p. 272) gives this proportion in 1826–28 as more than a quarter; (3) in noting the absence of earlier accounts, we must bear in mind not only the striking clinical and pathological features of the disease but also the fact that insanity had been carefully studied during the late 18th century from the aspects of nosology and brain pathology. One explanation of these observations is that dementia paralytica, from being a rare or non-existent disease, suddenly became very prevalent in Paris during the second decade of the 19th century. It was not recognized before because it had rarely or never occurred before; it was recognized by the Parisian alienists because it became so common there that it could not be missed[18]; it was not thought to be a new disease because physicians believed

---

[18] This would of course in no way lessen the merit of its first describers. The efflorescence of genius which led to and was evoked by the discovery of dementia paralytica is one of the most astonishing and glorious chapters in psychiatry. Baillarger (1860) considered this discovery the most important single achievement in the history of mental disease; Harrington Tuke (1859) wrote of Calmeil's *De la Paralysie* that it described general paralysis "with a terseness and success that may be considered as rendering his work unrivalled in medical literature". Robertson is no less emphatic: referring to the publication in 1826 of Bayle's *Traité des Maladies du Cerveau* and Calmeil's *De la Paralysie*, he says – "The appearance in the same year of two such books . . ., both dealing with a newly discovered disease in so masterly a fashion, is unique in the history of medicine. And, although much has been written about general paralysis during a century, the disease is described in these two books so fully, so faithfully and so convincingly that future additions to our knowledge seem little more than details. No other book devoted to this subject alone was written for two generations afterwards, nor was there any needed." I wish I could add the commendation of some general physician.

that diseases, like species, were enduring and immutable.[19] Another explanation, however, was put forward by Robertson (1923) in his excellent essay on the discovery of general paralysis. He considered that the Napoleonic wars must have produced "a large harvest of cases of general paralysis", many of which would come to the two great mental hospitals of Paris, Bicêtre and Charenton (the latter catering particularly for army officers). These hospitals had been re-organized by or under the influence of Pinel, who had introduced kindness and orderliness into the regime and insisted on full and careful case-records. "These symptoms of general paralysis", says Robertson, "are so striking that the great number of similar cases thus collected together could scarcely have been overlooked when Pinel's method of caring for the insane was adopted." This may be conceded and is not incompatible with the first explanation; but, unlike the first explanation, it does not account for the later history of dementia paralytica and for the evidence which suggests that, from its origin in northern France, the disease spread in a fairly well-defined manner across Europe, then to America and later still to less highly industrialized countries.

PART II

The earliest definite reference to dementia paralytica in France is, I think, that of Esquirol, who in 1814 wrote: "When paralysis is a complication of dementia, all the paralytic symptoms appear one after the other; first of all, articulation of sounds is laboured; soon after locomotion is made with difficulty; finally, there is loss of control of the excretions." The disease was certainly common at Charenton in 1816, when the cases described by Bayle began to be admitted; and we have Esquirol's word for it that by 1828 one-sixth of all admissions to Charenton were paretic and the disease was common at Bicêtre and at the St Yon asylum near Rouen (quoted by Prichard, 1835, p. 101). Yet it remained rare in the south of France (Esquirol, 1838, p. 273): between 1822 and 1825 Rech found no case among 132 admissions of insane patients to the hospital at Montpellier; in Toulouse, Delaye found only five cases among 111 patients (no date given); while in north Italy it was rarer still, as Esquirol himself confirmed in 1834. Even in 1849, Lunier concluded from personal observation that dementia paralytica was rare in the south of France. Yet by 1876 it must

---

[19] We might even hazard the guess that the honour of being the eponymous discoverer of dementia paralytica went to Bayle because, not being a pupil of Esquirol and having no great experience of mental disease, he saw his patients' behaviour without the preconceptions of instruction or of habit. Bayle was only 19 when he became interne under Royer-Collard at Charenton, and only 23 when he submitted his inaugural thesis (1822). But Georget, Delaye, Falret and Calmeil would be thoroughly familiar with the classification and opinions of their great teacher, Esquirol, and of his great teacher, Pinel; they were for many years unable to conceive that paralysis could be other than a mere epiphenomenon of insanity, as scurvy or phthisis might be; and Esquirol himself never abandoned that view (Baillarger, 1859, 1860). "There is a suspicion", says Robertson, "that antagonism to Bayle existed because he did not belong to the school of Esquirol." This is too mild. It is obvious that intense passions were aroused. Esquirol's pupils went out of their way to pour scorn on Bayle's ideas and to belittle his achievements. According to Toulouse (1922), even Pinel pronounced his work "premature and useless". We read with sorrow but without surprise that after his term of office as interne at Charenton ended in 1823, Bayle drifted away from the study of mental diseases to that of general medicine, anatomy, medical history and (*horresco referens*) bibliography. He died in 1858, two years before the writings of Baillarger convinced his compatriots that dementia paralytica might properly be called "la maladie de Bayle".

have become common, for we read that "in the south of France, if we may judge from the official returns, general paralysis has greatly increased during the last generation or two and at present is nearly equal to that in the north" (18th Report of the Commissioners in Lunacy for Scotland).

Two further observations may serve to suggest that for many years dementia paralytica was uncommon except in the environs of Paris. Salomon (1862) states, "France is the peculiar focus . . . Paris is the headquarters of the disease." Krafft-Ebing (1866) gives a list of the literature concerning dementia paralytica "from the earliest up to the most recent date" and has no reference to any but French writings until 1848. He missed some of the English literature but he is unlikely to have missed any German work.[20] The absence of early German references suggests that dementia paralytica was too rare in that country for the French descriptions to arouse much interest. This is confirmed by Mönkemüller's study (1911) of the case records preserved from the penitentiary and madhouse at the town of Celle, near Hanover. The records cover the period 1750 to 1831 and among 669 cases, Mönkemüller found 31 resembling dementia paralytica. They were distributed over the years as follows:

Years	Admissions	Cases resembling dementia paralytica
1750–1800	211	0
1801–1810	153	6
1811–1820	188	15
1821–1830	117	10

The diminished number of cases in the last decade is probably accounted for by Mönkemüller's observation that many cases were then being diverted to a new hospital at Hildesheim. It is of interest, too, that "a relatively large number" of the 31 cases were soldiers and had therefore probably been in conflict with Napoleon's armies.

In England, Burrows (1829) seems to have been the first to comment on the new disease. He refers to the descriptions of Georget, Bayle and Calmeil, and then (p. 177) remarks on the singular discrepancy in the prevalence of paralysis complicated by insanity in the French as compared with the English hospitals. In the latter, "from inquiry I know the number is comparatively trivial . . . In my own practice, the proportion has not been one in twenty." Conolly (1830), in his *Inquiry concerning the Indications of Insanity*, makes no mention of paralysis in spite of a reference to Bayle's "excellent work".[21] Prichard (1835) went to some pains to determine whether

[20] Meyer (1959) has pointed out that Griesinger, in the first edition of his textbook (1845) drew attention to the occurrence of "so-called general paralysis" in Germany.

[21] Conolly confirms Bayle's observation that many patients dying of consumption show *spes phthisica*. The reference is not, of course, to the pathologist Gaspard Laurent Bayle, who wrote the famous *Recherches sur la phtisie pulmonaire*, but to Gaspard's nephew Antoine and his *Maladies du Cerveau* (p. 551).

Burrows's opinion was correct but (p. 108) he "met with considerable difficulties in obtaining satisfactory information". He concluded, however, that the disease was "comparatively rare in private asylums" and, in the one public asylum (Gloucester) for which he gives figures, only 16 cases had been observed since 1828. Yet by 1849 the situation must have changed, for Conolly in his Croonian lectures says that general paralysis was common in all the asylums of England, France, Belgium and Germany, though rare in Italy and Spain. We may consider, too, the progress of the disease in one particular asylum, the Middlesex Lunatic Asylum at Hanwell, from figures given by its superintendents. Sir William Ellis makes no mention of dementia paralytica in his *Treatise on Insanity* of 1838. Two years later Millingen (1840) finds only twelve cases of paralysis among 1000 patients and contrasts this with the high prevalence at Charenton. By 1849, however, Conolly finds that among 690 deaths at Hanwell over the last ten years, the proportion of those due to general paralysis was 37% in males and 11% in females. These figures for a London asylum were probably well above the average for the country, as in 1876, when the annual reports of the Commissioners in Lunacy first give separate statistics, the proportion of deaths from general paralysis in all the asylums of England and Wales was 14% in males and 3% in females.[22]

The disease does not seem to have appeared in Scotland until 1839, nor was this due to lack of knowledge of it. "I saw the disease in Paris in 1832", says Browne (1875), "but did not recognize it in this country till 1839." It soon became fairly common in Edinburgh and Glasgow (Workman, 1858) but elsewhere remained rare or unknown for many years. Thus Skae (1860) says that his former pupil Howden, who had been well acquainted with the disease in Edinburgh, could not find a single case among the 300 patients of the Montrose Asylum; and during the years 1869–1872, among 200 admissions to the Fife and Kinross Asylum, Batty Tuke discovered only four cases (Bucknill and Tuke, 1874, p. 127). As late as 1879, Maudsley could remark that general paralysis was "hardly ever met with in the Highlands of Scotland". In that same year, however, the proportion of deaths due to general paralysis in all the asylums of Scotland was officially given as 18% in males and 3% in females.[23]

In the United States, dementia paralytica was not recognized until after 1840. I have been unable to consult the original reference of Luther Bell (his Annual Report for the McLean Asylum, Boston, 1843), but that he was the earliest to record the disease is confirmed by several writers. Thus Bucknill and Tuke (1874, p. 323)

---

[22] Nevertheless, in some asylums in England and Wales there were whole decades when a quarter or more of all the male admissions were paretic. These cases pursued a slow but relentless course to complete dementia and death, and it is not hard to imagine that the unrewarding and dispiriting task of nursing them was one reason why the high standards of humane care set up by the pioneers of non-restraint and moral management seem gradually to have deteriorated during the latter half of the 19th century.

[23] See the 41st Annual Report of the General Board of Commissioners in Lunacy for Scotland (1899, App. A, Tab. X). We may calculate a crude mortality rate for general paralysis in England and Wales and in Scotland, using the figures given in the Board of Control Reports for the year 1876 and the estimated population of the two countries in this year. Expressed as deaths per million of the population, the figure for England and Wales is over 50, for Scotland it is under 20.

say: "The late Dr Bell of America, writing in 1844, said it was only within three years that patients had been admitted to the McLean Asylum labouring under general paralysis. On looking over the register for the past years he could not find a case the description of which resembled the manifestations so graphically described by many English and Continental authors." Chase, writing in Philadelphia in 1902, says (p. 21): "As an illustration of the former rarity of the disease in this country, it is said that the eminent alienist, the late Dr Luther Bell, of Massachusetts, at the time of his first visit to England about fifty years ago, had never recognized a case of general paresis, a statement which seems almost incredible considering its rapid increase and spread in late years, especially during the past quarter of a century." There was no further report of cases of general paresis in the States until that of Pliny Earle in 1847 (MacDonald, 1877; Wagner, 1902). Recognition was even more tardy in Canada. "When I entered the Toronto Asylum in 1853", says Workman (1858), "there was not a single case, as far as I could judge, in the institution but it was not long before it began to make its appearance." That there was a characteristic mode of spread of the disease suggested itself very strongly to his fellow-countryman MacDonald (1877).[24] MacDonald says, "A curious point in the history of the disease is its gradual extension from one country to another and its gradual increase in localities where it has once appeared"; and he gives a table of asylum reports indicating that general paresis was still rare in the western and southern states compared with its prevalence in the central states and those of the eastern seaboard. In his own institution (the New York State Asylum) the numbers of paretics were increasing annually and although some of the increase might be explained by familiarity, yet "when all due allowance is made on this account there is still abundant evidence that the disease is steadily and rapidly extending". His observations led him to believe that in any one place the disease progressed in a manner shown by: first, its appearance and recognition in males; then, increased frequency in males and its appearance in females; increased frequency in both sexes with an increased

---

[24] MacDonald, Workman and Mickle were Canadians and had all studied at the Toronto School of Medicine. Mickle, who emigrated to England and became Superintendent of Grove Hall Asylum, London, was unimpressed by the American statistics of his two compatriots and dismissed them with the remark that "many statistics are utterly misleading . . . merely an index of the varying capacity of medical men to recognize the disease". But when we remember that this disease was recognized in America only at a time when every psychiatrist must have been familiar with its textbook description, and that the progress of any infectious disease across that vast and largely unopened continent must have been relatively slow, we may think the Americans had a better opportunity than Europeans of observing the spread of dementia paralytica.

Another statistical sceptic was Spitzka, professor of medical jurisprudence at New York, and originator of the maxim that general paresis was due to the three W's – wine, women and worry. He severely disapproved of "the widely circulated error" that general paresis was "travelling" from east to west of the American continent. His opposition to MacDonald's statistics was based (1883, pp 183, 208): (1) on the fact that in the German and French asylums, "where the diagnostic acumen of the medical officers is unquestionable", the disease was said to be increasing only very slightly; and (2) on the ad hominem argument that MacDonald had not only attempted to support the ridiculous theory of the Englishman Austin that in general paresis an affection of the left pupil was associated with mania and of the right with depression, but that he had got this association the wrong way round, so that his figures instead of supporting Austin's theory were at complete variance with it – a careless error which, says Spitzka, "constitutes a significant commentary on the reliability" of the author's work in general. Yet in fact it was not MacDonald but Spitzka who was the careless one, inasmuch as Austin (1859, p. 31) claimed mania to be associated with contraction of the left, MacDonald (1877) with dilatation of the right pupil.

proportion in females; and finally, changes in the nature of the disease, such as its duration and the age of patients attacked. He also quotes figures to show that dementia paralytica was at that time much more prevalent in Britain than in the United States; in 1874–76, for example, the percentage of cases in the asylums of Great Britain was 14.1 for males and 3.2 for females whereas in the USA the figures were 4.1 and 0.4. Workman had reached similar conclusions in 1878. Observing that there were markedly fewer paretic deaths in the Toronto Asylum during the eighteen-seventies than in English asylums of comparable size, he adds, "I have carefully examined over 130 reports of United States and Canadian asylums for the last three years. In more than half of this number I have found that paresis was either totally unmentioned or but very exceptionally noted in the obituary tables. I believe it is a recognized fact that in the Southern and farthest Western States the disease is unknown; or at least it has been unnoticed . . . To an English superintendent, who numbers his paretics by the score and shows a paretic death proportion of one in three or four, this fact could not fail to appear marvellous." During the next twenty years, however, dementia paralytica spread and increased in both Canada and the States, so that by 1894 Ballet and Blocq could write, "Central and Western Europe and North America have the unhappy privilege of furnishing the greatest number of cases." Dayton's figures (1940, p. 468) show that, of first admissions to the mental hospitals in the State of Massachusetts between 1917 and 1933, the proportion of paretics was 10.6% for males and 3.0% for females.

The spread of dementia paralytica among the negro population of North America is also worth noting. Long after it had become common among whites, the disease was still rare in negroes. As late as 1883 and 1886, asylum superintendents in North Carolina and in Georgia could claim never to have met with general paresis among their coloured patients (Moreira and Penafiel, 1907). In the New York Asylum, Spitzka (1883, p. 180) found the proportion of cases lower among negroes than among whites and indeed used this finding to support his belief that general paresis was "more frequent with races of a high than of a low cerebral organization". Berkley, in 1893, drew the same conclusion for the Northern States generally; but a few years later, in his *Textbook on Mental Diseases* (1900, p. 194), he writes of dementia paralytica in the negro: "Before the civil war and for some few years afterwards the disease was unknown among them. Little by little the number of cases grew in frequency. Such patients were at first regarded as curiosities, but at present in Baltimore paretics represent approximately the same percentage, according to the total population, in negroes as they do among Caucasians; nor do the general types of the disease differ materially in the two races." Emil Kraepelin (1913) quotes an investigation "very kindly undertaken for me by Hoch in New York" which showed that in seven large asylums the average rate for paresis in negroes was over twice that in whites. Green (1914) wrote, "For many years it was claimed that general paresis was seldom met with in the negro race. That this claim is untrue is generally accepted today"; at the Georgia State sanitarium he found the proportion of general paresis among negro admissions was twice that of the whites. Plaut, in 1926, again found a higher rate of general paresis among negroes than whites in America, and in the same year Kraepelin

Table 1 Number of cases of dementia paralytica admitted to the Kommune Hospital, Copenhagen (from Smith, 1926)

Year	1876–1880	1881–1885	1886–1890	1891–1895	1896–1900	1901–1905	1906–1910	1911–1915	1916–1920	1921–1925
Males	88	138	139	188	202	222	169	316	308	305
Females	3	23	37	57	89	104	97	149	121	116
Ratio M/F	29	6.0	3.8	3.3	2.3	2.1	1.7	2.1	2.5	2.6

(1926) lent the weight of his authority to the "remarkable fact" that general paresis had been extraordinarily rare in North American negroes 40–50 years earlier but was now very common among them. Figures quoted for Massachusetts mental hospitals from 1917 to 1933 by Dayton (1940, p. 411) and for New York State Hospitals in 1935 by Rosanoff (1938) indicate that general paresis continued at least twice as common among negroes as among whites; while recent work (Malzberg, 1953) indicates that in New York State this comparative factor has risen to more than five.

The spread of dementia paralytica in certain other countries may be mentioned more briefly. In Ireland, the disease was generally acknowledged to be rare at least up until the 1870s. Thus Ashe (1876) found no cases in the asylums of Belfast or Cork and only one in Londonderry and drew the conclusion that "general paralysis is scarcely to be found in Ireland". Deas, in 1879, echoes "the undoubted fact that general paralysis is all but unknown in Ireland", and seven years later Mickle (1886, p. 259) can still say that "Ireland enjoys an extraordinary immunity from general paralysis". Yet the Reports of the Inspectors of Lunatics (Ireland) in 1890 (the first year in which separate figures are given) indicate 30 deaths – more than 3% – from general paralysis, a number and proportion which increases in later years. In the Isle of Man, the immunity to the disease seems to have lasted even longer, Richardson (1891) reporting that "during the past six years I have seen no instance of it in a patient of Manx parentage", though two cases had occurred in immigrants. In Denmark, figures given by Heiberg (1932) suggest that dementia paralytica was uncommon there until the late 1860s. The number of paretic deaths at the St Hans Hospital, Copenhagen, in 1866 was five; but the average annual deaths for the decades from 1866–1925 were 8.6, 14.0, 23.1, 35.8, 41.3 and 51.7. Heiberg also gives reasons for believing that the figures represent "with a rather high degree of accuracy" the actual number of paretic deaths in the city of Copenhagen. Smith's figures (1926) for admissions to the Kommune Hospital in Copenhagen from 1876–1926 show the same general trend (Table 1).

Similar trends are to be found in reports from other countries. In Brazil, according to Moreira and Penafiel (1907), there were five cases of paresis admitted to the National Hospital for the Insane in Rio de Janeiro in 1889; but the average annual number admitted during the three quinquennia from 1890–1905 was 10.1, 17.4 and 21.2, while the percentage of paretic admissions increased from 3.1 to 4.0 and 5.3. They also observe that the disease was commoner in immigrants than among natives, a differential prevalence which held true of other countries until quite recent times. Thus Lennox (1923) observes that although syphilis was three times as common in China as in America, the incidence of neuro-syphilis was less than one-seventh as great; and he quotes "writers of experience" who, during the years 1907–1916, hardly ever saw general paresis in Chinese, and where it occurred the patient was found to have been infected from a non-Chinese source. Although Lennox thought the rarity of neuro-syphilis among the Chinese might to some extent be due to lack of facilities for diagnosis, yet he concluded that this would "probably not account for all the observed racial differences". Stewart (1924) quotes a report by Christidis of 1922 that among 3000 cases of syphilis in Persia he did not find a single paretic; paresis was also rare in European residents who had acquired syphilis in Persia but was common in those infected from outside sources.

The general facts related above always appeared sufficiently remarkable to contemporary workers to demand an explanation. Before considering some of the earlier explanations, I will suggest that these facts seem broadly explicable on the hypothesis that a mutant neurotropic strain of the syphilitic spirochaete appeared in northern France and then spread by venereal infection along the trade routes of the world. On this hypothesis, the new disease would tend to spread first to those countries having the closest commercial intercourse with the country of origin; and on reaching a new country overseas, would appear first in the port towns and only later spread inland. Again the disease would tend to spread more quickly among peoples of similar cultural and ethnic group and only move slowly to other groups. The facts that dementia paralytica is a chronic disease and that a variable interval of 5–20 years separates the initial infection from the appearance of symptoms would account for the absence of any explosively obvious outbreak of cases. Such an epidemiological hypothesis could hardly have been put forward before 1913 as until then the infectious nature of dementia paralytica was unsuspected or unproved; and by 1913 the disease had become fairly evenly distributed over the civilized world and it was easy to dismiss the older statistics as valueless because they had not been based upon objective methods of diagnosis.

The diagnosis of dementia paralytica became objective during the years 1896–1912, when the specific reactions of the cerebrospinal fluid were elucidated by Babcock, Alzheimer, Wassermann and Lange. Before this, diagnosis during life had to be made entirely on clinical grounds, though post-mortem examination added much to the accuracy. (It is worth noting that, according to the reports of the Commissioners in Lunacy, the proportion of post-mortem examinations carried out on patients dying of general paralysis in the asylums of England and Wales between 1901 and 1911 was over 70%. We have no post-mortem figures for earlier years, but no reason to suppose they were less.) No doubt in the statistics of dementia paralytica were included some cases of arteriosclerotic, alcoholic and epileptic dementia, cerebral syphilis, cerebral tumour, pellagra and plumbism; but it had been recognized almost from the start that these conditions entered into the differential diagnosis, while conditions that were differentiated only later, such as the dementias of Pick and Alzheimer, were too rare to be of statistical importance. No doubt, too, the diagnosis was made more carefully in some centres than in others, but this is true of all diseases..The consequence would be that the edges of the statistical picture were blurred by a penumbra of misdiagnoses and the problem is – whether the size of this penumbra was such as to fog the true picture beyond recognition.[25] In assessing the value of these 19th-century statistics, it is perhaps useful to reflect that the diagnosis of dementia paralytica at that time was probably much more accurate than is the present day diagnosis of schizophrenia,[26] for the former disease presented not only mental changes but physical signs and characteristic post-mortem appearances and was uniformly fatal within a few years. Although it seems probable that before 1906 there was some degree of confusion as to what should be included in the diagnosis of dementia paralytica, yet I cannot find that, on the whole, there was any sudden fluctuation in the reported incidence or mortality of the disease after the introduction of objective methods of diagnosis.[27]

It is a curious historical fact that during the 19th century each generation of psychiatrists was confident of its own ability to diagnose dementia paralytica but was very ready to doubt the diagnostic accuracy of its predecessors. Thus an anonymous reviewer of the 48th Annual Report of the General Board of Commissioners in Lunacy

[25] Kraepelin (1927, p. 1137) discusses the unreliability of the 19th-century statistics on dementia paralytica and gives his opinion that "they are set about with so many sources of error as not to allow any definite conclusion on the actual alterations in frequency of the disease". Nevertheless, he in fact permitted himself to draw general conclusions: for example (p. 1145), "from these considerations we may take it as very probable that dementia paralytica was formerly uncommon, then underwent a progressively rapid increase from the beginning of last century and for some time now has been gradually diminishing"; and again, discussing the sex incidence (p. 1150), "although the figures may be considerably influenced by the sources of error mentioned above, yet there can be no doubt of the overall increase in the danger to the female sex from dementia paralytica".

[26] It is sometimes urged that the present-day diagnosis of schizophrenia is too uncertain for epidemiological studies of this disease to be meaningful. The history of dementia paralytica suggests that we should be unwise to neglect such studies. In 1857, Esmarch and Jessen had drawn attention – rather apologetically – to the statistical relations between syphilis and paresis. Another early piece of evidence for the syphilitic hypothesis was provided by Sankey, who, in 1866, pointed out the close association between the incidence of syphilis and of paresis in different social classes. But this delicate flower was withered by the scorn and authority of Mickle, who, in his textbook (1880, p. 105) dismisses it with the inappropriate remark that "even if true this does not establish any connection between the syphilis and the general paralysis". Krafft-Ebing, on the other hand, was so impressed by the statistical evidence that he was emboldened in 1894 to inoculate nine paretic patients with syphilis; but, as Berkley (1900, p. 174) and others observed, this proved nothing, for persons infected with syphilis do not necessarily develop symptoms, patients with longstanding syphilis may acquire the infection anew, and other investigators (see Diefendorf, 1906) repeated Krafft-Ebing's work with contrary results. Yet this doubtful experiment caught hold of the popular fancy, convinced many who had been sceptical of all the patiently accumulated statistics, and is still regularly quoted as one of the landmarks in the history of dementia paralytica.

[27] The difficulties of clinical diagnosis were indicated by the problem of 'pseudo-paralysis' (see, for example, Hyslop, 1896). It is likely that these difficulties increased at the end of the 19th century on account of the rapid changes in the proportions of the different clinical types of dementia paralytica. However, it seems that the difficulty lay more in the initial than in the final diagnosis: Kraepelin says of the period 1892–1907, "at that time we had the tendency to diagnose the condition as early as possible from the clinical picture . . . Consequently we made many wrong diagnoses later discovered by regular follow-up" (1927, Vol. I, p. 958).

Objective diagnosis became common after Wassermann's demonstration, in 1906, that his complement-fixation test was given by the cerebrospinal fluid of paretics; and was further refined after 1912 when Lange discovered the specific reaction of the fluid to colloidal gold. With these facts in mind we may note that in England and Wales:

(1) The Registrar General's figures from 1901 onwards for deaths due to general paralysis of the insane show no change other than a continued downward trend (Figure 2, see p. 66);

(2) The change in sex ratio of deaths from general paralysis of the insane is closely paralleled by that from tabes, the accurate diagnosis of which was probably little influenced by the new techniques (Figure 1, see p. 62);

(3) First admissions to asylums of cases diagnosed as general paralysis of the insane are recorded in the annual reports of the Board of Control. These show a sudden decrease in the numbers in both sexes for 1914, an occurrence which may be attributed to the outbreak of the first world war; otherwise, neither the numbers nor the sex ratio show any sign of short term change between 1900 and 1928.

for Scotland (*Journal of Mental Science*, 1907), referring to the continued increase in admission rate and deaths of general paralysis during the past 25 years, says: "The reviewer is convinced that a few years ago many of the cases now returned as having died from general paralysis would have been described as cases of cerebral softening, disseminated sclerosis, and cerebral paralysis."[28] Twenty-one years before this, Mickle had written (1886, p. 248), "It is difficult to say how far the apparent increase of general paralysis among women of late years is due to a former defective recognition of it and faulty diagnosis, owing to the less salient features and less dramatic course of general paralysis as it occurs in women than as in men." Twenty-six years before this, Skae (1860) had said, – "for many years (general paralysis) must have been imperfectly known and recognized even in large asylums, if we may judge from the small proportion of cases mentioned in the annual reports of these asylums, compared with the large number which now figure in the tables of these reports. The only other explanation of this fact is that the disease has been increasing in frequency in this country of late years." And twenty-five years earlier than this, Esquirol (1838, p. 274) took Burrows to task with the words: "This worthy writer attributes the frequency of paralysis in Paris to our bad management and our failure to take proper precautions in guarding our insane from exposure to inclement weather; whereas in England, he says, the patients are very well cared for . . . I am convinced that once the symptoms of paralysis complicating insanity are better understood, there will be found in England and particularly in London as many paralytic insane as there are in Paris."

Although the statistics of earlier authors could always be dismissed as unreliable, yet the reported variations in the prevalence of dementia paralytica at any one time could not be so dismissed, because they were again and again confirmed by experienced psychiatrists from personal observations.[29] Of the explanations offered, however, none was adequate and many were self-contradictory. The lower consumption of alcohol was held by Lunier (1849) to account for the lower prevalence of dementia paralytica in southern France; by Wise (1869) for the "remarkable rarity" of the disease among the natives of India; and by Kraepelin (1913) for its rarity in upper-class European women, in non-Europeanized peoples and in Mohammedans. Yet this

[28] This reviewer seems to have been particularly unguarded in his assertion. The Annual Report gave a table of deaths, not only from general paralysis but also from "apoplexy and paralysis" and the numbers in this latter table did not vary over 30 years and showed no sex difference: clearly the Scottish doctors had been at pains to separate "cerebral softening" and "cerebral paralysis" from general paralysis. As for disseminated sclerosis, the Reports of the Commissioners in Lunacy give the number of deaths in England and Wales from cerebral and spinal sclerosis in 1901 as 8, in 1906 as 18, in 1910 as 9; the number in Scotland would be proportionately less and it seems clear there had been little variation in the statistically negligible number of such cases. Again, a fellow-reviewer writing twelve years earlier on the 36th Annual Report (*Journal of Mental Science*, 1895) had said, "There can be no reasonable doubt, even after making due allowance for possible greater certainty in diagnosis, that of late years there has been a steady and by no means inconsiderable increase (in general paralysis), notably in the male sex."

[29] One of the strongest objections to the Theory of Evolution was that, as no one could see evolution taking place, the theory was merely a hypothetical explanation of events long past and incapable of proof or disproof; and a recent demonstration that the evolutionary process can actually be observed today in certain species of seabirds has been claimed as valuable additional evidence. In the same way, many 19th-century psychiatrists found it hard to believe that the prevalence of dementia paralytica in different countries could have changed significantly during the century; but its rapid increase among American negroes, a phenomenon that took place under the very eyes (so to speak) of Kraepelin, was a practical and almost irrefutable demonstration that such changes could occur.

explanation would certainly not account for the low prevalence of dementia paralytica in Northern Scotland and in Ireland, nor for the observation that "the Irishman has to go to America to be attacked by it, for at home he seems immune" (Berkley, 1900, p. 193). Clouston (1883, p. 379) considered "hard muscular labour" was among the exciting causes of dementia paralytica, yet Maudsley (1879, p. 433) attributed its rarity in Scottish highlanders to their taking "a great deal of bodily exercise". An attack of malaria or relapsing fever soon after syphilitic infection has been held to account for the rarity of dementia paralytica in the tropics, but McCartney (1946) has pointed out that neuro-syphilis is rare in the Marshall Islands where there is no malaria; and malaria would not explain the rarity of dementia paralytica in many colder countries such as Ireland and Norway. Towards the end of the 19th century the association between syphilis and dementia paralytica became increasingly well-established and the importance of the former as an exciting cause of the latter disease was summed up in the famous 'civilization and syphilization' aphorism of Krafft-Ebing at the Moscow Congress in 1897. But as Mott pointed out in 1900, dementia paralytica was rare in some countries (Persia, Japan, Egypt) where syphilis was very common, a fact with which Kraepelin (1913) concurred and which he was at a loss to explain. The belief that 'civilization' was a factor determining the prevalence of dementia paralytica had long been held, though there was disagreement whether the effects were due to the excessive sensitivity of more highly civilized beings or to their degeneracy. Salomon (1862) thought the peculiar susceptibility of Frenchmen to the disease was the result of their "insatiable thirst after 'la gloire'". Mickle (1880, p. 97) taught that "a life absorbed in ambitious projects, with all its strenuous mental efforts, its long-sustained anxieties, deferred hopes and straining expectation . . . chagrins, forced erethism of the intellectual faculties . . . exposure to constant sources of annoyance – all these predispose to general paralysis". Stewart (1896) considered the recent increase in the disease as due to "increasing moral and physical decadence, lessening power of resistance and diminishing vitality, and increasing tendency to premature and rapid racial decay"; though a few years later (1901), when subsequent figures indicated a slight fall in the number of paretics, he was happily able to conclude that the tendency to racial decay in England and Wales had undergone a reversal.[30]

[30] Nineteenth century ideas on the aetiology of dementia paralytica provide material for a historical study which might illustrate our contemporary views on a disease such as schizophrenia where the aetiology is still obscure. Not only do many of these ideas seem very strange to us now, but they led to the advocation of 'rational' methods of treatment and prevention which might seem even more strange were it not that the history of medicine is full of such things. For example, the hypothesis that dementia paralytica was caused by sexual excess led to the prophylactic advice that wives should be "cautioned against being too loving to their lords" (*Journal of Mental Science*, 1873). Of course, not everyone agreed with such a view; Mickle (1880, p. 105) was contemptuous of it, on the grounds that married women were not lascivious bacchantes and stood in no need of such advice.

For a long time, one of the most unlikely of these speculations was that dementia paralytica was due to syphilis. The statistical and epidemiological evidence in favour of this view, however, became increasingly strong at the end of the 19th century. But statistical evidence is never proof and as late as 1902 Nonne could state that in his opinion "progressive paralysis is not a specific syphilitic disease of the brain". Kraepelin, in 1904 (and this was two years before Wassermann showed that his antigen reaction was given by the spinal fluid of paretics), was bold enough to commit himself absolutely to the syphilitic hypothesis, but for the more cautious or less statistically-minded psychiatrist there was no sure path through the speculative labyrinth until the autumn of 1912, when, in the paretic brain sections sent to Noguchi by Moore, the pale visage of a few spirochaetes sufficed to disinherit chaos.

Kraepelin (1913, 1926, 1927) was much occupied with the problem presented by variations in prevalence of dementia paralytica in different countries. When in Java in 1904, he had been unable to discover a single case among the natives and he did not believe that the reported variations in prevalence could be explained by variations either in the prevalence of syphilis or in the recognition and diagnosis of paresis. He admits that the theory of a special strain of syphilis would explain the otherwise very difficult fact that dementia paralytica is rare in some countries where syphilis is common but he rejects this theory on two counts. The first count is that "we see Europeans become paretics after infection with the same syphilis to which the nervous tissue of the natives is immune". He gives no reference for this statement and it would clearly never be easy to establish that a European acquired syphilis from a native rather than from an immigrant or in another country. The second count is that "in Constantinople the different races show a very different susceptibility for paresis although the syphilis of the Turks, Greeks, Jews and Armenians is certainly the same". From this statement it would appear that Kraepelin conceived of different strains of syphilis being statically distributed in different countries and that he did not have in mind the concept of a new strain in the process of spreading from Europeanized to non-Europeanized countries; yet it is on this latter concept that most of the facts seem explicable.

The same belief in a static distribution of a neurotropic strain is evident in S. A. K. Wilson's writings. In his *Neurology* (1941, Vol. I, p. 462; 2nd edition (1954), Vol. I, p. 485), he states: "Another allegation, often quoted by those who believe in the dualist theory, is to the effect that in certain countries where syphilis is rife, neurosyphilis is conspicuous by its relative absence . . . But most of such claims are proving visionary in the light of advancing knowledge. In 1926 Plaut showed that the incidence of general paralysis among American negroes is actually higher than among whites." Wilson seems here to be supposing that the earlier statistics on the scarcity of dementia paralytica in negroes were simply false. He was not alone in such a belief, for there are many references in the literature to the legend that dementia paralytica did not occur or was very rare in certain communities and to the advancing knowledge which showed such legends to be false (see, for example, Barnes, 1891, quoted by Moreira and Penafiel, 1907; Samuels, 1916; Marie, 1922). Yet Kraepelin definitely rejected the legend theory,[31] and it would seem altogether more reasonable that real increases in the prevalence of dementia paralytica occurred; and

[31] "In countries where the social care of the insane is not adequately carried out, only a fraction of the psychotic patients enjoy medical attendance, but it is highly improbable that general paretics will be missing amongst these few, all the more so as their symptoms are usually very disturbing. If accordingly I experienced that, in a hospital containing several hundred native patients, not one case of general paresis could be found by excellently trained medical officers, we must infer that the disorder cannot in any way be as common in those parts as it is at home" (Kraepelin, 1926).

A more recent example of the legend theory is provided by two studies made in Bosnia and Herzegovina. In 1888, Gluck and others had reported that although syphilis was widespread in these "remote provinces", only 0.65% of native-born syphilitics developed dementia paralytica, compared with 9% of the foreign-born (Kraepelin, 1927, p. 1149). The investigation was repeated by Kojog (1939) who found that the proportion of paretics to syphilitics was the same as in Europe (5–10%). Kojog drew the conclusion that Gluck's work was entirely inaccurate; but the different findings might alternatively reflect the fact that the first world war and the general development of communication had made this part of Yugoslavia a much less remote place.

it would then be at least as satisfactory to explain these increases in terms of the spread of a neurotropic strain as by such vague hypotheses as "unknown protective influences" or "factors incidental to civilization" (S. A. K. Wilson, *op. cit.*, pp 536, 486).

Changes in sex ratio

From the time of its discovery, dementia paralytica has always appeared to be more common in men than women, but the figures given for the proportion of male to female cases have varied widely in different times and places. "The comparative figures can vacillate between one to two and one to seventeen or even higher values", said Kraepelin (1926); he thought the variation could not be attributed to sex differences in the incidence of syphilis but, apart from suggesting that a low consumption of alcohol might account for the rarity of the disease in upper-class European women, he offered no explanation. The statistics have been discounted as fallacious but otherwise there has not, as far as I know, been any general attempt to explain these variations in sex ratio.

In hazarding a partial explanation, I suggest that if factors of time and place are taken into account it becomes possible to discern a fairly constant pattern of change, similar to that suggested by MacDonald in 1877, viz. that when dementia paralytica first appears in a country, the sex ratio (males to females) is high but gradually falls to a more or less steady value of between four and two to one. This is the pattern which would be expected on the hypothesis of the spread of a neurotropic strain of spirochaete. On this hypothesis, the strain would tend to reach a new country by the agency of travellers and seamen; from these men the infection would pass principally to prostitutes in the coastal towns and from them to native males. As the number of male clients is in general much higher than the number of prostitutes, the disease would at first show a preponderance of males and would only gradually spread to other females. In time, however, a balance would be reached and thereafter the sex ratio of dementia paralytica would tend to be more stable. The rapidity with which a steady ratio is reached seems to have varied markedly from country to country, and this could possibly be explained by variations in cultural attitudes to sexual behaviour. I will quote figures to indicate the early rarity and later increasing proportion of female cases in different countries.

In Paris, the sex ratio was never very high and seems to have fallen to a low level in a short time. Bayle (1826, p. 568), at the Charenton Hospital, found the ratio of males to females eight to one during the years 1816–1823; at the same hospital from 1823–1826 Calmeil (1826, p. 370), as the result of a "scrupulous examination", found the ratio to be three to one; a decade later, Foville found it 2.3 to one (Griesinger, 1861, p. 400). In 1886 (p. 245) Mickle quotes the proportion in France as 2.5 to one and a similar figure is given by Idanoff (1894). In Germany, Neumann (1859) believed that women were "very seldom" the victims of dementia paralytica. Other early writers put the ratio in Germany as 10 to one (Griesinger, 1861, p. 400); Sander (1870) found this ratio at the Charité Hospital, Berlin. In 1877, Krafft-Ebing put the figure at eight to one but twenty years later (1894) concluded that the proportion of females had considerably increased. By 1913, Kraepelin (p. 142) could say that "the relative number of women is certainly increasing in Germany" and that whereas the sex ratio had been seven or eight to one in earlier decades it had fallen to between five and two to one. In the St Hans Hospital, Copenhagen, Heiberg's figures for paretic deaths during the years 1876–1890 show a gradually increasing proportion of females from 12–30%; from then on (to 1930) this proportion remains almost constant. Smith (1926) has given figures for the annual admission of paretics to the Kommune Hospital, Copenhagen, from 1876–1925; the numbers in quinquennial periods are shown in Table 1, and from this it is evident that the relative proportion of male cases was at first very high but after the end of the 19th century remained steady at about 2.5 males to one female.

In England, the sex ratio of deaths seems to have been fairly steady at about four to one for most of the 19th century. In the earliest reference to the subject which I can find, however, Prichard (1835, p. 110) records that of the 16 cases seen at the Gloucester asylum since 1828 only one was female. Conolly (1849) says that at Hanwell Asylum during the decade 1839 to 1849 there were 146 male and 33 female deaths from general paralysis, adding that "in private practice I have never yet met with a case of general paralysis in a woman". Similar figures for provincial asylums are given by Wilson (1857) and Boyd (1865). From 1876 the Annual Reports of the Commissioners in Lunacy give statistics for general paralysis of the insane in England and Wales; these indicate a relatively constant sex ratio of about four to one until the second decade of the 20th century when there is a slight increase; from 1925 there is a progressive decrease until by 1945 the ratio is 2.3 to one. These recent trends are reflected in the Registrar General's reports (Figure 1). Discussing his earlier experiences of dementia paralytica in Scotland, Browne (1875) said he had never been able to convince himself of the presence of the disease in the female, and Skae (1860) said that at the Royal Edinburgh Asylum he had "very seldom more than one female paralytic under my care at any one time" but rarely fewer than 22–25 male cases. From the Annual Reports of the General Board of Commissioners in Lunacy for Scotland, however, we learn that the male-to-female ratio of deaths was soon in the region of four to one and continued at this level into the early part of the 20th century.

The same picture of dementia paralytica being at first rare in females and later much more common seems evident in North America. Between 1841 and 1843, Luther Bell (quoted by MacDonald, 1877) found 16 cases of the disease at Boston, but only one of these was female. Workman (1858) wrote: "In five years I have not in the Toronto Asylum met with a single case of general paralysis in a female . . . Why is it that in America general paralysis of the insane is almost if not entirely confined to males and why in Europe is there so considerable a number of exceptions to this rule?" Twenty years later (1878), Workman wrote on the subject again: during the period 1865–1877 he had had 95 cases of general paresis at Toronto, of whom only eight were female; and in the New York State Lunatic Asylum at Utica, where "the records are perfectly reliable", the sex ratio of paretic deaths from 1849–1877 was 16 to one and in New York itself the ratio was between 15 and 20 to one. "Why a

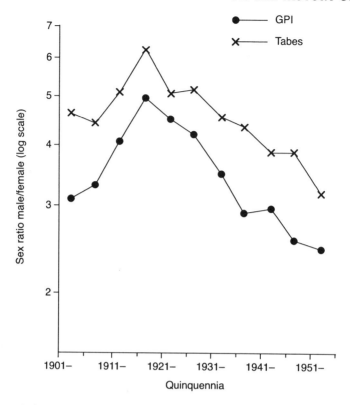

Figure 1. Sex ratio, by quinquennia, of deaths from General Paralysis of the Insane (GPI) and from tabes
(from the Registrar General's Annual Reports for England and Wales).

New York city asylum should show a lower proportion than an English asylum,
I fail to understand." MacDonald's opinion (1877) on the gradual increase in the
proportion of female cases has already been noted and his figures suggest a higher
sex ratio in the Western than in the Eastern States. Figures for various asylums in the
United States during the latter decades of the 19th century show a ratio of about
eight to one (Wagner, 1902) and Berkley (1900, p. 171) makes the observation that
the sex ratio had decreased during the past 10–15 years from nine or ten down to
seven or eight. The ratio continued to decrease. Dayton's figures (1940, p. 468) show
that in Massachusetts mental hospitals between 1917 and 1933, the male-to-female
ratio was about four to one. In New York State hospitals between 1932 and 1941
this ratio decreased progressively from four down to three (Arieti, 1945), and figures
of the US Bureau of the Census (quoted by Iskrant, 1945) show the ratio for paretics
in all mental institutions in 1940 was three to one.

The commonest – indeed the only – general explanation put forward to account
for the increasing proportion of female paralytics in any one locality and their varying proportion in different countries was that the statistics were misleading. Thus

Austin (1859, p. 59) thought the disparity had been "over-stated"; Mickle (1886, p. 245) asserted that, as the relative proportion of male to female cases in England was four to one, Krafft-Ebing's earlier estimate of an eight-to-one rate was "inaccurate"; and the anonymous reviewer in the *Journal of Mental Science* (1907) believed that the increasing proportion of females was due to the fact that in this sex "the disease is now diagnosed with greater accuracy". However, we should note that although dementia paralytica may have been less dramatic in females than in males, it was not therefore less well diagnosed, for in both sexes the simple dementing type and the depressed type had been clearly described by Calmeil in 1826 and the hypochondriacal type by Baillarger in 1857. Again, if the clinical diagnosis in the female was more difficult and less often made, we should expect to find that when objective methods of diagnosis were developed early in the present century the proportion of female cases would appear to increase, but in England, at any rate, the opposite occurred, as is shown by the reports of the Board of Control and the Registrar General. The change in sex ratio of dementia paralytica during the early 20th century is unlikely to reflect any change in diagnostic habit, as a very similar change occurred at the same time in tabes (Figure 1).

Changes in type and prevalence

When a population is exposed to infection by a new virulent organism, the resulting disease tends in the course of years to undergo an evolution from forms which are acute and severe towards those which are milder and more chronic. This seems to have happened, for example, in the great 15th century epidemic of syphilis. If some such evolution can be shown to have occurred in dementia paralytica since its definite recognition 140 years ago, this may be taken to support the hypothesis that it was at that time a new disease. I will briefly consider evidence for supposing that there has been a gradual change in the proportion of clinical types of dementia paralytica and, more recently, a natural decline in its prevalence.

Both Bayle and Calmeil recognized that in its early stages dementia paralytica could be characterized either by grandiose delusions or by depression or by simple dementia, but neither of them had any doubt that of these three types the grandiose was much the commonest. Thus Bayle (1826, p. 547) says that although not every case shows monomania yet "exceptions are very rare and are probably due to the fact that detailed observation was lacking during the first two stages of the disease". Calmeil (1826, p. 325 ff.) considered that ideas of grandeur were present in "a very great number" of insane paralytics and that simple dementia and depression (or *lypémanie* as he then called it, following Esquirol's classification) were rare. Falret, in his *Recherches sur la Folie Paralytique* (1853, p. 29), still stated that expansive delusions were the commonest mode of onset of the disease. During the second half of the century, however, changes in the relative proportion of the types began to be observed. In 1859 Calmeil published his second major work on dementia paralytica, the *Traité des Maladies Inflammatoires du Cerveau*; here (Vol. I, p. 276) he states that the depressive type had become more common during the past twelve years until now it was almost as common as the expansive type. According to Westphal (1868) "it is now established beyond contradiction that ideas of the most varied, yea even opposite description, frequently exist during the whole course of the disease or only for a certain period of it", and he adds that Bayle's belief in the overwhelming preponderance of the grandiose type "must be considered as completely refuted". Krafft-Ebing, in his monograph of 1894 (p. 25) observes that "comparison between past and present is misleading because for several decades the nature of general paralysis has been changing and in place of the classical, dramatic, obstreperous type we see more and more of the simple, dementing type". Of the various German and Austrian figures quoted by Kraepelin (1913), none puts the proportion of the expansive type as higher than 30%; the percentages of the depressive type range from 10–20%, and of the demented type from 40–60%.

The same gradual changes are apparent in Great Britain, though the classical type seems to have remained common for a longer time than on the continent. Thus Conolly (1849) says, "The disease is so generally associated with ideas of wealth and grandeur that when these prevail strongly in any patient we expect the paralysis to supervene. It is scarcely ever combined with melancholia." The low proportion (45%) of the grandiose type found by Austin (1859, p. 59) is perhaps to be explained by the unusually large number of females (nearly one-third) among his 135 cases,[32] for as late as 1871 Blandford, lecturer in psychological medicine at St George's Hospital, still taught that "almost all, certainly 19 out of 20, paralytics are full of ideas of their greatness, importance and riches" (p. 260). Bullen (1893), from observations at the Wakefield Asylum, Yorkshire, between 1880 and 1890, concluded that the grandiose type was diminishing and the depressed and simple dementing types increasing in frequency (the proportion among his cases over a decade being 64%, 13% and 21% respectively); he also quotes Claye Shaw as saying, "I have no doubt that we get more cases of the demented and paralysed form than we used to, and that the percentage of these is not only greater, *quoad* other forms of insanity, than formerly, but that amongst general paralytic cases it is the most common form." A later study at the Wakefield Asylum by Baird (1905) for the years 1896–1902 showed the proportion of grandiose cases to have fallen to 46%, with corresponding increases in other types, principally the melancholic. Clouston of Edinburgh, in the sixth edition of his textbook (1904, p. 342) says of the simple dementing type, "about one-third of all the cases of the disease that I used to see were of this character, and nearly all the older medical officers of asylums say that this type is increasing while the classical grandiose type is diminishing in frequency". In a study at Brentwood Mental hospital, Power (1930) found that between 1907 and 1922 there was a slight decrease in the number of grandiose cases, from 43 to 40% and an increase in the demented type from 30 to 50% Stoddart (1921) makes the generalization that the depressed form "is almost as frequent as, if not at present more frequent than, the expansive form".

---

[32] All authorities have agreed that grandiose delusions were less common in female paretics. According to Stoddart (1921, p. 433) this peculiarity was ascribed by Krafft-Ebing and Regis to the relative poverty of ideation in women.

More recent continental work indicates a continued decrease in the proportion of the classical grandiose type, though a newly distinguished type, 'euphoric dementia' appears. Thus Bostroem (1930), in 1218 cases studied at Munich between 1920 and 1930, found the grandiose type in 10%, euphoric dementia in 30%, simple dementia in 34% and the depressed type in only 7% Among 680 paretics admitted to the St Hans Hospital, Copenhagen, between 1922 and 1935, Lomholt (1944) found 14% expansive or grandiose, 2% depressive, but 60% with fatuous, euphoric dementia. Froshang and Ytrehus, studying paretics admitted to hospitals in Oslo between 1915 and 1954, found that the proportion of the classical type gradually decreased from 10% to 4%

Although a distinction between the various types of dementia paralytica is not always easy to make (especially as, during the course of the illness, the clinical picture may fluctuate) yet it seems reasonable to detect certain major changes during the past 140 years. The grandiose type, from being much the most common, has gradually become uncommon and indeed rare. The depressive type, originally rare, became more common during the latter half of the 19th century (between 20% and 50% of cases) but has again become rare. That there have been changes in the relative proportion of types, few if any authorities have seriously questioned. The changes cannot be accounted for merely by changes in the sex ratio, for in England they occur during a period when the sex ratio was constant; nor can they be held due to changes in prevalence of the disease, for the decline in proportion of the grandiose type continued when the prevalence was increasing during the 19th century and when it was decreasing during the 20th.

There is some evidence that this decline in prevalence of dementia paralytica in the present century cannot, in England at least, be altogether or even principally ascribed to the effects of medical intervention. Figure 2 shows the mortality in England and Wales from dementia paralytica, tabes and aortic aneurysm since 1901 (the first year for which the Registrar General's reports list general paralysis of the insane and tabes separately). In 1940, the Registrar General adopted the Fifth Revision of the International List for the classification of causes of death (in which "aneurysm of the aorta" replaced the previous comprehensive category of "aneurysm") and also in the same year changed the method of selecting the assigned cause from the death certificate ("the choice now being in the main that inferred from the statement of the certificate instead of being determined by arbitrary rules of precedence"). In 1950, the Sixth Revision of the International List was adopted, by which "aneurysm of the aorta" excluded both dissecting aneurysm and aneurysm specified as non-syphilitic. These changes in method of classification account for the breaks in the curves of Figure 2. They are of little consequence for the mortality from dementia paralytica and tabes; but they imply that the figures for aortic aneurysm must, in the earlier years, have included many deaths from non-syphilic aneurysms, so that the real decline (if any) in mortality from syphilitic aneurysm must be less than that represented by the curve (indeed, for females, the Registrar General's actual figures of average mortality from 1946–1955 are higher than those from 1901–1910). This comparatively slight decline (or perhaps rise) in

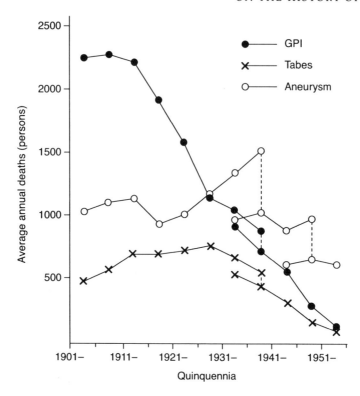

Figure 2. Average annual deaths, by quinquennia, from general paralysis of the insane (GPI), tabes and 'aneurysm' (from the Registrar General's Annual Reports for England and Wales). The breaks in the curves are explained in the text.

mortality from aortic aneurysm is in accordance with the figures quoted by King (1958) that the number of cases of syphilis of more than year's duration showed no appreciable decline between 1931 and 1952. The decline in mortality from dementia paralytica and tabes cannot, therefore, be attributed to the prevention or early treatment of syphilis. Yet the decline in mortality from tabes cannot be attributed to any specific treatment, for until penicillin was introduced after 1945 no specific treatment was known[33]; this decline has probably, therefore, been a natural one. From the close similarity between tabes and dementia paralytica we might argue that the decline in mortality from dementia paralytica has also been a natural one. Even if we disallow this argument, the decline is far greater than could be attributed to the effects of malarial treatment. Thus Nicole (1943) found that of 401 paretics receiving malaria only 32% were finally discharged from hospital and the same proportion is mentioned by Hutton (1941) and, from the USA, by Iskrant (1945). Even if none of

---

[33] Walshe (1947, p. 174) says that he "cannot claim ever to have been satisfied that anti-syphilitic treatment influences the course of tabes".

the discharged cases was recorded as dying from dementia paralytica, this would only lead to a mortality reduced from pre-malarial days by a factor of 1.5 whereas the mortality has in fact been reduced by a factor of 18. There remains a further possibility. The paretics who remained in hospital after treatment and who died perhaps years later of intercurrent disease may not all have been recorded as dying from dementia paralytica. If the proportion of such cases was sufficiently high, this could account for the reduction in mortality. Yet it would not explain the fall in mortality that occurred before malaria therapy was introduced, nor would it explain the continued fall in mortality after the therapy had become established. Moreover, no explanation of reduced mortality in terms of treatment would account for the very general experience that the morbidity has been declining for many years and that nowadays a case of dementia paralytica is almost a rarity. I am informed by the Board of Control that the numbers of admissions (including re-admissions) of general paralysis of the insane to mental hospitals in England and Wales fell from 1246 in 1930 to 408 in 1950.

Conclusion

Sir Humphrey Rolleston (1927a,b) observed that many diseases have undergone modifications in form, in severity and in prevalence during historical times. Such modifications may be ascribed either to changes in the habits or constitution of the host, or to changes in an infecting organism. The disappearance of chlorosis, for example, was probably related to the disappearance of the fashion for tightly-laced corsets; the diminished prevalence of urinary calculus can be attributed to changes in dietary and drinking habits. Diphtheria, on the other hand – "a disease so sharply cut that it can hardly have been overlooked until Brettonneau of Tours" (who gave the first clear description of it in 1821) – is seen by Rolleston as probably arising *de novo* from the mutation of a hitherto harmless diphtheroid. In the same way, it may be suggested that dementia paralytica may also have been a new disease arising from a mutation in the syphilitic 'virus' towards the end of the 18th century. In summary, this hypothesis is based on four considerations:

1. There is evidence (not universally accepted) that the syphilitic 'virus' underwent some change at the end of the 15th century and that this was responsible for the great epidemic of that time. With regard to other changes in the nature of syphilitic disease, Klotz (1926) pointed out that there are no satisfactory descriptions of aortic aneurysm until the beginning of the 16th century, when they become common.

2. Although dementia paralytica presents (or did present, when it first became prevalent) a very striking clinical picture, yet there is no clear description of it and certainly no evidence that it was at all common until the Parisian outbreak described by Esquirol, Georget, Bayle and Calmeil.

3. The hypothesis of a mutant strain of spirochaete spreading by venereal infection from a centre somewhere in northern France would largely explain the varying times at which dementia paralytica was recognized in different countries and the

variations in prevalence and sex ratio reported in these countries during the years after its first recognition.

4. There is evidence that during the past 140 years the disease has shown gradual modifications in clinical form and a recent natural decline in prevalence. These changes are comparable with the changes that took place in the clinical course of syphilis during the years that followed the 15th century epidemic.

The existence of a neurotropic strain of treponema must, in the absence of laboratory proof, remain only a more or less probable hypothesis. The attempt to support this hypothesis has been my excuse for drawing attention to the history of dementia paralytica. It is a disease which, in a relatively short time, has shown marked changes in its prevalence, distribution and clinical characteristics; and whatever may be the explanation of these changes, they permit us to reflect on a theme which it is perhaps the business of medical history to emphasize – the mutability of disease (But see also this volume, note 7, chapter 6, p. 123).

Acknowledgment

I am much indebted to Dr Alexander Walk for his helpful criticism and advice.

References

Arieti S. (1945) General Paresis in Senility, *Amer J Psychiat* **101**: 585.
Arnold T. (1786) *Observations on the Nature, etc. of Insanity*. London.
Ashe I. (1876) Some Observations on General Paralysis. *J Ment Sci* **22**: 82.
Austin TJ. (1859) *General Paralysis, its Symptoms, Causes and Seat*. London.
Baillarger M. (1857) Délire hypocondriaque des déments paralytiques. *Gaz des Hôpitaux* pp 55, 218, 477.
Baillarger M. (1859) De la découverte de la paralysie générale, I. *Ann Méd-Psychol* **5**: 509.
Baillarger M. (1860) De la découverte de la paralysie générale, II. *Ann Méd-Psychol* **6**: 1.
Baird H. (1905) Statistical Observations on General Paralysis *J Ment Sci* **51**: 581.
Ballet G and Blocq P. (1894) In: Masson G (ed.) *Traité de Médicine* Vol 6, Paris, p. 1011.
Bayle ALJ. (1822) *Recherches sur l'arachnitis chronique, la gastrite et la gastro-entérite chroniques, et la goutte, considerées comme les causes de l'aliénation mentale*. Paris.
Bayle ALJ. (1826) *Traité des Maladies du Cerveau*. Paris.
Berkley HJ. (1893) Dementia Paralytica in the Negro *Johns Hopkins Hosp Bull* **4**: 94.
Berkley HJ. (1900) *A Treatise on Mental Disease*. New York.
Blandford GF. (1871) *Insanity and its Treatment*. London.
Bonnet H and Poincaré – . (1868) Recherches sur l'anatomie pathologique et la nature de la paralysie générale. *Annal Méd-Psychol* **12** (4th series): 169.
Bostroem A. (1930) In: Bumke O (ed.) *Handbuch der Geisteskrankheiten* Vol 8, Berlin, p. 165.
Boyd R. (1865) Vital Statistics, etc. in the Somerset Lunatic Asylum. *J Ment Sci* **10**: 491.
Browne WAF. (1875) New Cerebro-psychical Diseases. *Amer J Insan* **32**: 198.
Bucknill JC. (1857) The Diagnosis of Insanity. *J Ment Sci* **3**: 141.
Bucknill JC and Tuke DH. (1858) *A Manual of Psychological Medicine*. London, p. 17.
Bucknill JC and Tuke DH. (1874) *A Manual of Psychological Medicine* (3rd edn). London.
Bullen FStJ. (1893) Inquiries into a Variation of Type in General Paralysis. *J Ment Sci* **39**: 185.
Burrows GM. (1829) *Commentaries on the Causes, etc. of Insanity*. London.
Calmeil LF. (1826) *De la Paralysie considérée chez les Aliénés*. Paris.
Calmeil LF. (1859) *Traité des Maladies Inflammatoires du Cerveau*. Paris.

Cantarow A and Trumper M. (1944) *Lead Poisoning*. Baltimore, p. vii.

Castiglioni A. (1947) *A History of Medicine* (2nd edn, transl Krumbhaar EB, New York).

Chase RH. (1902) *General Paresis*. London.

Clouston TS. (1883) *Clinical Lectures on Mental Diseases*. London.

Clouston TS. (1904) *Clinical Lectures on Mental Diseases* (6th edn). London.

Conolly J. (1830) *An Inquiry concerning the Indications of Insanity*. London.

Conolly J. (1849) *On Some Forms of Insanity*. London.

Cullen W. (1769) *Synopsis Nosologiae Methodicae*. Edinburgh.

Dayton NA. (1940) *New Facts on Mental Disorders*. Illinois.

Deas PM. (1879) Five Years of Statistics, etc. *J Ment Sci* **25**: 8.

Diefendorf AR. (1906) The Etiology of Dementia Paralytica. *BMJ* ii: 744.

Ellis WC. (1838) *A Treatise on the Nature, etc. of Insanity*. London.

Esmarch F and Jessen W. (1857) Syphilis und Geistesstöring. *Allg Ztschr f Psychiat* **14**: 20.

Esquirol E. (1814) Dementia. In: *Dictionnaire des Sciences Médicales*.

Esquirol E. (1838) *Des Maladies Mentales*. Paris.

Falret J. (1853) *Recherches sur la Folie Paralytique*. Paris.

Froshang H and Ytrehus A. (1956) A Study of General Paralysis with special reference to the Reasons for the Admission of these Patients to Hospital. *Acta Psychiat Neurol Scand* **31**: 35.

Garrison FH. (1929) *An Introduction to the History of Medicine* (4th edn). London.

Georget EJ. (1820) *De la Folie*. Paris.

Green EM. (1914) Psychosis among Negroes – a Comparative Study. *J Nerv Ment Dis* **41**: 697.

Griesinger W. (1861) *Mental Pathology and Therapeutics* (transl 1867, Robertson CL and Rutherford J). London.

Guthrie D. (1945) *A History of Medicine*. London.

Guthrie LG. (1903) 'Myasthenia Gravis' in the Seventeenth Century. *Lancet* i: 330.

Haslam J. (1798) *Observations on Insanity*. London.

Haslam J. (1809) *Observations on Madness and Melancholy*. London.

Heiberg P. (1932) Variations in the Number of Reported Cases of Syphilis and in the Number of Deaths from General Paresis. *Acta Psychiat Neurol Scand* **7**: 189.

Hirsch A. (1885) *Handbook of Geographical and Historical Pathology* Vol 2 Chap 2. (transl from 2nd edn by Creighton C). London.

Hutton EL. (1941) Recent Advances in the Aetiology and Treatment of Neurosyphilis. *J Ment Sci* **87**: 1.

Hyslop TB. (1896) Pseudo-General Paralysis. *J Ment Sci* **42**: 303.

Idanoff ID. (1894) De la Paralysie Générale chez la femme. *Ann Méd-Psychol* **19**: 382.

Iskrant AP. (1945) The Economic Cost of Paresis in the United States. *J Ven Dis Inf* **26**: 175.

Journal of Mental Science (1873) Discussion on The Causation of General Paralysis **19**: 164.

Journal of Mental Science (1895) Review of the 36th Annual Report of the General Board of Commissioners in Lunacy for Scotland. **41**: 116.

Journal of Mental Science (1896) Discussion on Pseudo-General Paralysis. **42**: 646.

Journal of Mental Science (1907) Review of the 48th Annual Report of the General Board of Commissioners in Lunacy for Scotland. **53**: 154.

King A. (1958) 'These Dying Diseases'; Venereology in Decline? *Lancet* i: 651.

Klotz O. (1926) Concerning Aneurysms, 3rd Gordon Bell Memorial Lecture, University of Toronto Studies, Pathological Series (quoted by Rolleston, 1927b).

Kojog F. (1939) Die endemische Syphilis in Bosnia und Herzegowina. *Dermatologica* **79**: 361.

Kraepelin E. (1913) General Paresis. *Nervous and Mental Diseases Monograph No 14* (transl Moore JW). New York.

Kraepelin E. (1926) The Problems presented by General Paresis. *J Nerv Ment Dis* **63**: 209.

Kraepelin E. (1927) *Psychiatrie* (9th edn, Vol 2). Leipzig.

Krafft-Ebing R von. (1866) Zur Geschichte und Literatur der Dementia Paralytica. *Zeitschr f Psychiat* **23**: 627.

Krafft-Ebing R von. (1894) *Die Progressive Allgemeine Paralyse*. Vienna.

Lancet. (1957) A new disease? ii: 285.

Lees R. (1950) Syphilis – a historical and modern problem. *Trans Med-Chir Soc Edin* **129**: 58.

Leigh D. (1955) John Haslam MD 1764–1844, Apothecary to Bethlem. *J Hist Med* **10**: 17.
Lennox WG. (1923) Neurosyphilis among the Chinese. *Arch Neurol Psychiat* **9**: 26.
Lomholt M. (1944) Clinic and Prognosis of Malaria-treated Paralysis. *Acta Psychiat Neurol Scand* Suppl 30.
Lunier ML. (1849) Recherches sur la paralysie générale progressive. *Annal Méd-Psychol*, p. 183.
McCartney JL (1946) Why is Neurosyphilis uncommon in the Tropics? *Mil Surgeon* **99**: 21.
MacDonald AE. (1877) General Paresis. *Amer J Insan* **33**: 451.
Major RH (1954) *A History of Medicine*. Oxford.
Malzberg B. (1953) Mental Disease in Negroes in New York State 1939–41. *Ment Hyg* **37**: 450.
Marie MA. (1922) In: *La Paralysie Générale Centenaire de la Thèse de Bayle* (Vol 2). Paris, p. 139.
Maudsley H. (1867) *The Physiology and Pathology of Mind*. London.
Maudsley H. (1879) *The Pathology of Mind*. London.
Maudsley H. (1895) *The Pathology of Mind* (2nd edn). London.
Meryon E. (1864) *Practical and Pathological Researches on the Various Forms of Paralysis*. London, p. 153.
Mettler CC. (1947) *A History of Medicine*. Philadelphia.
Meyer A. (1959) A Note on the Concept of Dementia Paralytica at the time of Robert Schumann's death in 1856. *J Ment Sci* **105**: 116.
Mickle WJ. (1880) *General Paralysis of the Insane*. London.
Mickle WJ. (1886) *General Paralysis of the Insane* (2nd edn). London.
Millingen JG. (1840) *Aphorisms on the Treatment and Management of the Insane*. London, p. 46.
Mönkemüller –. (1911) Zur Geschichte der progressiven Paralyse. *Zeit f d ges Neurol Psychiat* **5**: 500.
Moore M and Solomon HC. (1934) Contributions of Haslam, Bayle and Esmarch and Jessen to the history of Neurosyphilis. *Arch Neurol Psychiat* **32**: 804.
Moreira J and Penafiel A. (1907) Contributions to the Study of Dementia Paralytica in Brazil. *J Ment Sci* **53**: 507.
Morris H. (1912) Observations on the History of Syphilis. *Lancet* **ii**: 497.
Morton LT. (1954) *Garrison and Morton's Medical Bibliography* (2nd edn). London, p. 418.
Mott FW. (1900) *Arch Neurol (London)*. **1**: 166.
Mott FW. (1908) Recent developments in our knowledge of Syphilis in relation to Diseases of the Nervous System. *BMJ* **i**: 10.
Neumann H. (1859) *Lehrbuch der Psychiatrie*. Quoted by Krafft-Ebing, 1894.
Nicole JE. (1943) Malaria in Neurosyphilis 1923–1943. *J Ment Sci* **89**: 381.
Nonne M. (1902) *Syphilis und Nervensystem*. Berlin, p. 543. Quoted by Zilboorg and Henry, 1941.
Padget P and Moore JE. (1936) Syphilis, a review of the recent Literature. *Arch int Med* **58**: 901.
Pinel P. (1798) *Nosographie Philosophique ou Méthode de l'Analyse appliquée à Médecine*. Paris.
Pinel P. (1809) *Traité Médico-philosophique sur l'Aliénation Mentale* (2nd edn). Paris.
Plaut F. (1926) *Paralysestudien bei Negern und Indianern*. Berlin, p. 25.
Power TD. (1930) The Aetiology of General Paralysis of the Insane. *J Ment Sci* **76**: 524.
Prichard JC. (1835) *A Treatise on Insanity*. London.
Report together with the Minutes of Evidence and an Appendix of Papers from the Committee appointed to consider of Provision being made for the better Regulation of Madhouses in England (1815). London.
Richardson –. (1891) Asylum Reports for 1890. *J Ment Sci* **37**: 604.
Robertson GM. (1923) The Discovery of General Paralysis. *J Ment Sci* **69**: 1.
Rolleston H. (1927a) Changes in the Clinical Aspects of Disease. *BMJ* **i**: 87.
Rolleston H. (1927b) Clinical Variations in Disease from the Historical Point of View. *BMJ* **ii**: 205.
Rosanoff AJ. (1938) *Manual of Psychiatry* (7th edn). New York, p. 341.
Salomon E. (1862) On the Pathological Elements of General Paresis. *J Ment Sci* **8**: 365.
Samuels WF. (1916) General Paralysis of the Insane in the Federated Malay States. *J Ment Sci* **62**: 411.
Sander W. (1870) Die paralytische Geistesstörung beim weiblichen Geschlecht. *Berlin Klin Woch* **7**: 81.
Sankey WHO. (1864) The Pathology of General Paralysis. *J Ment Sci* **9**: 467.
Sankey WHO. (1866) *Lectures on Mental Diseases*. London.
Semelaigne R. (1894) *Les Grands Aliénistes Français*. Paris.
Semelaigne R. (1930) *Les Pionniers de la Psychiatrie Française*. Paris.

Skae D. (1860) Contributions to the Natural History of General Paralysis. *Edinburgh Med J* **5**: 885.

Smith JC. (1926) Notes on the Appearance of Dementia Paralytica and the relation between its Frequency and the Antisyphilitic Treatment. *Acta Psychiat Neurol Scand* **1**: 346.

Spitzka EC. (1883) *Insanity, its Classification, Diagnosis and Treatment.* New York.

Stewart RM. (1924) General Paralysis; its unsolved problems. *J Ment Sci* **70**: 33.

Stewart RS. (1896) The Increase of General Paralysis in England and Wales; its Causation and Significance. *J Ment Sci* **42**: 760.

Stewart RS. (1901) Decrease of General Paralysis of the Insane in England and Wales. *J Ment Sci* **47**: 41.

Stoddart WHB (1921) *Mind and its Disorders* (4th edn). London.

Sudhoff K. (1926) *Essays in the History of Medicine.* New York, Chap 22, p. 259.

Toulouse E. (1922) In: *La Paralysie Générale, Centenaire de la Thèse de Bayle* (Vol 2). Paris, p. 11.

Tuke H. (1859) On General Paralysis. *J Ment Sci* **5**: 575 and **6**: 200.

Wagner CC. (1902) The Comparative Frequency of General Paresis. *Amer J Insan* **58**: 587.

Walshe FMR. (1947) *Diseases of the Nervous System* (5th edn). Edinburgh.

Westphal C. (1868) On the present state of our knowledge regarding General Paralysis of the Insane. *J Ment Sci* **14**: 162.

Whitwell JR. (1940) *Syphilis in Earlier Days.* London.

Willis T. (1672) *De Anima Brutorum.* Translated in *Dr. Willis' Practice of Physick* by Samuel Pordage, London, 1684. Part II, Concerning the Soul of the Brutes, Chap 9, *et seq.*

Wilson JH. (1857) General Paralysis of the Insane. *Liverpool Med-Chir J*, p. 231.

Wilson SAK (1941) *Neurology.* 2nd edn (1954) edited by AN Bruce, London.

Wise –. (1869) General Paralysis of the Insane. *Indian med Gaz* **4**: 75.

Workman J. (1858) Pathological Notes. *Amer J Insan* **15**: 1.

Workman J. (1878) On Paresis. *Canada Lancet* **10**: 357 and **11**: 1.

Zilboorg C and Henry GW. (1941) *A History of Medical Psychology.* London, Chap 13.

4

The two manias:
A study of the evolution of the modern concept of mania

PART I

In the year 1899 there occurred an event which has had great consequence for psychiatry. This was the publication of the sixth edition of Emil Kraepelin's textbook, where he introduced for the first time his distinction between manic-depressive insanity and dementia praecox. It was a distinction which rapidly became accepted almost everywhere in the world, and it still forms the basis of our thinking about the nature of the functional psychoses. Kraepelin's concept of mania was quite different from the concept of mania held during most of the 19th century; and so, historically speaking, there are two manias, more or less sharply separated by the Kraepelinian revolution. The purpose of the present essay is to give some account of the term 'mania' in its pre-Kraepelinian sense and of the events which led Kraepelin to his new concept; and also (in Part II) to put forward a new idea of why this revolution came about.

Although Kraepelin's new concepts were accepted fairly quickly – that is to say, over a span of 10–20 years for English-speaking countries – something of the old concepts lingered on, especially in textbooks, causing confusion in the minds of students until quite recently. The story of chronic mania illustrates this, and may serve as an introduction to my subject. But first, I give a note about my sources and about the term 'dementia'.

Textbooks tend to go through many editions, and I have generally quoted from the earliest edition easily available to me. In the life of a successful textbook, one particular edition may come to be thought of as the standard or definitive one (the 8th edition of Kraepelin, for example), and then the earlier editions may become rare. It is not easy to consult a 1st edition of Kraepelin or even of Henderson and Gillespie. Moreover, in later editions of 19th century textbooks the date of the original publication often goes unmentioned.

For foreign-language textbooks I refer in the text to the publication date of the edition I quote, but the passages quoted are generally from an English translation. Fortunately, most of these translations were made within a short time of the original publication, and the English terminology will be in line with usage then. From the historical point of view, therefore, the contemporary translations are more useful than a modern translation could be.

I have for the most part used the term dementia in its 19th century sense. Bucknill and Tuke (1879, p. 177) describe the early stage of dementia as a confusion of thought and a failing of memory, and the late stage as one in which the patient is unable to tell his name, often dirty in his habits, and occupied – if occupied at all – only in purposeless activity. The dementia which commonly followed mania or melancholia was not, during the 19th century, distinguished in its clinical manifestations from that associated with senility or general paralysis. The distinction was made only by age of onset or the presence of characteristic physical signs and postmortem appearances. It was, of course, this usage of dementia which Kraepelin intended in his 'dementia praecox'. But he accepted Bleuler's alternative name, 'schizophrenia', partly because he came to agree with Bleuler that dementia did not always occur and partly, no doubt, because schizophrenia was a word with a convenient adjectival form.

Chronic mania

The specific term chronic mania does not seem to have been used by textbook writers until about the middle of the 19th century, but its existence is clearly implied before that time. Thus Pinel (1801, p. 235) says of a case of mania that the patient became "sunk into continued mania"; and Esquirol (1838, p. 392) describes mania as "a disorder which is emphatically chronic". Griesinger (1865b, p. 323), discussing states of mental weakness, says that "chronic mania and dementia constitute the vast majority of the insane". Chronic mania (he goes on) "is always a secondary disease, developed out of melancholia or mania; in it, the emotions of the acute illness disappear"; there is a dullness and weakness, an absence of sentiment, an indifference; left to themselves, the patients become absorbed in their delusions and there is eventual deterioration into apathetic dementia.

In their *Manual of Psychological Medicine* Bucknill and Tuke (1879, p. 303) say that, "when mania becomes chronic, we witness the almost hopeless form of insanity which is only too common". Advanced chronic mania "is so little distinguishable from dementia" that physicians disagree which is which. And 13 years later, in his *Dictionary of Psychological Medicine* (1892, under 'Mania'), Tuke observed that patients who do not recover or do not die early from a maniacal attack "tend to fall into chronic dementia or what is called chronic mania. With the latter affection there is a considerable degree of permanent loss of mental power, so that it is really akin to chronic dementia. However, it may for descriptive purposes be differentiated by the retention of delusions". According to Thomas Clouston (1892, p. 192), the typical picture of a patient with chronic mania was that of the mad Mrs Rochester in Charlotte Brontë's novel *Jane Eyre* (published 1847); and the same picture, though perhaps in a milder form, is reflected in Maudsley's statement (1895, p. 264) that the chronic manic patient displays absurd hallucinations, senseless conversations with himself, odd acts, imaginary enemies, various delusions and a gradually increasing weakness of mind.

The opinion of contemporary German writers on the subject of chronic mania was summarized by Schott (1904). He recognized that many cases in which chronic over-activity and excitement terminated in obvious dementia could properly be included in Kraepelin's category of dementia praecox. But there was also, he said, a type of case which began as mania (in the Kraepelinian sense) but in which there gradually developed a weakness of memory and skill, with loss of initiative and insight and with deterioration of habits. Kraepelin, who in the sixth edition of his textbook (1899, p. 385) had recognized that some degree of general deterioration might occur in severe and long-standing cases of mania, accepted in his eighth edition (1913a, p. 16) the picture of chronic mania as delineated by Schott. He made no mention, however, of Schott's comment that these cases constituted "a special type of dementia". Kraepelin's reference to Schott was widely quoted in English textbooks and may have led a later generation of English-speaking psychiatrists to forget that the term chronic mania had been in common use long before then.

The history of chronic mania during the first three decades of the 20th century has been summarized by Wertham (1929). He recognized that prolonged manic excitement might be an end-state of various groups of psychoses; but he thought the term ought to be reserved for a rare condition, developing only in persons of manic constitution and pyknic physique, and benign in the sense that it did not lead to severe mental deterioration. Yet he accepted that, even within his delimitation, delusions and 'intellectual reduction' might occur. Wertham's views were similar to those of many American authors, but were represented by only one British textbook – that of Henderson and Gillespie, whose account and whose illustrative cases remained almost unchanged through successive editions from 1929 to 1962.

The general view among British writers was that, even within Kraepelin's classificatory system, chronic mania tended to mental deterioration. At first these assertions were made unreservedly – Cole (1913), for example, says "in time the memory becomes affected and the process tends to secondary dementia", and similar views were expressed by Yellowlees (1932) and, as late as the 1950's, by Tredgold and Tredgold. Chronic mania, says Yellowlees, is analogous to chronic melancholia, "but with the exceedingly interesting difference that the great majority of patients who remain in a state of even fairly mild elation for any great length of time begin to show distinct evidences of mental degeneration and become untidy, careless and degenerated, often to a remarkable degree". Tredgold and Tredgold (1943) say that "most patients with chronic mania have exacerbations . . . After each of these, intellectual deterioration is usually more pronounced, and eventually, it may be after many years, dementia supervenes". The statement is repeated in the third edition of their textbook (1953).

But later opinions become less definite and tend increasingly to account for the deterioration in terms of personality change, old age, arteriosclerosis or, more simply, a wrong diagnosis. Thus Anderson (1964) says of patients with chronic mania "there is not, until age overtakes them, any evidence of intellectual deterioration". The first edition of Mayer-Gross et al. (1954) says that chronic mania "provides a lasting and terminal picture of shallow and monotonous hilarity, querulousness and irritability" – though we should note that their third edition (1969) omits this and merely states that when mania becomes chronic, lithium treatment is often helpful.

I think it is fair to say that, over the past 20 years, the interest of textbook writers in the subject of chronic mania has steadily waned. The eighth edition of *Modern Clinical Psychiatry* (Kolb, 1973) says no more of chronic mania than that it is uncommon before the age of 40; and chronic mania is not mentioned at all in the 1974 edition of Arieti's *American Handbook of Psychiatry*.

Thus chronic mania, from having been an important concept for 19th century psychiatrists and from having survived (though in an emasculated form) the first decades of the Kraepelinian revolution, has gradually over the last 20 years or so seeped away until today it must be thought of – if thought of at all – as a mere ghost still haunting a few textbooks but without substance or clinical significance.

Mania before Kraepelin

In their authoritative textbook, Bucknill and Tuke refer to "the constant tendency of mania, and other forms of mental derangement, to pass into dementia" (1879, p. 304). This observation sums up the 19th century concept of mania as a condition commonly leading to mental (i.e. intellectual) deterioration. Clouston (1892, p. 205), discussing the prognosis of mania, says there is complete recovery in about half the cases, death in 5%, partial recovery (that is, chronic mania) in 15%; and in the remaining 30%, dementia – adding that "the bulk of chronic patients in asylums are of this class". Melancholia had a similar outcome, and it is evident that the concepts of mania and melancholia in the 19th century included cases of what we would now call schizophrenia and which Kraepelin called dementia praecox; indeed, Kraepelin specifically makes this point (1913a, p. 193).

The question may then be asked, did Kraepelin's concepts of manic-depressive insanity and dementia praecox spring fully armed, as it were, from the head of Jove, so that he saw in a sudden flash of inspiration what had been there all the time but which no one else had seen; or had a gradual change been taking place in the understanding, or in the clinical manifestations, of mental disorders, such that a distinction between these two groups must soon have become obvious to many observers? It is this question which I am going to consider. The attempt to answer it will involve a search among the complex and changing patterns of 19th century classifications for the emergence of the idea that there were some types of insanity, characterized by excitement or depression or both, which did not progress to dementia.

I propose to examine four strands from this vast pattern: the ideas related to (1) periodicity, (2) partial insanity, (3) simple mania, and (4) recoverability.

Periodic insanity

Because we are apt to think of affective disorder (in its modern sense) as typified by a tendency to recurrence, an examination of the concept of periodic insanity might seem a promising one for our purpose. But Pinel was only recalling what had been recognized for centuries when he wrote in 1801 (p. 5) about insanity in general that, "intermittent or periodical insanity is the most common form of the disease"; and this is why, he says, he begins his treatise with the subject of periodical insanity. It was of course this general tendency to periodicity which gave rise to the mediaeval English word 'lunatic', meaning a person affected with intermittent insanity – the intermittency being attributed to changes in the moon. A claim is sometimes made that Jean Pierre Falret, a pupil of Esquirol, 'discovered' manic-depressive insanity in his delineation of circular insanity, which he called 'folie circulaire' (1854). Thus in Hinsie and Campbell's *Psychiatric Dictionary* (1970), folie circulaire is described as "Falret's term for the condition known today as manic-depressive psychosis, circular or alternating".

Falret indeed described a disorder characterized by alternating attacks of mania and melancholia, in which there were lucid intervals between each attack. The attacks were of the simple form of mania and melancholia – that is to say, without incoherence or intellectual disturbance. And yet, he says, although the simple forms are more curable than most insanities when occurring in isolation, it is a remarkable fact that when they were united to form folie circulaire he had never known a case with complete cure or even a lasting remission; and that, even in the lucid intervals, the patient only seemed recovered and tried to conceal his intellectual loss and delusions. The prognosis of folie circulaire, he said, was particularly grave, indeed it was *désesperant* – hopeless. This view was generally accepted. Bucknill and Tuke (1879, p. 304), in observing that mania may pass into melancholia, add that "if the two conditions alternate, it assumes the very unfavourable form of circular insanity". Maudsley (1895, p. 279) says that the prognosis of alternating recurrent insanity is always bad: it causes "the mind eventually to become weaker and the disease to last for life".

Clearly, Falret's folie circulaire cannot be simply equated with our modern affective disorder. On the other hand, Falret says of his folie circulaire that it is strongly hereditary and that it affects females much more than males. And in spite of Falret's explicit statement about the bad prognosis, Kraepelin included "the so-called periodic or circular insanity" within his category of manic-depressive insanity. However, Kraepelin did not use periodicity as a distinguishing feature of the manic-depressive insanities because (he said) periodicity is also characteristic of epileptic insanity, hysterical insanity, and certain forms of dementia praecox (1913a, p. 189).

Thus the original concept of periodic or alternating insanity does not seem to lead us directly to the reason for the Kraepelinian divide.

Partial insanity

The 19th century inherited two opposing views on the nature of the mind and, in consequence, on the nature of mental disease. One view – of which John Locke was a proponent – saw the mind as an indivisible unity, like the soul. On this unitarian view, the mind was incapable of suffering any partial derangement: if diseased, it would be diseased throughout, and therefore all insanities were essentially the same, varying only in their mode of onset or in the comparative severity of symptoms. This view was incorporated in the 19th century concept of the *Einheitspsychose*, held in Germany by Griesinger and in Britain by Sankey and to some extent by Maudsley. It is reflected in Bucknill's remark that when a man is a lunatic he is a lunatic to his fingers' ends, a remark which is quoted with approval by Maudsley (1867, p. 343), and is repeated in Tuke's Dictionary (1892) in the article on 'Hair of the Insane', together with Darwin's comment – that Tuke might have added "and often to the extremity of each particular hair".

The other view of the mind was that its activities could be considered under distinct categories, particularly those of feeling, thinking, and willing, as set out by Emanuel Kant. This view allowed the concept of partial insanity. Already in the 18th century William Cullen – who was a disciple of Linnaeus and therefore a classifier – had classed insanity into partial (which he called melancholia) and general (which he called mania). Pinel (1801) took the same view, but, unlike Cullen, he divided mania into two types according to whether or not it was accompanied by 'delirium' (see Appendix). Pinel's mania without delirium, or *folie raisonnante* as he called it, became the prototype of partial insanity during the 19th century. But to consider the further development of this concept, we need to remind ourselves of the classification of Pinel's successor, Esquirol.

In his *Maladies Mentales* of 1838, Esquirol classified insanities into partial and general, and he called partial insanities 'monomania', i.e. mad in only one aspect. He divided partial insanity into two types, according to the dominant mood being sad or gay. The gay type he called 'monomania proper', and he further subdivided it according to the faculty chiefly disordered: that is to say, he divided it into intellectual, affective, and instinctive types. He says that his affective monomania is equivalent to Pinel's *folie raisonnante*. Yet we should be wrong if we thought that Esquirol's gay affective monomania represented what we now call mania or hypomania. For we have to note: first, that Esquirol defined his monomania as insanities in which the delirium was partial and permanent, so that by definition affective monomania was an incurable condition; and second, that, to quote Esquirol, "in the character of Don Quixote, we find an admirable description of monomania" (p. 331).

During the course of the 19th century, the partial insanity which Esquirol called monomania passed through a series of names, such as 'primary systematized mania' (Maudsley 1895, p. 299) and 'systematized insanity', and finally came to cover a group of disorders under the general name of paranoia – a group which worried Kraepelin because, as it included cases showing all gradations between those which ended in dementia and those in which the personality and intellect seemed perfectly preserved, he had difficulty in deciding whether or not to include it in his dementia praecox group.

Thus the concept of partial insanity does not seem to lead us towards the Kraepelinian (and present-day) idea of affective disorder.

Simple mania

If then we are to find the equivalent of our modern idea of mania in Esquirol's classification, we must look among his group of general insanities, and particularly perhaps in his concept of simple mania. Esquirol divided general insanities into two groups, mania and dementia, and he says of mania that if it is simple, then it is the most certainly curable of all forms of mental alienation (p. 395).

Later in the century it became common to refer to simple mania and simple melancholia, meaning conditions which were uncomplicated by delusions or incoherence. Thus Griesinger (1865a, p. 299) described simple mania as a form of incompletely developed mania, "a relatively mild mode of expression of certain desires and instincts, in which the patient still shows no striking disorder of the intelligence". We might think that sounds a promising candidate for Kraepelin's mania. But, says Griesinger, this is the maniacal form of *folie raisonnante* and though it might end in recovery, it might also "pass into a state of mental weakness . . . with silly foolish acts and desires and childish play"; and he adds that "in no single case of mania is the conscious thought, the intelligence, perfectly free from any disorder" (p. 302). Maudsley, in 1867, grouped together Pinel's *folie raisonnante*, Esquirol's monomania and Prichard's moral insanity as being only phases of what he called affective disorder or affective insanity – terms which he later equated with simple mania; but he went on to say that these were conditions "which, continued, usually end in positive intellectual disorder or dementia" (p. 322). Bevan Lewis, in his Textbook (1899, p. 201), says that "simple uncomplicated mania is a remarkably recoverable affection". Yet the table he gives (p. 221) of the outcome of 1800 cases admitted to the West Riding Asylum, Yorkshire, shows simple mania to have an outcome no better than acute mania: for only 60% recovered, 12% died during the attack, and 16% passed into the chronic state with "permanent mental enfeeblement".

Thus we cannot easily find Kraepelin's mania – that is, a condition which never leads to profound dementia – in the simple mania of the second half of the 19th century.

Recoverability

There was a long tradition, upheld by John Monro (1758), that insanity was incurable. This was a prejudice which, said Esquirol, "has proved exceedingly fatal to maniacs" (1838, p. 389), because it led physicians to neglect both the treatment of such patients and the study of mental disorder. With the worthy aim of refuting this prejudice, Esquirol – and Pinel before him – was concerned to show that insanity was not necessarily a hopeless condition. "Experience has proved", he wrote, "that mania is not incurable" – but it is disappointing that neither he nor Pinel mention the proportion of their manic patients who recovered. Later in the century, during the era of asylum building, it became the concern of medical superintendents, with an eye on public relations and the reports from other asylums, to claim as high a cure rate as possible. Perhaps it was partly for these reasons that there seems to have been no very serious effort to define what was meant by cure or recovery. Thus recovery might mean only that the patient did not die or did not immediately pass into a state of dementia.

The more thoughtful writers gradually began to observe that those patients who were considered to have 'recovered' nevertheless often failed to return to their former state. Thus Griesinger, in 1867, said, "It is not at all unusual, although it has hitherto been very little attended to, to observe a mental state characterized by moderate (mental) weakness occasionally ensure after apparent recovery from other forms (of insanity), and to remain persistent" (p. 322). Hack Tuke, in his Dictionary (1892 under 'Mania'), says that "it is usually found that recovery from any form of mania is preceded by a state of dullness . . . recovery may take place with a certain mental enfeeblement (the *Heilung mit Defekt* of Neumann)". Maudsley (1895, p. 259) says that recovery from mania occurs in about half the cases, but the recovery "is not invariably quite so perfect as it looks": there is a moral blunting and "some degree of impairment of intellectual memory may be detected sometimes after acute mania".

Nevertheless, attempts were being made to isolate a group of disorders which recovered in a stricter sense – in the sense that they were never associated with decline into dementia. Here the contributions of Mendel and Kahlbaum are important.

Mendel, as Privat Dozent at the University of Berlin, published in 1881 his *Die Manie*, a book in which he put forward a new name and a new concept – hypomania. He proposed this name for "that form of mania which typically shows itself only in the mild stages, abortively, so to speak" (p. 36). This form of illness, he says, can't properly be called simple mania because simple mania has come to be equated with Pinel's *folie raisonnante* (mania *sine delirio*) which has characteristic features – as we have noted above. Nor can it properly be called *excitation manique* because that has been used to cover states of excitement due to various types of recognized brain disease. Mendel describes his hypomania as an illness "similar to the state of exultation in typical mania, (but) with a certain lesser grade of development" (p. 38), and which never comes to incoherence of speech. He says that all his cases of hypomania were cured (p. 185), and to that extent we may accept Mendel's hypomania as one of the earliest descriptions of a purely affective psychosis which did not lead to mental (i.e., intellectual) enfeeblement.

Kraepelin was to take over the term hypomania and use it as the equivalent of the mildest form of (his) mania. But it is a curiosity of history that the term hypomania was soon replaced, in the textbooks of writers who adopted the Kraepelinian scheme, by that of simple mania – a term which, as we have seen above, had been commonly used for cases ending in dementia; and Kraepelin himself, in the ninth edition of his textbook (1927), reverts to the use of 'simple' for the mildest degree of mania. For some decades after Kraepelin, the distinction between acute mania and simple mania was still based on the presence or absence of incoherence. But incoherence, in its 19th century sense of incomprehensible and raving speech, became increasingly uncommon during the 20th century both as a technical term and as a clinical state; and this is no doubt why the distinction between simple and acute mania went out of fashion. When that happened, a new word was needed for that form of mania which was even milder than Kraepelin's simple mania, and it was to fill this need that Mendel's term hypomania has recently staged a come-back (Hare, 1976).

Kahlbaum and cyclothymia

A more explicit account of affective disorder not leading to dementia was given by Kahlbaum. Although Kahlbaum is chiefly remembered for his book *Die Katatonie* of 1874, I think he deserves at least as much credit for his paper 'On Circular Insanity' (1882), in which he put forward the view that there was a type of circular disorder characterized by attacks of excitement and depression but which, unlike typical and recurrent attacks of mania and melancholia, did not end in dementia. To appreciate this, we must recall the almost universal belief that attacks of mania (in the pre-Kraepelinian sense) were generally preceded by a period of melancholia. Thus

Griesinger had said (1865a, p. 276), that "in the majority of cases, melancholic states precede the maniacal"; and Maudsley (1879, p. 395), talking of mania, said "most often there is a forewarning of calamity, a precursory stage of depression". Such statements, which must certainly have reflected contemporary experience, have dropped out of modern textbooks. But during the 19th century, the repeated sequence of depression leading to excitement was the form called 'typical circular insanity'. It was from this group that Kahlbaum extracted what he considered to be a generically distinct type, a type that did not end in dementia and which he called 'cyclothymia' ("we need a new name for the non-deteriorating group, and for this group I propose the term cyclothymia"). And he went on to say that there are pure states of depression and pure states of exaltation which also do not lead to dementia and for which he proposed the names 'dysthymia' and 'hyperthymia'.

These ideas were re-moulded by Kraepelin. Just as Kraepelin took over the concepts of catatonia and hebephrenia (which had been delineated by Kahlbaum and by Kahlbaum's pupil Hecker) and made them into aspects of his dementia praecox, so he took over Kahlbaum's cyclothymia, dysthymia and hyperthymia and made them into aspects of his manic-depressive insanity. He then used Kahlbaum's term cyclothymia in an altogether difference sense, the sense in which we still use it.

Krafft-Ebing, building on Kahlbaum's observations, clearly distinguished in his textbook (1898) – and as far as I know, for the first time in the history of psychiatry – between types of insanities which were curable and types which were not. His classification seems unsatisfactory today because it was based on the then still persisting ideas of Morel on degeneracy. Thus he held mania and melancholia to be acquired disorders, and to be curable because they were acquired; and he classified them under the heading of 'psychoneuroses'. Other types of insanity, which tended to dementia, did so because they were due to hereditary degeneration. Kraepelin took over the concept of mania and melancholia as recoverable, but unlike Krafft-Ebing he recognized the hereditary factor. Indeed, one of the points on which he based his opinion that manic-depressive insanity represented a single morbid process was that its varieties showed mutual replacement in heredity.

PART II

From the above considerations, it appears to me that the distinction between mental disorders which tended to progress to permanent mental enfeeblement (what the 19th century called dementia) and those which did not – a distinction which Kraepelin considered to be a fundamental one – first clearly emerged in the early 1880's with the publications of Mendel and Kahlbaum. If that is so, then we may pertinently ask why the distinction emerged at that time. If the distinction is really a permanent and enduring feature in the nature of mental disorders, why was the discovery not made earlier?

There is one straight-forward explanation why Kahlbaum was able to delineate the non-dementing forms of insanity and why this had not been done before. Under the influence of Griesinger, psychiatry had become an academic subject in Germany by the mid-19th century. But it was dominated by Griesinger's concept of the *Einheitspsychose*, and so the university climate was unfavourable for the study of syndromes and classification. Moreover, university research and teaching is likely to have been based (as so often, even now) on acute cases, studied over a short period of time. Kahlbaum, on the other hand, worked for more than 30 years at a single institution and was therefore well placed to detect syndromes on the basis of long-term outcome.

But although this explanation is reasonable, it does not seem to me sufficient. The classification of insanities had been very carefully studied since the end of the 18th century, and it is not easy to believe that Esquirol and the many very able members of his school, who studied their cases in institutions and not in university clinics, would have missed the particular class of non-dementing insanities if it had been clearly there. Again, the explanation does not account for the very widespread belief that all insanities tended to dementia. This belief was held by the ablest observers throughout much of the 19th century, whereas today, of course, the most casual experience would refute it. To take account of these points, I propose an additional explanation.

The mutability of disease

This explanation is based on the belief – or the fact – that diseases are continually undergoing change. The mutability of diseases has not attracted much attention from clinicians or historians; and after more than a hundred years, Darwin's ideas have still not made any great impact on medical thinking. It is a curious fact that when Linnaeus proposed the first satisfactory method for classifying species of plants and animals, his method was immediately adopted by medical men; and Linnaeus himself, though not a physician, wrote a book (*Genera Morborum*, 1763) on the classification of disease – including mental disease – in which he, like his followers, treated each disease as though it were a species comparable to the species of living organisms (which at that time were considered immutable). Diseases are not closely comparable with species, but I think there is an analogy in the sense that diseases, like species, represent the balance of a process by which living organisms struggle to adjust to a continually changing environment. The main difference is that diseases change much more quickly than species do. And perhaps psychiatric diseases change more quickly than others because their expression is largely psychological and follows changing fashions in the mode of expressing mental distress.

Such changes make the understanding of disease more difficult. The simplest, and perhaps the best, way in which the vast mass of medical experience can be brought under intellectual control is by constructing a classification of disease. But when diseases are changing significantly within a few decades, the attempt to classify them becomes like an attempt to describe the changing shape of a cloud. The innumerable classificatory systems of 19th century psychiatrists no doubt reflect to some extent a growing insight into the nature of the disorders. But I think they also represent an attempt to keep pace with the continually changing manifestations of the disorders.

McKeown (1979) has emphasized the relatively rapid change which has occurred in the incidence and severity of many common diseases in Western Europe since the beginning of the 19th century. The progressive fall in death rates during the

19th century from such diseases as tuberculosis, typhoid fever, measles and scarlet fever are attributed by him not to medical treatment but to the effects of better nutrition, better hygiene (especially as regards drinking water and milk) and smaller families (which allows more food and parental care for each child and diminishes the chance of cross infection). These effects, he suggests, led to increasingly better health and to a greater constitutional resistance to disease among the general population.

Changes in mental disease

If one accepts McKeown's thesis, then it is worth considering what effect the continuing improvement in health and constitutional resistance may have had on the manifestations of psychiatric disease in Western Europe during the last 150 years or so. A striking fact which emerges from a study of 19th century psychiatric textbooks is that the diseases described there are not much like the kind of psychiatric diseases we see today. One has only to consider their descriptions of typical cases of acute mania to realise this – and it does not matter whether they were describing cases of what we would now call mania or what we would now call catatonic excitement: such cases are certainly rare now among the native-born population in Britain. This is only one of many such changes.

Thus in the mid-19th century, between 10% and 20% of admissions to asylums in this country were for general paralysis. We are apt to believe the disappearance of general paralysis was a triumph of medical science, but there is evidence that this is not the full story (Hare, 1959; see this volume, Chapter 3).

A hundred years ago, between 5% and 10% of admissions to asylums were for epileptic insanity. Epileptic insanity was not merely a condition in which a patient might have a manic-like attack after a fit – epileptic furor – but a condition in which there typically developed changes in personality, often with delusions and hallucinations, and generally progressing to dementia, a dementia which, apart from the fits, seems to have been indistinguishable from that consequent upon attacks of mania and melancholia. Esquirol (1838, p. 381) said that epilepsy, "which is so often a cause of idiocy and dementia, also produces mania". "Of the 400 epileptic patients that we now have in the Salpêtrière, 50 at least were maniacs after every attack. The fury of epileptics is blind, terrible, and dangerous in the extreme". According to Griesinger (1865a, p. 405) "a very large number of epileptics are in a state of chronic mental disease even during the intervals between attacks . . . The most persistent psychical disorder to which epileptics are subject is dementia". Maudsley says of epileptic mania that it "differs chiefly from ordinary mania by the extremity of its blind fury and reckless violence"; and that epilepsy tends to progress to epileptic dementia, "which differs from ordinary insanity only in being more accompanied by hallucinations and more prone to outbreaks of excitement and violence".

Yet today, I think, we never see such cases; and we too easily account for that by thinking of the great advances in the treatment of epilepsy when we should also be considering whether epilepsy itself has become a rarer disease or milder in its consequences than it used to be. In relation to the effects of better general health, Clouston (1892, p. 444) has an interesting observation. He says that the proportion of admissions of British asylums for epileptic insanity varied from 11% in the poorer agricultural counties to 5% in the better-off mining and manufacturing counties, and he goes on to note the "curious fact" that in Edinburgh, in his department for the richer classes, there was not one case of epileptic insanity among 800 admissions over 19 years.

Chronic alcoholism is a condition which is probably commoner in Britain now than it was a hundred years ago. But what has become of alcoholic insanity? During the latter part of the 19th century, about 5% of asylum admissions were for alcoholic insanity, a disorder which, like epileptic insanity, was commonly associated with delusions and hallucinations and which pursued a downward course to dementia. It was of course the general similarity between the symptoms and course of insanities associated with mania, melancholia, general paralysis, epilepsy and alcoholism which led to the idea that all insanities were essentially the same and that all tended towards dementia.

Another striking difference between the psychiatric disorders of the 19th century and today is in their mortality rate. There is considerable agreement among the textbook writers of the 19th century that the mortality rate of an attack of acute insanity was about 10% – and this even when cases of general paralysis, epilepsy and alcoholism had been excluded. From a study of 3800 deaths in Scottish asylums, Mitchell (1879) concluded the death rate there was between six and eight times that of the general population and that the excess death rates were higher in the younger age-groups. Part of the high mortality was due to general paralysis, but even at Bethlem Hospital, which did not admit epileptic or paralytic cases or cases where the duration of the illness had been more than a year, the mortality rate was between 5% and 9% (Griesinger, 1865b; Robinson, 1865).

However much the statistics may be open to doubt, there seems no escaping this evidence of high mortality in acute attacks of insanity during the last century. Once again it is easy to suppose that the improvement in mortality rate between then and now is simply the consequence of earlier admission, better care and better treatments. But it seems to me at least as plausible to attribute it to improvements in general health and in constitutional resistance to disease, in consequence of better nutrition and the other factors which McKeown (1979) noted.

The amelioration of insanities

Such conditions as these lead, I suggest, to the reasonable supposition that psychiatric disorders taken as a whole were becoming less severe during the 19th century, particularly during its second half. There is indeed plenty of evidence that the later textbook writers of the 19th century noticed that acute mania was becoming a less serious condition than had been described by earlier writers. Thus Bucknill and Tuke (1879, p. 296) say that mania, or raving madness, "is to be found at the present day much better described in books than observed in asylums", and they add that Arnold's statement (of 1782) that the patient raves incessantly, "is not applicable to nearly so large a proportion of cases of maniacal insanity as it was when Arnold wrote". And Clouston (1892, p. 154) says that "the raving madness of the older authors, or acute mania, is perhaps the type of all insanity both in the popular and professional mind . . . Yet this type of disease is nowadays not at all so common as others"; and among 297 cases of acute mania he could find "not more than 20 which could have sat to Esquirol's pictures".

The idea that the manifestations of psychiatric disorder were changing during the last century is reinforced by the many studies which have indicated a change in the manifestation of psychiatric disease in the last few decades. There is general agreement that the prognosis of schizophrenia has notably improved, that catatonic stupor has practically disappeared, and that the various sub-types which Kraepelin delineated have become much less well defined. I think marked changes must have occurred too in that form of mental disorder which used to be called involutional melancholia. It has faded away and can hardly be made out nowadays – and in this respect has followed a similar course to that of its counterpart, chronic mania.

Dementia in dementia praecox

The view that psychiatric disorders were ameliorating during the 19th century allows us to consider in what ways this might have occurred to permit Kraepelin to reach his distinction between manic-depressive insanity and dementia praecox; and also to consider whether this can be linked with the changing manifestations of schizophrenia in Western society during the present (20th) century. Apart from genetic disposition, there are two factors contributing to the severity of a disease. One is the prevalence and virulence of environmental causes and the other is the patient's constitutional resistance to disease. For the major classes of mental disorder we know little about the causes, but we can say something about the general standard of a person's health. Thus his health as an adult will be determined by the state of his mother's health during pregnancy; by complications of pregnancy and delivery; by the standard of nutrition he received, particularly in early childhood; by the amount of infection to which he was exposed – particularly virus infections which may be associated with encephalitis; and by the general standard of care he received from his parents, which would include how far he was protected from accident and violence. These determinants have greatly changed over the past 150 years in industrialized countries; and it is their changes, I suggest, which have been a major factor in the amelioration of the course of psychotic disorders.

Good general health, in so far as it is indicated by good physique, has long been recognized as a favourable prognostic sign in schizophrenia. Clouston (1888) said that the cardinal problem of psychiatry was, "How can we avert dementia?"; and his suggestions for prophylaxis, or early treatment, were of "rapidly fattening the patient, life out of doors, regular exercise" and so on – in other words, an attempt to build up the patient's physique and therefore by implication his resistance to dementia. Kraepelin, 25 years later, gave almost exactly the same advice (1913b, p. 279); and it is worth noting that most of the 'successful' treatments for schizophrenia have had the effect, if not primarily the intention, of increasing the patient's appetite and thus fattening him up. We might also reflect that until a few decades ago it was the common opinion that schizophrenia in young persons was associated with various physical stigmata which were referred to as the somatic manifestations of schizophrenia (Shattock, 1950). We do not see such manifestations now, and that may be simply because the general health of patients has further improved.

One of Kraepelin's criteria for his dementia praecox group was that, unlike manic-depressive insanity, its course tended to profound dementia. But nowadays (in Britain at least) schizophrenia rarely leads to profound dementia, and to that extent the Kraepelinian distinction has worn thin. The improvement which has occurred in the prognosis of schizophrenia is commonly attributed to advances in care and treatment. No doubt they are a factor, but it seems clear that the improvement had begun well before the introduction of modern methods of treatment and particularly before the introduction of the phenothiazines (Ödegaard, 1967).

Dementia in manic-depressive psychosis

In spite of much careful study, it was not until the 1880's that any clear evidence emerged for a group of insanities which did not tend to dementia. But even in Kraepelin's day, the prognosis of his manic-depressive insanity was by no means of the entirely non-dementing kind which we nowadays tend to associate with affective disorder. Kraepelin accepted that his manic-depressive insanity might progress to a type of psychic weakness – and indeed found this to have occurred in 37% of nearly a thousand cases which he had studied (1913a, p. 117). He described the nature of this weakness as simple personal peculiarities, such as occur in the families of manic-depressive patients. It is perhaps strange that, although he did not feel it necessary to give any particular explanation for the dementing process of dementia praecox, he was nevertheless at some pains to explain – to explain away, as it might seem – the "permanent peculiarities" in manic-depressive insanity. Thus he suggested that this weakness might be due to a severe hereditary taint, or to long residence in an institution, or to approaching age, or even to a postulated aetiological relation between manic-depressive insanity and arteriosclerosis (p. 161). Moreover he did not make it clear in what way the psychic weakness differs from a mild degree of schizophrenic deterioration – and nowadays a schizophrenic deterioration is often manifested as no more than a defect of personality. Nor does this distinction become clear in the writing of later authors. Lewis (1966), for example, discussing the course and prognosis of affective disorder, states that "in the more chronic forms, or after a series of attacks, there may be impaired initiative and judgement, irresoluteness, dullness and social deterioration – none of them conspicuous", a description which would do very well for a mild state of schizophrenic defect. I suggest that in such descriptions we still see the tail end, the ghost as it were, of a process of mental enfeeblement which can occur in affective psychosis and which generally did occur, to a more severe degree, until towards the end of the 19th century.

Conclusion

I have suggested that the mental deterioration which was the common sequel of insanity during the 19th century was due, at least in part, to the relatively poor state of general health then, and to the consequent low resistance to disorders affecting mental function. This idea permits a reconciliation of two opposing views held during that century: the view that all insanities were essentially similar and tended to dementia, and the later view that there was a type of insanity in which the intellectual function was not significantly involved. Thus we can say that, under the conditions of poor hygiene and poor general health which existed during much of the 19th century, most insanities did tend to dementia. But as the general health of the population gradually improved, this tendency became less; and the effect of this was first apparent in the group of affective disorders, so allowing their identification late in the century as a distinct, non-dementing group. And we may then suppose that the same cause has continued to act, and that its effect has more recently become apparent in Kraepelin's dementia praecox group; and this would explain why we no longer see the profound dementia which was still the characteristic end-state of the disorder in his day.

References

Anderson EW. (1964) *Psychiatry.* Baillière: London, p. 134.

Arieti S. (1974) *American Handbook of Psychiatry* (2nd edn). Basic Books: New York.

Bevan Lewis W. (1899) *Textbook of Mental Diseases.* Griffin: London, p. 1185.

Bucknill JC and Tuke DH. (1879) *A Manual of Psychological Medicine* (4th edn). Churchill: London.

Clouston TS. (1888) Presidential address to the Medico-Psychological Association. *J Ment Sci* **34**: 325–348.

Clouston TS. (1892) *Clinical Lectures on Mental Diseases* (3rd edn). Churchill: London.

Cole RH. (1913) *Mental Diseases.* Hodder and Stoughton: London, p. 120.

Cullen W. (1800) *Nosology* (First published in Latin, 1772). Creech: Edinburgh.

Esquirol JED. (1838) *Des Maladies Mentales.* Baillière: Paris. Translated by Hunt EK (1845) as *Mental Maladies: A Treatise on Insanity.* Lea and Blanchard: Philadelphia (facsimile edition by Hafner: London, 1965).

Falret JP. (1854) Sur la folie circulaire. *Bulletin de l'Académie de Médecine* **19**, 382–400.

Griesinger W. (1865a) *Die Pathologie und Therapie der Psychischen Krankheiten* (2nd edn). Braunschweig: Wredon. Translated by Robertson CL and Rutherford J (1867) as *Mental Pathology and Therapeutics.* New Sydenham Society: London.

Griesinger W. (1865b) The prognosis in mental disease. *J Ment Sci* **11**: 317–327.

Hare EH. (1959) The origin and spread of dementia paralytica. *J Ment Sci* **105**: 594–626. [See this volume, p. 36]

Hare EH. (1976) Hypomania. *Bethlem and Maudsley Gazette*, Summer: 3–5.

Henderson DK and Gillespie RD. (1929) *A Textbook of Psychiatry* (2nd edn). Oxford University Press: London.

Hinsie LE and Campbell RJ. (1970) *Psychiatric Dictionary* (4th edn). Oxford University Press: New York.

Kahlbaum KL. (1882) Über cyclisches Irresein. *Der Irrenfreund* **10**: 145–157.

Kolb LC. (1973) *Modern Clinical Psychiatry* (8th edn by Noyes AP and Kolb LC, 1st edn 1934). Saunders: London, p. 381.

Kraepelin E. (1899) *Psychiatrie* (6th edn). Barth: Leipzig.

Kraepelin E. (1913a) *Psychiatrie* (8th edn). Translated by Barclay RM (1921) from Vols 3 and 4 as *Manic-Depressive Insanity and Paranoia.* Livingstone: Edinburgh.

Kraepelin E. (1913b) *Psychiatrie.* Translated by Barclay RM (1919) from Vol. 3, Part II as *Dementia Praecox and Paraphrenia.* Livingstone: Edinburgh.

Krafft-Ebing R von (1898) *Lehrbuch der Psychiatrie* (3rd edn). Enke: Stuttgart.

Lewis A. (1966) In: Scott RB (ed.) *Price's Textbook of Medicine* (10th edn). p. 1185.

McKeown T. (1979) *The Role of Medicine*. Blackwell: Oxford.
Mayer-Gross W, Slater E and Roth M. (1954) *Clinical Psychiatry*. Cassell: London, p. 207.
Maudsley H. (1867) *The Physiology and Pathology of Mind*. Appleton: New York.
Maudsley H. (1879) *The Pathology of Mind*. MacMillan: London.
Maudsley H. (1895) *The Pathology of Mind* (3rd edn). MacMillan: London.
Mendel E. (1881) *Die Manie*. Urban and Schwazenberg: Vienna.
Mitchell A. (1879) Contribution to the study of death-rate of persons in asylums, *J Ment Sci* **25**: 1–4.
Monro J. (1758) *Remarks on Dr Battie's Treatise on Madness*. John Clarke: London.
Ödegaard O. (1967) Changes in the prognosis of functional psychoses since the days of Kraepelin. *Brit J Psychiatry* **113**: 813–822.
Pinel P. (1801) *Traité Médico-philosophique sur l'Aliénation Mentale*. Brosson: Paris. Translated by Davis DD (1806) as *A Treatise on Insanity*; Cadell and Davies: Sheffield (facsimile edition by Hafner: New York, 1962).
Robinson CL. (1865) Comparative statistics of Bethlem Hospital and English county asylums. *J Ment Sci* **11**: 307–317.
Sankey WHO. (1884) *Lectures on Mental Disease* (2nd edn). HK Lewis: London, p. 118.
Schott A. (1904) Klinischer Beitrag zur Lehre von den chronischen Manie. *Monatschrift für Psychiatrie und Neurologie* **15**(1): 1–19.
Shattock FM. (1950) The somatic manifestations of schizophrenia. A clinical study of their significance. *J Ment Sci* **96**: 32–142.
Tredgold AF and Tredgold RF. (1943) *A Manual of Psychological Medicine*. Baillière: London, p. 119. 3rd edn 1953.
Tuke DH. (1892) *Dictionary of Psychological Medicine*. Churchill: London.
Wertham FI. (1929) A group of benign psychoses: prolonged manic excitements. *Amer J Psychiatry* **9**: 14–76.
World Psychiatric Association (1971) *Common Psychiatric Terms in Four Languages*. Basle.
Yellowlees H. (1932) *Clinical Lectures in Psychological Medicine*. Churchill: London, p. 48.

Appendix

An essay might be written on the vagaries of the word delirium and the misunderstanding it has caused in psychiatry. The Latin word *delirium* became the French *délire*, but in the 18th and early 19th centuries the English equivalent was *raving*. During the course of the 19th century, raving was quietly dropped from English medical terminology; and delirium, which had formerly included raving madness, became restricted to conditions where there was evident brain disease, fever or exhaustion (see Tuke's Dictionary, 1892). Their places were taken by two terms denoting different aspects of insanity. These terms were incoherence and delusion.

Incoherence, which had formerly been used as a synonym for dementia, came to refer to speech which, being illogical or too rapid, had "a want or absence of cohesion or connection" (Tuke's Dictionary).

Delusion referred to false beliefs, but its connotation was wider then than nowadays. It included a patient's false belief of hearing voices (Sankey's "auditory delusions"), or of his feeling extremely fit when in fact he was suffering from mania. A further difficulty was that delusion is a peculiarly English word. In France, the word *délusion* had become obsolete by the 17th century. Sankey (1884) wrote that "In French there is no such word as *délusion*; the French for the English word delusion is *illusion*, and the French for the English word illusion is *hallucination*". However, from at least the 1890s the term '*délire chronique* or *délire chronique partiel*' has been used for chronic delusional or paranoid states; the term for 'a delusion' is *idée délirante*, and particular forms of delusion are indicated by *délire* followed by an appropriate noun, as *délire de persécution*, etc. Perhaps the passage of nearly 100 years has seen some progress. In the World Psychiatric Association's *Common Psychiatric Terms in Four Languages* (1971), hallucination and illusion are given as equivalent terms in French and English, and the French equivalent of delusion remains *délire* (which in German is *Wahn* or *Delirium*).

5

Was insanity on the increase?

At the autumn meeting of the Medico-psychological Association in 1871, Maudsley – at that time President of the Association – read a paper entitled 'Is Insanity on the Increase?'. The question was then one of profound concern both to the British public and to psychiatrists. Not only had there been for years a constant need to build new asylums – a cause "of terrible discouragement and complaint with the ratepayers" (Arlidge, 1859) – but also, as was clearly apparent in the publications of the Poor Law Office and the Annual Reports of the Commissioners in Lunacy, the number of the registered insane was increasing every year, far out of proportion to the increase in the population (see Figure 1). This circumstance, it was said, "might well give rise to alarming apprehension of a mental degeneracy" in the country (Arlidge, 1862).

The increase was occurring not only in England and Wales, but in Scotland and Ireland too. "There can be no question", said Maudsley in his paper of 1872, "that there are a great many more insane persons shut up in asylums in this country now than there ever were at any other period of its history, or, perhaps, in any country at any period of the world's history". But the explanation of this increase was 'more easily disputed than decided'.

Among medical men, the dispute was long and bitter. In one camp were those who believed that the incidence of insanity was increasing at an alarming rate and that the same was happening in Europe and in the USA: in the other camp were those who believed that the undoubted increase in the numbers of the recognized insane did not necessarily imply an increase in incidence and could be accounted for in other ways – ways which we might nowadays call 'nosocomial'. The term 'nosocomial' means 'of hospitals' (OED); but it has been usefully used in the special sense of embracing all those factors, other than the disease itself, which determine whether a person with the disease comes to be included in a register of hospital cases.

This sharp difference of opinion – between the alarmists who thought insanity was increasing and the nosocomialists who thought it was not – continued throughout the 19th century. In the early 20th century, determined efforts were made by a specially appointed Statistical Committee of the Medico-psychological Association to devise ways in which the issue might be finally decided (*Journal of Mental Science*, 1904; 1905). But their efforts were interrupted by the Great War of 1914; and soon after that war, it became apparent that the question had lost its urgency. In his Maudsley Lecture of 1926, George Robertson discussed the statistics of insanity in Scotland for the years 1910–1924, and showed that the evidence indicated a decrease

The Fifty-sixth Maudsley Lecture of the Royal College of Psychiatrists, 19 November 1982

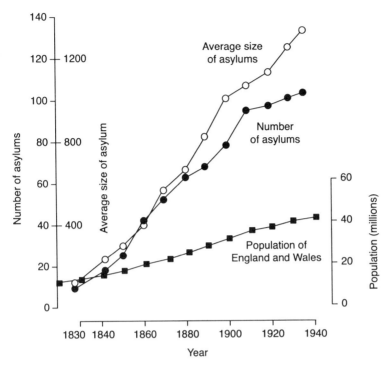

Figure 1 The asylum era. Number and average size (places) of county and borough asylums in England and Wales, 1827–1936, and total population. Data for 1827 and 1842 are from Jones (1955); the remainder are from the Annual Reports of the Lunacy Commissioners and the Board of Control.

rather than an increase in rate during that period. He concluded that "in these statistics there is no cause whatever for alarm". The old bogey, of insanity in Britain being "fearfully on the increase", seemed at last to have been laid to rest; and I cannot find that there was any further discussion of the matter during the next 50 years.

So the question raised by Maudsley, at this autumn meeting of ours in 1871, was never resolved; and indeed, it has been said that it never could have been resolved because the appropriate data were not collected, or were not collected for a sufficient period of time. Yet it is my impression that since 1939 at least there has existed a silent presumption that the nosocomialists were right and that the incidence of mental disorder in Britain during the 19th century did not increase to any significant extent. Such a presumption would be in line with the widely accepted conclusion reached by Goldhamer and Marshall in their book *Psychosis and Civilisation* (published in 1953) that, except for the psychoses of old age, there was no change in the incidence of psychotic illness in the USA between the 1840's and 1940. It would also be in line with a general opinion (as expressed, for example, by Dunham in 1971) that the incidence of schizophrenia is probably about the same in all parts of the world.

These views have recently been challenged. In particular, the work of Goldhamer and Marshall has been criticised in the United States by the sociologist William Eaton (1980) and by the psychiatrist Fuller Torrey (1980). Reading their criticisms, it occurred to me that it might be of interest to re-examine, from a historical point of view, the 19th-century controversy over the increase of insanity in Britain. Such a study would be more than mere antiquarianism. The incidence of a disease, and its possible variations in time, are of basic importance in epidemiology; and although no decisive answer might be found, the probabilities could be re-assessed, and these might then be relevant for present hypotheses of the aetiology of the functional psychoses.

The case for the nosocomialists

The Lunacy Act of 1845 not only obliged counties to build asylums for the care of their insane poor, but placed on the Commissioners in Lunacy the power and the duty to inspect asylums and to make returns of the numbers of persons brought to their notice as 'insane' (the term was used to include lunatics and idiots). From 1846 until 1914 (when they were succeeded by the Board of Control), the Commissioners produced Annual Reports – the so-called 'lunacy Blue Books' – which gave statistics of insane persons in public and in private asylums, in workhouses (under the Poor Law Acts) and in home care. The collection of such nationwide figures on what might be considered essentially a medical condition was something quite new, and it needed a few years before the system was considered to be satisfactory. But the establishment of this system, and the fact that it then continued almost unchanged for 60 years, is a remarkable tribute to the determination and efficiency of the Commissioners.

From their Annual Reports, and from the continually increasing demand for asylum accommodation, it appeared incontrovertible that, in one sense at least, insanity was on the increase. Thus it was upon those who held that this increase was not a real one – i.e. was not due to an increasing incidence – that the burden of proof lay. I shall therefore present first the case for the nosocomialists.

The 1850s

In their earliest Reports, the increasing numbers of registered insane were attributed by the Lunacy Commissioners to the incompleteness of previous records. However, the increases continued even when the system of recording seemed to be adequate. In their Ninth Report (Bucknill, 1855) the Commissioners, noting that during the past eight years the numbers of pauper lunatics in asylums had increased from about 10 000 to about 16 000 (i.e. by 64%), observed that this increase "may appear at first sight startling" and might lead to the "painful and disheartening" inference that the incidence of insanity was increasing. But, they said, the increase in numbers could be explained in other ways. These were: first, that asylum care caused the insane to live longer there than they would have done outside, so that long-stay cases were accumulating; second, that the effect of various Acts of

Parliament had been to increase both the numbers of persons ascertained as insane and the numbers admitted to asylums who might previously have been cared for at home or in workhouses; and third, that "the far more comprehensive as well as scientific view of insanity" had led to the recognition of cases which "from not exhibiting any strongly developed symptoms, were in former times, wholly over-looked". They concluded that the increase of insanity was more apparent than real.

These three reasons, lower death rate, more complete registration, and more accurate detection, which the Commissioners first put forward in the early 1850s, appear to have been generally accepted for a number of years. In 1866, for example, the *Lancet*, while observing that the "three large asylums for the county of Middlesex are full" and that "extended accommodation for the insane poor is urgently required all over England", could add "It must not be thought that insanity is increasing because more asylums are required". Likewise the *Pall Mall Gazette*, in an article of 1869 on the alleged increase of insanity, was still able to find in the arguments of the Lunacy Commissioners a satisfactory explanation for the evidence that the number of insane paupers in proportion to the population of England and Wales had more than doubled between 1836 and 1868 (*Journal of Mental Science*, 1869).

The 1860s and '70s

As time went on, however, and the pressure for asylum places continued, the matter came to be studied more closely. Lockhart Robertson (1869) dealt with the problem in his presidential address of 1867, and he added something to the arguments of the Commissioners. The Lunacy Act of 1845, he said, "forms a new era in the history of lunacy, and it cannot be wondered that the greater care bestowed upon the insane should lead to a larger knowledge of their numbers as well as their conditions". Moreover, the Lunacy Registration Act of 1853 required the medical officers of (pauper) Unions to make quarterly returns of the numbers of pauper lunatics not in asylums; this added to the accuracy of the total numbers. Similarly, the Irremovable Poor Act of 1861, by which a pauper lunatic became chargeable to the common fund of the Union instead of to his own parish, led to increasing numbers (especially of idiots) being sent to asylums because, whereas parishes had tended to maintain their insane poor at home in order to keep down the local rates, this inducement was now removed. The effect of these measures, it was argued, could account for the increase in asylum numbers; and the time would come when all lunatics had been ascertained and transferred, and there would be no further increase. Indeed, this seemed already to be happening, because the rate of increase of the numbers in asylums was falling, as was the rate of increase of admissions (see Table 1). "I think I am justified in saying", Robertson concludes, "that we see the limits of our labours in providing for the care and treatment of the insane poor; and further, that we have nearly gained the desired end. It is

Table 1 Yearly rate of increase in asylum population, 1844–1868 (Robertson, 1869, Table IX)

Period	Mean yearly rate of increase
1844–49	5.64%
1849–54	6.09%
1854–59	3.41%
1859–64	4.83%
1864–68	3.82%

allowing a wide margin in our calculations for the future if we place the possible total number of lunatics and idiots at one in 400 of the population . . . We should thus require, with a population of 22 million, 33 000 beds in public asylums. Of these, 26 000 are already provided." (Table 2).

Maudsley, in the paper of 1872 which I have mentioned, took a similar view: most of the increase was due to better recog-

Table 2 Ratio of insane to total population of England and Wales (Robertson, 1869, Table I)

Year	Total insane	Proportion of population
1844	20 611	1 in 802
1852	26 352	1 in 691
1858	35 347	1 in 544
1868	50 118	1 in 432

nition; part of it to a wider range of conditions being included (though this might be simply the result of administrative factors[1]); and part of it to a diminishing recovery rate (though he implies that the asylum system itself might be partly to blame for this[2]). As to the admission rate, he accepted that it had been increasing, but was this increase (he asked) greater than might be accounted for by the causes he had enumerated? He thought not; and "for my part", he concluded, "I think that one might fairly venture a prophecy that, 12 years hence, the ratio of admissions to the population will not be greater, if it be not less, than it is now."

We might notice here another paper of Maudsley's, published five years later, in which he refers to this prophecy of 1871, a prophecy which, he admits, "does not seem at all likely to be fulfilled in regard of pauper patients." But the fact that the admission rate was continuing to increase could now be attributed, he said, to the so-called 'Four Shilling' Act of 1874, whereby the Government granted four shillings towards the local authority cost of maintaining each asylum patient – or, as Maudsley put it, an Act whereby the Government said, in effect, to parish officials, "We will pay you a premium of four shillings a head on every pauper whom you can by hook or crook make out to be a lunatic and send into an asylum". As to the likely collapse of his former prophecy, "how was it possible (he asks) to foresee in 1871 that a Conservative Government would come into power and forthwith put a direct premium on the manufacture of lunacy? It was impossible" (Maudsley, 1877).

The 1880s and '90s

The question of increasing insanity was debated as vigorously during the 1880s and 1890s as it had been during the '60s and '70s. From 1880 until his death in 1895 at the age of 67, Daniel Hack Tuke was the editor of the *Journal of Mental Science*, and his

---

[1] "What with the opening of county asylums, the stringent statutory provisions with regard to the insane, the prosecutions for receiving insane persons without compliance with these, and the official stricture on their management in workhouses, it has come to this; that people now see lunacy in forms of imbecility and illness in which they would never at one time have dreamt of doing so." (Maudsley, 1872).

[2] The lower percentage of recoveries, according to Maudsley (1872), "is probably owing, in great part, if not entirely, to the hopeless character of the disease in many of those who have been admitted during the last 25 years . . . Still it is a question deserving of more attention than it has yet received in this country whether the present practice of crowding the insane of all sorts into large asylums, where the interests of life are extinguished, and where anything like individual treatment is well nigh impracticable, is so much superior to the old system in affecting recoveries as other persons imagine."

position as editor, we may presume, added to the influence of his strongly-held opinion that insanity was not on the increase. In an article of 1886, he re-emphasized that the only sound test of increasing insanity was the proportion of 'occurring cases' – what we would now call the incidence rate. An increase in the number of existing cases in asylums (i.e. an increase in prevalence) was not a sound test, as this could be due to an accumulation of cases from falling rates of death or discharge. He gave figures to show a recent fall in asylum death rates, and a calculation to show that this fall would imply 3 000 fewer deaths and therefore 3 000 more patients in asylums. He noted, as Lockhart Robertson had done 20 years before, that the rate of increase in the numbers of insane had been falling, and also that the rates for first admissions (i.e. total number of admissions less transfers and re-admissions) had actually shown a decrease. Finally, he gave a graph of admission rates for 'first attacks', returns for which had been available in the lunacy Blue Books since 1876. He concluded: "these figures are very satisfactory so far as they exhibit no increase in the amount of occurring insanity since the year 1878." (Table 3).

Table 3 'First' admission rates to asylums in England and Wales, 1871–1885 (adapted from Table E in Tuke, 1886)

Period	Admission rate (per million population)	Change in rate
1871–75	429	
1876–80	461	+7.4%
1881–85	452	−1.9%

We should notice here some of the technical difficulties which Tuke had to contend with. At no time during the 19th century does there seem to have been any clear understanding, in the statistical study of insanity, of the need for what we would now call the definition of a case. The idea of a 'first-ever admission to an asylum' being a good working definition of a case of insanity and a basis on which a study of changes in incidence rate could usefully be made was never fully reached. Tuke did not consider 'first admission' a satisfactory index, partly because it was not necessarily a 'first-ever' admission (the patient might have been previously admitted to some other asylum) but more because, as Tuke rather cumbrously put it, "first admissions . . . are not identical with first attacks, for obviously a patient may be admitted for the first time into an asylum and yet not be labouring under his first attack." He evidently believed that a true index of occurring insanity should refer only to recent cases, and that cases of insidious onset and cases where there had been earlier attacks not needing admission should be excluded. But his usage of 'first attack' was criticized, particularly from America, and Tuke himself (1894) was later ready to accept that the returns for first attacks were untrustworthy.[3]

Another major contribution to the debate came from a statistician, Noel Humphreys. His article 'Statistics of insanity in England, with special reference to its

[3] Sanborn (1894) wrote of Tuke's 1886 paper, "I distrust very much the record of *first attacks*; so far as my observations goes . . . there is nothing in the proverbially doubtful statistics of the insane more dubious than those affecting to give the date of a first attack." Tuke, in his last paper on the subject (1894), said he was unable to supply updated information on his 1886 table of first attacks because "I have now reason to believe that the returns which have since been published cannot be trusted." The untrustworthy later returns had shown a very marked increase in the rate of first attacks.

alleged increasing preva-
lence' was published in the
*Journal of the Royal Statistical
Society* in 1890. He ob-
served – what everyone accepted – that the available
statistics did not allow of
a sound and trustworthy
answer, but he introduced

Table 4 Numbers of insane found at census and by the Lunacy Commissioners in 1871 and 1881 (Humphreys 1890, from Table A)

Year	Census enumeration	Numbers ascertained by Lunacy Commissioners	Deficit in ascertainment
1871	69 019	56 755	18%
1881	84 503	73 113	14%

a new argument. He compared the numbers of registered insane, as found by the Lunacy Commissioners, with the numbers enumerated at the censuses of 1871 and 1881 (Table 4): these censuses had included a question on the number of residents in each household who were 'imbecile or idiot, or lunatic'.[4] The differences between the census numbers and the registered numbers, he said, must indicate the numbers of the unregistered insane; and the fact that the proportion of unregistered insanity was lower at the later census was an indication of 'the increasing accuracy of registration'. Thus the ever-increasing number of the insane, as shown in the Reports of the Lunacy Commissioners, was to be accounted for by a gradual mopping-up of the pool of un-registered cases. Humphreys does not mention – nor indeed does Hack Tuke, who uses this argument in his last paper of 1894 – that the Census returns, completed (we must presume) by householders of widely varying knowledge, opinion and responsibility in these matters, might not constitute a very reliable source of data on so emotional a topic. Another comment which might be made in retrospect is that many, perhaps most, of the non-registered insane reported in the censuses would have been idiot chil-dren, the group most likely to remain at home; and that the decrease in the size of the non-registered pool might in part reflect a decreasing proportion of mentally retarded children in the community because of the fall in birth-rate dating from the 1870s, which implies a fall in family size and in the number of children born to older women.

Better recognition and registration was one reason, Humphreys said, for the in-creasing numbers of the existing cases of insanity.[5] Another reason for the accumu-lation of patients in asylums was the diminishing death rate there: "It is beyond

---

[4] During the earlier part of the 19th century, the term 'imbecility' was used for what later came to be called 'dementia.' Thus Conolly says (1849) that young and promising persons may become insane "and after some months of excitement fall into hopeless imbecility" (p. 2); and "the extreme of imbecility is that state of inactivity of all the faculties, to which the term dementia is now generally applied". Humphreys was still using 'imbecile' to describe persons suffering in later life from chronic dementia. This does not affect his argument, which is based on the numbers of the insane (i.e. lunatics plus idiots). But his usage, and the requirement of the census forms, indicates that a distinction was still being made between a lunatic (one who at the time of his admission was in a state of what would now be described as a florid psychosis) and an imbecile (one admitted in a state which we would now describe as chronic schizophrenic deterioration).

The term 'idiot' was also used at one time for the final state of disordered intellect consequent on an attack of madness (Cox, 1806).

[5] The historical problems of statistical nomenclature are illustrated by the title of Humphreys' paper and also by his statement that the increase of existing cases of insanity "has been mis-called an increasing prevalence of insanity". What he calls 'prevalence' we would now call 'incidence'; but Humphreys, like Farr before him, perfectly understood the principle. Hack Tuke (1886) also used prevalence in this sense.

question that the rate of mortality in asylums has declined" he said, and he gave figures to show that this was so both in lunatic asylums (Table 5) and in the metropolitan asylums for imbeciles and idiots. Concerning the use of first admissions as an index of incidence, Humphreys had the same doubts as Tuke; there was no way, he said, of determining what proportion of first admissions were really new cases and how many were previously existing in the reserve of cases in workhouses or with relatives.[6] For what they were worth, the figures showed no increase in rate during the previous ten years, and indeed a decline during the last quinquennium. Humphreys's final cautious conclusion was that "without venturing to say there has been no increase of insanity in England in recent years, many reasons have been pointed out for refusing to accept any insanity statistics that we at present possess as conclusive evidence for a real increase in the rate of occurring insanity".

Table 5 Annual asylum death rates in England and Wales, 1859–1888 (from Humphreys, 1890, Table D, p. 228)

Period	Death rate
1859–68	10.31%
1869–78	10.17%
1879–88	9.55%

The last study to support the nosocomialist view that there was no need to suppose any increase in the incidence of insanity in England and Wales was the special report of the Commissioners in Lunacy on the alleged increase of insanity (1897). Essentially a summary of previous arguments, it also provided one new one, based on the age distribution of asylum patients. One of the major deficiencies of the statistics collected by the Lunacy Commissioners was, as Humphreys had observed, the absence of any routine data on age at admission to asylums or age at death there. The importance of age-specific rates only gradually become recognized during the latter half of the 19th century, and although Maudsley had remarked on it in his 1872 paper, no routine data became available. However, the censuses of 1881 and 1891, which had enumerated the insane in asylums, provided data on their ages. In the Commissioners' Special Report a table shows that for insane persons in the age group 20–45 – the period of greatest liability to insanity – the proportion relative to the population was no greater in 1891 than it had been in 1881. The "obvious inference", says the Report, was that "accumulation and not fresh production had been the most influential factor" in the increased numbers of asylum patients.[7] This, together with the weight of previous arguments, led the Commissioners to the

[6] "The value of the Commissioners' statistics of admissions to asylums is vitiated", says Humphreys, "by the impossibility of separating the really new cases from those already existing in workhouses, or from pauper cases residing with relatives, or from the large reserve of unrecognized cases." Here Humphreys seems to be accepting the opinion of Tuke that a distinction must be made between first attacks and first admissions.

[7] There is a difficulty in accepting this inference. What was needed was the ages of patients at the time of first admission, whereas the Census returns gave only the age at the census date and took no account of mean duration of stay, proportion of re-admissions, or age distribution of first admissions, any of which might have changed from one census to the next. The Commissioners supported their inference with a table giving age at admission for the years 1883–1895, but this gives only numbers, not rates, for patients aged 25–44 at admission. The number admitted in 1883 was 6833, and in 1895 it was 8341 an increase of 22%. The increase in the general population of all ages between these two years was only 9%.

following conclusion: "We have thus, we think, demonstrated at least the probability that much of the apparent increase of insanity has been due, not to an increase in the incidence of that disorder, but to the aggregation of persons affected by it and to their re-distribution". These are words which, we might now be tempted to think, reflect the uneasy compromise of a committee divided in its opinions; but this was to be the last authoritative statement on the subject until George Robertson's Maudsley Lecture of 1926.

The case for increasing incidence

Those 19th-century psychiatrists who believed that the incidence of insanity was increasing had, on the face of it, a much easier case to make. They did not deny that some of the undoubted increase in prevalence was to be explained in the way the nosocomialists claimed, i.e. by increased recognition of cases and by patients staying longer in asylums, but they argued that such effects could only be temporary, whereas the increase in numbers of the insane had been continuous from the time of the earliest statistics. If Acts of Parliament or better diagnosis drew attention to cases previously unrecognized, the time should come when the pool of undiagnosed cases had been mopped up;[8] and if patients lived longer in asylums than they would have done outside – and there was no proof of this – then after 20 years or so these patients would have reached the natural limit of their lives and so there should be no more accumulation from that cause.[9] In any case, the admission rate to asylums showed a generally increasing trend; and even though there was considerable year-to-year fluctuation in this rate and the statistics of first admissions were somewhat unsatisfactory, the reasonable conclusion was of a real increase in the number of new patients being admitted.

The number of insane in Britain

Harrington Tuke, in his presidential address of 1873, observed that Dr Lockhart Robertson had "adduced all that can be brought forward in advocacy of the hopeful view that the statistical returns lead to a fallacious conclusion . . . I regret to say that the elaborate Annual Reports of the Commissioners in Lunacy, and the inference to be drawn from them, seem to me unanswerably to demonstrate the reverse." These

---

[8] Duncan (1870) quoted figures to suggest that the effect of the 1861 Act on increasing the numbers in asylums lasted only two or three years. As the numbers continued to mount (he said), "we are bound to accept the fact that there is a steady increase in the lunacy of the population of England & Wales and Ireland." Eames (1885), in his presidential address, concluded that accumulation could not account for such a large increase in numbers as had occurred at the Cork Asylum (from 687 patients in 1873 to 926 ten years later); whatever the cause, insanity was "decidedly on the increase". Corbett (1893) began his criticism of the nosocomialist view with the words: "the theory promulgated by the majority of the Lunacy Commissioners with resolute persistency, in the face of facts and figures that should convince the most casual observer to the contrary, is that 'the increase is only apparent'." See also Boyd (1871) and Brushfield (1872).

[9] For Scottish asylums during the 1870's, Mitchell (1879) showed the overall death rates to be some five times as high as those of the general population, and for the younger age groups to be nearly ten times as high. Among patients in the West Riding Asylum, Crichton Browne in 1868 found no increase in life span during the previous 40 years.

statistics, together with a table divided into age-groups, prepared for him by William Farr, "appear to prove", said Tuke, "that a great wave of insanity is slowly advancing." The discussion which followed his address, and which was reported in the *Journal of Mental Science*, clearly shows the conflict of expert opinion at this time.

Much of the evidence for increase came not from the lunacy statistics but from medical men with long and close experience of particular districts. In 1869, Dr MacCabe, Superintendent of the Waterford District Asylum, contended that there were 'tolerably accurate returns' of the numbers of the insane in all parts of Ireland. Between 1851 and 1861 these numbers had increased by 6%, while the population had fallen 12%. In his own district during this time, the proportion of persons found to be insane had almost doubled, from 1 in every 690 to 1 in 350.

The increase in lunacy in Ireland, he believed, was a well-established fact. This opinion continued to be expressed by Irish physicians. In his paper of 1894, Thomas Drapes, Superintendent of Enniscorthy Asylum, compared statistics for first admissions to asylums in Ireland with those in England and Wales. For Ireland, the first admission figures were derived from those of all admissions, less transfers and re-admissions; but they included admissions from workhouses, a group which had been omitted from Hack Tuke's tables on the ground that such cases were not first attacks. It is clear now that, insofar as a first admission to an asylum would have been the best definition of a case of insanity, Drapes' procedure was right here and Tuke's was wrong. Drapes concluded that the increasing first admission rate in Ireland "must be regarded as indicating a decided increase in occurring insanity". As regards the cause of the increase, he noted that there was no good evidence for an increase in the part played by heredity or consanguineous marriage, and that the effects of emigration had probably been over-estimated, though he rather spoils these sensible observations, we might now think, by attributing the increase to the Celtic temperament: "the quick-witted, passionate, versatile and vivacious Celt has, for those qualities which make him so charming, too often to pay the price of instability".

Like Ireland, Scotland was for the most part a thinly populated country where a man might acquire close knowledge of a local community. Jamieson was physician at the Royal Aberdeen Hospital, and in 1876 he expressed his opinion, based on 35 years' professional experience, that "the most remarkable phenomenon of our time has been the alarming increase of insanity". Whereas in 1840 there had been seven asylums in Scotland, in 1876 there were 24; and whereas in 1844 the asylum in Aberdeen had held 150 patients, now it had 480, and in addition there were three new asylums, each with 100 patients in them.[10]

---

[10] An unsigned (presumably editorial) comment on Jamieson's paper says that 'no-one who has given serious attention to the question will feel quite satisfied' with his conclusion. Over several decades the editors of the *Journal of Mental Science* displayed a marked bias towards the nosocomial view. Articles or reports pointing to an increased incidence of insanity are generally given adverse editorial criticism, whereas those of the opposite view are uncriticized or approved. One paper, entitled 'Insanity is decreasing' (Chapman, 1896), is of such poor quality that its acceptance for publication surely lay in its title rather than its substance.

The number of insane abroad

The question of an increase in insanity was also being debated in other countries, but I will here refer only to such observations as were noted in the *Journal of Mental Science*.

In France, the asylum population increased rapidly between 1838 and 1862 (Lunier, 1870; Robertson, 1871); but Lunier, observing that the rate of increase had then begun to fall off slightly, attributed most of this increase to an increased public confidence in the use of asylums, adding that any increase in incidence was "une proportion insignificante du chiffre total des entrées". Yet a few years later, at the discussion of Harrington Tuke's presidential address, a Parisian physician said that the intermarriage of families where insanity prevailed was one cause of the continued increase in the numbers of the insane in France (Tuke, 1873, p. 479); and in the discussion of Humphreys' paper (1890), it was remarked that the increase in the number of lunatics in France had gone on in recent years at a more rapid rate than in England.

In the United States, the increase in the number of the insane had caused concern since at least the early 1850s, when Jarvis (1852) concluded that "insanity is an increasing disease".[11] From a study of the statistics of insanity in Massachusetts, which showed an 80% increase in the number of first admissions between 1868 and 1886, Pliny Earle (1887) concluded that the figures "appear to show that there has been a considerable increase, even in recent insanity, out of proportion to the gain in population". His opinion was reinforced in a later paper by Sanborn (1894) entitled 'Is American insanity increasing?' Sanborn accepted that the three factors of better care, better registration and a wider definition of insanity could have accounted for some of the earlier increase in the number of insane. Yet, "still we find this insane accumulation going on as fast as 50 years ago, and in the face of influences that ought to yield just the contrary result". For this reason – and because, as he indicated, the statistics of insanity in Massachusetts had been particularly reliable over the preceding 15 years – he believed that there must have been a very substantial increase in the incidence of insanity there and, "I doubt not, in most of the United States . . . If any other interpretation can be put upon the figures given, nobody will be more pleased than myself; but that seems to me hardly possible."

An assessment of the evidence

I shall now attempt to assess the evidence for and against the view that insanity was increasing in Britain during the second half of the 19th century. Contemporary authors could of course consider only the statistics available to them at the time, whereas we can now take a longer view. To an epidemiologist, the main deficiency

---

[11] Twenty years' further experience only strengthened his opinion. In 1871, Jarvis wrote: "in the United States, Great Britain, Ireland, and other civilized nations as far as known, there has been a great increase of provision for the insane within 40 years, and a very rapid increase within 20 years. Hospitals have been built seemingly sufficient to accommodate all lunatics within their respective state, county or district. These have been filled, and then crowded, and then pressed to admit still more. They have been successively enlarged, and then other institutions built and filled and crowded as the earlier houses were." Yet the number of the insane at that time (1871) had "all but doubled" twenty years later (Corbett, 1893).

of the Lunacy Commissioners' statistics is that they were designed to serve administrative rather than medical ends; but we have also to remember that epidemiology was then an undeveloped science and that the need for case definition and for age-specific rates of first-ever admissions was not recognized, or was recognized too late to be useful. In addition, of course, 'insanity' was a legal rather than a medical concept, and embraced not only all varieties of mental illness ('lunacy') but all varieties of retardation ('idiocy') as well.[12]

Prevalence statistics

I will first consider the arguments used by the nosocomialists to support their view that the obvious increase in the numbers of ascertained insane did not necessarily imply an increase in the incidence of insanity. There were three types of argument.

Previously unrecognized insanity. The first was there had been a large number of cases of unrecognized insanity in the population, and that these were gradually being recognized as a result of various Acts of Parliament, greater medical knowledge, and increased public confidence in asylums. It was argued that although this recognition had been the cause of the increasing numbers of insane under care, the pool of unrecognized cases was being emptied and the time would come when the numbers of recognized insane would no longer continue to increase. Lockhart Robertson, in 1869, believed this desired end had almost been achieved, and he predicted that the proportion of the insane in the general population would never fall below 1 in 400, and that the limit of the need for asylums would be 1500 beds per million population. Yet as Figure 2 shows, his prediction of the maximum prevalence rate was overtaken within five years, and by the year 1914 the proportion of the insane to the population was 1 in 266, and the proportionate number of asylum beds was more than twice his maximum, (at 3100 beds per million). We have already noted Maudsley's prophecy of 1872, that in 12 years time the admission rate would show no further increase. In fact, by that time the rate had increased by nearly 15%, and in another 12 years was to be increased by 50%. Hack Tuke in 1886, and Humphreys in 1890, also argued that the admission rates were levelling off, and indeed that the last quinquennial average had actually shown a fall. This was true, but as we can now see (Figure 5), the effect was only temporary and the rate rose as steeply as ever during the next three quinquennia.

Accumulation of patients. The second explanation for the increase in the number of the recognized insane was that chronic cases accumulated in asylums. Accumulation occurs whenever the number of admissions exceeds the combined numbers of discharges and deaths. Unfortunately, the lunacy statistics were not always such as to enable a simple calculation to be made, and arguments had to be based on a consideration of rates of recovery and of deaths. Clearly, if either of these rates were

---

[12] Idiots were admitted to county and borough asylums except where special idiot establishments existed (principally in the metropolitan area). The only common variety of mental illness which was more or less clearly distinguishable from the rest was general paralysis of the insane (GPI), separate statistics for which were first given in 1878.

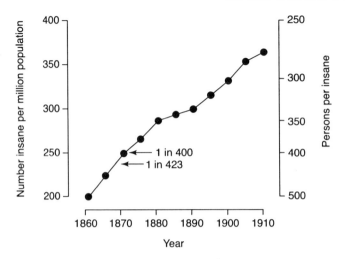

Figure 2   Numbers of ascertained insane per million population in England and Wales: quinquennial averages 1859–1913. Data from the First Report of the Board of Control (for 1914), Table II.

falling, there would be more patients remaining in asylums. The best statistic for recovery rate was based on the number per 100 admissions who were 'discharged as recovered'. Tuke, in 1886, noted that this rate had shown little change since 1870, when the data first became available, and concluded that recovery rate did not appear to be 'a disturbing element'. Humphreys (in 1890) found the statistics of recovery to be 'so vitiated by the disturbing elements of relapses' that no useful conclusion could be drawn from them. On the other hand, the evidence for a decrease in recovery rate was used by the Lunacy Commissioners in their Special Report of 1897 as an argument for accumulation. The actual numbers (Figure 3) point to a clear fall in recovery rates from about 1890, though we might think that when the Special Report was being written, the trend towards a fall was not then clear enough for the Commissioners' case to be very sound.

Death rates in asylums (expressed as the number of deaths divided by the

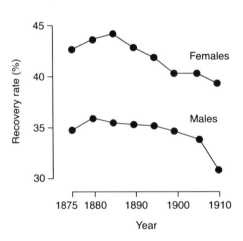

Figure 3   Asylum recovery rates in England and Wales, expressed as number of stated recoveries per 100 admissions: quinquennial averages 1873–1912. Data from the First Report of the Board of Control (for 1914), Table VII. Note: these rates cover county and borough asylums, hospitals, licenced houses, state institutions and private single patients. Table V of the Report gives decennial averages for asylums only, which show essentially the same trends.

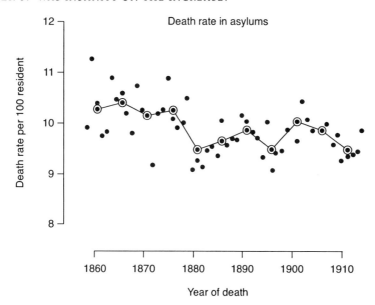

Figure 4 Asylum death rates in England and Wales, 1859–1914, calculated as deaths per 100 residents (daily average). Yearly rate are shown by dots, quinquennial averages are circled. Data from Annual Reports of Commissioners in Lunacy. Note: these data include hospitals, licenced houses, etc. Table VI of the First Report of the Board of Control gives decennial averages, by sex, of death rates in asylums only.

daily average resident number) were more clear-cut than recovery rates, though the absence of any break-down by age at death much decreased their value. Humphreys took the evidence for decreasing death rates as supporting the case for accumulation, though he accepted that the interpretation was uncertain because the death rate would increase if the average age of patients increased and would decrease if ('as is probably the case') the proportion of acute cases diminished. Hack Tuke, in 1894, used the same argument, saying that the mortality rate in asylums 'is distinctly lower than it was 20 years ago', and the Commissioners followed suit (1897). However, the figures collected in the Board of Control's Report (1914) show there was a decline in the death rate between 1870 and 1885, but no such trend thereafter (Figure 4). Thus once again the nosocomialists were using evidence which supported their view when taken over a relatively short preceding period, but which was uncharacteristic of a longer period. A further difficulty in the use of death rate is that, when considered by sex, the male rate shows a general decrease and the female rate an increase.

Private patients. The third argument – and to my mind much the weakest – for the increase in the insane being due to nosocomial factors was that the increase had been mainly in pauper patients and had been relatively small in the private class. The argument was used by the Commissioners as far back as 1855, when they noted that the increase in the number of lunatics over the preceding eight years had been 64% for paupers, and only 15% for private patients. Forty years later, an editorial review in the *Journal of Mental Science* (1895) drew attention to the fact that the number of private patients in Scotland had not been increasing and commented that this was "one of the strongest indicators that there is no real increase in the amount of mental disorder in the country" because if the alleged increase were due to the strain of modern life then "it ought to show itself especially in the classes above the ranks of manual labour". The same argument was urged in the Special Report of the Commissioners in 1897. The lunacy statistics do indeed show a fall in the ratio of private patients to the population between 1880 and 1895, but thereafter a fairly rapid increase. In any case, a separate consideration of private cases seems, from the medical point of view, to be unsatisfactory. Not only does private care reflect the varying play of market forces but, as Maudsley pointed out in 1872, insanity was a pauperising disease, so that many once well-to-do patients had come down in the world by the time institutional care was needed.[13]

Conclusion. There is no doubt that some of the increase in the numbers of insane was due to nosocomial factors – increased recognition (in the statutory sense) and increased length of asylum stay. The question is: how much? In the absence of hard data, there could only be, and still can only be, opinions. But from the above considerations, I conclude that the arguments of the nosocomialists, though reasonable enough at the time they were made, do not hold up when a longer view is taken of the statistics.[14] To a much more considerable degree than the nosocomialists were prepared to admit, the increase in the numbers of the insane did represent an increase in the real prevalence rate of insanity; and if the prevalence rate was increasing, then it was not unlikely that this was due, at least in part, to an increase in incidence rate.

Admission statistics

By the 1890s it had become generally accepted that "the only true criterion of the increase or decrease of insanity is to be found in the number of first attacks" (Drapes, 1894), but it was later agreed that Hack Tuke's and the Lunacy Commissioners' restriction of first attacks to recent acute illness leading directly to asylum admission was unfortunate. Data for first admissions were available from 1869 though, as Tuke stressed, these were not first-ever admissions but only first admissions to a particular institution. First-ever admissions were not recorded until

---

[13] There are other reasons for thinking that no satisfactory conclusion could be drawn from the statistics of private cases. The total number was relatively small, about a tenth of the number of pauper cases; the sex ratio was different from that of paupers, and indeed underwent a reversal (there had been an excess of males up to 1880, but thereafter an increasing excess of females); and from 1870 an increasing proportion of private patients were in county and borough asylums.

[14] During the 19th century, when the numbers and proportion of the insane continually increased, many of the most distinguished psychiatrists set out to show that this didn't necessarily mean insanity was increasing. On the other hand, George Robertson in 1926 found that the numbers and proportions of the insane had decreased in Scotland over the preceding period of 15 years. He drew optimistic conclusion from this; and no-one, so far as I know, suggested that the figures did not necessarily mean insanity was decreasing.

1898, so that only a small series is available up to 1914. However, yearly figures for total admissions (excluding transfers and admissions to idiot establishments) are available from 1869 onwards, and there is reason to believe they can be of value. The first admissions for each of the years 1869–1897 show a ratio to the total admissions which is constant within very narrow limits at about 88% (r = 0.992). Similarly, there is an almost constant ratio between first-ever admissions and total admissions for the years 1898–1914 (about 82%, r = 0.995), and this is true for each sex. In other words, there are very close correlations between first admissions, as variously measured, and total admissions. It is thus reasonable to suppose, I think, that the admission rate for total admissions during the period 1869–1914 gives a pretty accurate index for the 'first-ever admission' rate (Figure 5 and Figure 6). With slightly less reliability, this argument can be extended back to the earliest

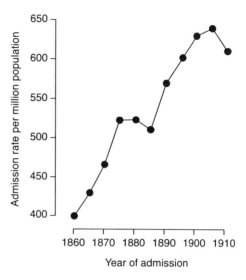

Figure 5 Asylum admission rates for England and Wales based on the total population: quinquennial averages, 1859–1914. Admissions include re-admissions but exclude transfers and admissions to idiot establishments. Rates calculated from admission numbers: data from Drapes (1894), and Reports of the Lunacy Commissioners and Board of Control. Rates for 1859–1868 estimated from numbers of admissions plus transfers (see text).

date for which admission figures are available, 1859.[15] Although we do not have the age-specific rates, I find it difficult to avoid the conclusion that between 1859 and 1900 there was a very considerable increase in the admission rate of new patients to institutions for the insane in England and Wales, and therefore a very considerable increase also of the incidence rate of insanity.

We might also notice here that the decade after 1900 seems to have been a watershed for lunacy statistics. Not only did the admission rate cease to rise (*Journal of Mental Science*, 1909; Commissioners, 1911), but two other distinct trends occurred: the asylum death rate, which had been essentially unchanged since 1860, began to fall; and the recovery rate (a less satisfactory statistic), which had been falling since about 1880, began to rise. We can only guess at the reasons for these phenomena, but they may explain why the question which so alarmed the 19th century – was insanity on the increase? – lost its urgency in the 20th.

---

[15] The earliest admission date in the lunacy Blue Books (from 1859) are given only terms of the numbers admitted each year, including re-admissions and transfers. For the years 1869–1877 we are able to compare these numbers with those of all admissions (excluding transfers): over these nine years, the correlation coefficient is 0.9. The close relation between numbers of first admissions and of total admissions had been noticed by Drapes (1894).

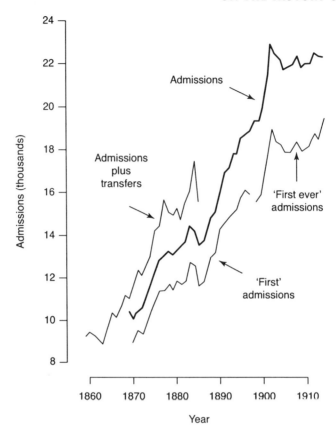

Figure 6 Numbers of patients admitted into county and borough asylums, etc. in England and Wales, showing the close correspondence between different categories of admission. Admissions (heavy line) include re-admissions but exclude transfers and admissions to idiot establishments. 'First' admissions were first admissions to a particular asylum. The figure shows the years 1859–1914 for which data in each category are available. The high numbers of admissions-plus-transfers in 1877 and 1884 reflect high transfer numbers consequent on the opening of the new asylums. Data from Drapes (1894) and the Reports of the Commissioners in Lunacy and the Board of Control.

Explanations of the increase

The earlier evidence

The only other person, so far as I am aware, to have made a recent study of the 19th-century English lunacy statistics has come to the same conclusion as myself. In his book *Museums of Madness* (1979), Scull pointed out that the system of enumerating the insane remained substantially unchanged from 1846 onwards, and that this weighed against the view that registration became more accurate, i.e. that a pool of unrecognized cases was being mopped up. He argued that if accumulation of patients in asylums had been the main cause of increased prevalence, then patients in private hospitals should also have accumulated, for the mortality rate there was about the same as in the asylums and the recovery rates were even lower: but this did not happen. Scull also drew attention to the national statistical studies of the first half of the century, which had later been dismissed as inaccurate. He concluded that they were carefully made and agreed with local studies, and that there was no good reason to doubt their accuracy.[16]

The rapid increase in prevalence rate shown by these early statistical studies reflected a very general impression, dating from the late 18th century, that insanity was becoming commoner. Jonathan Swift, like Maudsley after him, provided a sum of money for the establishment of a hospital for the mentally ill. But in his will, Swift expressed doubt that a sufficient number of insane persons could be found to occupy the modest building he had in mind, and so he directed that any spare places should be given over to physically ill patients. That was Dublin in 1747. Some 60 years later, William Halloran (1810) undertook an enquiry into the cause of the extraordinary increase of insanity in Ireland, having found that between 1789 and 1809 the numbers of insane in the city of Cork (where he was asylum physician) had "advanced far beyond the extent upon which the humane founders had calculated".

Similar impressions were being recorded in England. Thomas Arnold (1782) referred to the "vast increase of the disorder", which he could attribute only to "the present universal effusion of wealth and luxury". William Perfect (1787) referred to the belief that "instances of insanity are at this day more numerous in this kingdom than they were at any former period", and he suspected that one factor might have been "the epidemic catarrh, more generally known by the name of the *Influenza*, which raged with such violence . . . in the year 1782". William Pargeter (1792) wrote that the lack of progress in understanding and treatment of maniacal disorders was shown by this "hideous malady which so amazingly prevails at this day".

Such observations continued into the 19th century. In his *Practical Remarks* (1811), Bryan Crowther referred to insanity as 'an affection so rapidly becoming prevalent among all orders of society', and Alexander Morison (1826) noted the recent increase of mental disorder both in Great Britain and France (ascribing it to 'free governments and political commotions').[17] Prichard (1835) discussed the question at length, listing the differences of opinion; he concluded that "the apparent increase is everywhere so striking that it leaves on the mind a strong suspicion . . . that cases of insanity are far more numerous than formerly". The remarkable output of treatises on insanity in the latter part of the reign of George III (Pierce, 1919) was, one might think, as likely to have been due to the general impression of its increasing

---

[16] Sir Andrew Halliday (1828), who made an extensive study of the numbers of the insane, wrote "I have been persevering and strict in my inquiries. I have laboured incessantly now for twenty-five years."

[17] It has been suggested that, as most of these writers were proprietors of private mad-houses, they had an interest in spreading this view, but at least one such proprietor was taking the opposite view in 1820, and by 1828 was convinced of a 'general diminution in the number of lunatics' (Burrows, 1828). But Burrows admitted that the only ground he had for this belief was that, because of the superior mode of treatment available in asylums, the proportion who recovered was greater than before and consequently 'the aggregate number of the insane must be lessened'.

prevalence as to the more commonly accepted explanation of public interest in the King's illness.[18]

This impressionistic and statistical evidence from the late 18th and early 19th centuries, taken with the firmer evidence of the Reports of the Lunacy Commissioners, make it reasonable to suppose that the prevalence rate of insanity in Britain was increasing throughout the 19th century. There are no useful data on admission rates before 1859 and therefore none on which the incidence of insanity before then can be estimated. Only by analogy with later events could an argument for increasing incidence in the first half of the 19th century be supported, but to my mind the analogy is a fair one.

Why the admission rate increased

I now turn to consider possible reasons for such an increase, and in particular why the first admission rate to asylums should have increased during the last four decades of the 19th century. There are two possibilities. The first, the one that understandably so frightened the public, is that the incidence of insanity increased without there being any diminution in the severity of the condition. The second, and more reassuring, possibility is that the increase was due to the admission of increasingly milder cases. We have no sure way of determining the relative contribution of these two factors. Scull, in his analysis, does not consider the first possibility at all: and he finds an adequate explanation solely in terms of milder cases. To the question why so many milder cases should be admitted when there was a continued pressure for new beds, Scull gives a sociological answer, which may be summarized in his statement that "on the whole it was the existence and expansion of the asylum system which created the increased demand for its own services, rather than the other way round".[19]

Now while it is very probable that milder cases were being admitted – cases which would earlier have gone, in the first instance at any rate, to a workhouse – I find it difficult to accept that the whole or even a large part of the increased number could for so long a period of time have simply been milder cases. In particular, Scull's view that the asylum system expanded first and then new patients were found to fill it up is hard to reconcile with the 'terrible discouragement and complaint' of the rate-payers faced with the demand for new asylums. One would suppose rather that the reasons for that demand must have been urgent, compelling and inescapable. Moreover, if

---

[18] In France, Esquirol considered the increased interest in the subject of insanity to be due to the writings of Pinel, and the increased numbers of the insane to be due to greater public confidence in asylums (Burrows, 1828). But later (in 1845) Esquirol conceded that there must have been some real increase – caused, he thought, by the laxity of French morals during the 1820s and 1830s (Schwab and Schwab, 1978).

[19] Scull considered that asylum doctors welcomed more admissions, not only because they believed their institutions were benevolent and therapeutic, but also because the more the public recognized the serious problem of insanity the more importance and prestige would accrue to the experts who dealt with it. He also considered that the more the public recognized asylum beds to be increasingly available, the more it made use of these as 'dumps for the awkward and inconvenient'. No doubt there is some truth in this, but we cannot tell how far the patients whom Scull describes as 'the simple-minded and those who had simply given up the struggle for existence' were suffering from what we would now call chronic schizophrenia.

milder cases had been the main cause of the increasing admission rate, then the asylum death rate should have decreased and the recovery rate increased, whereas in fact the death rate was static and the recovery rate declined markedly from the mid-1880s.

There is also other evidence that the prognosis of asylum cases was worsening. Granville (1877) believed that the proportion of patients who passed into a state of chronic dementia had increased (he blamed it on non-restraint). Savage (1890) was of the opinion that "the form of insanity was worse" than formerly, though he could not back it up with statistics. The Commissioners in Lunacy (1899), noting that the recovery rate was falling although the appliances for skilled treatment were steadily mounting, concluded that this "can only be due to the admission of less favourable cases". The same idea was voiced in America, where Pliny Earle (1887) referred to "the not improbable fact that insanity, as a whole, is really becoming more and more an incurable disease".

From these considerations there appears to me to be a strong case for thinking that a considerable, perhaps a major, part of the increase in the asylum admission rate was due to a real increase in the incidence of insanity, of a kind not less severe than formerly.

Which disorders increased?

"If lunacy be on the increase", wrote Lockhart Robertson in 1871, "it should be shown in which of its varieties the increase occurs". He himself suggested that the increase might be in general paralysis, "as it is in France". But that was before separate statistics on general paralysis were published in the Blue Books, and it is evident from these that the admissions for general paralysis were about about 7% or 8% of the total (and only about 2% for females), and that their proportion to the total did not change much over the years.[20]

We can get an idea of the relative proportions of the different forms of insanity from the official statistics for the years 1909–1913 (Board of Control, 1914). These show that the group of conditions which we would now include in the term 'functional psychoses' – mania, melancholia, delusional insanity and secondary dementia – formed at least 75% of the total. There is no reason to think that the organic cases could have been responsible for a major proportion of the overall increase in admission rate,[21] and the conclusion must be that most of the increase was associated with the functional psychoses. But whereas we can say that delusional insanity, together with primary and secondary dementia, would have been closely related to what we now call the

[20] There was a general opinion that, even if the incidence of insanity as a whole was not increasing, that of general paralysis might be (Tuke, 1894). But by 1899 the statistical evidence indicated no increase in the proportion of admissions for general paralysis when compared with total admissions (Commissioners in Lunacy, 1899, p. 5; Board of Control 1923, p. 5). Since almost all admissions for general paralysis may be taken as cases of severe insanity, the absence of a decrease in this proportion is a further argument against any disproportionate increase in the admission of milder cases.

[21] There was certainly a gradual increase in the proportion of patients admitted at the age of 65 or over, but not all these had senile dementia. Our best evidence lies in the tables of the Commissioners and of the Board of Control, which give numbers of admissions categorized by form of disorder. Between 1879 and 1913, the proportion of admissions classed as senile dementia (all ages) rose from 4.2–5.8%. For age at admission and re-admission with senile dementia etc., see Table VII in The First Report of the Board of Control (1914).

paranoid and schizophrenic psychoses, we have no way of distinguishing the relative proportions of schizophrenic and affective psychoses among the manias and melancholias, for the Kraepelinian delineation of dementia praecox had not then been adopted (Hare, 1981).

There is, however, some information to be gained from these figures. If the increase had been principally among the affective disorders, we should have expected an increase in the rates of recovery and readmission and a decrease in the death rate; but these did not occur. In fact, the evidence for the accumulation of chronic cases, together with the lack of any marked change in the

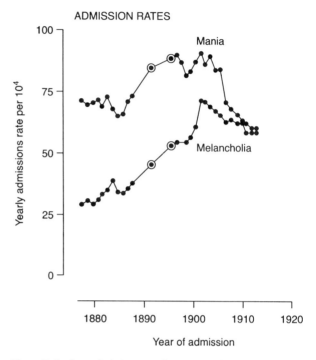

Figure 7 Asylum admission rates for mania and melancholia: data from Reports of the Commissioners in Lunacy. Between 1887 and 1897, the only data available are quinquennial averages (circles).

death rate (until after 1905) suggests that it was the condition we now call schizophrenia which was most likely to have been the main cause of the increased admissions. Another piece of statistical evidence which seems to support this is the change which occurred in the relative proportions of admissions for mania and for melancholia (Figure 7). This change was, of course, recognised at the time. Clouston in 1891 noted 'the unprecedented increase' in the admissions for melancholia to the Royal Edinburgh Asylum. He attributed it to the influenza epidemic of 1889–90: "the influenza poison burns up nervous energy and leaves the brain in some cases unable to recuperate". Robert Jones (later Sir Robert Armstrong-Jones), in his presidential address of 1906, wondered whether the early physicians knew of the condition increasingly referred to as dementia praecox – a condition "then apparently so rare, now so common" – and said that such cases almost invariably begin in depression. "It was justifiable to conclude that they were classed as melancholia", he thought, and that would account for the rise in the relative proportion of admissions in that class.[22]

---

[22] A long-term change in the mania : melancholia ratio can also be seen by comparison of these ratios with those from the early part of the 19th century (e.g. Rorie, 1900; Parry-Jones, 1972). The relation between influenza and mental illness was the subject of many papers: see particularly the *Journal of Mental Science* for 1892 and 1893.

I suggest therefore that there are reasons for thinking that, insofar as there was an increase in the incidence of insanity in Britain during the latter part of the 19th century, this increase was principally in that type of insanity which, in the 1890s, Kraepelin called dementia praecox and which we now call schizophrenia.

An epidemiological hypothesis

Now it is evident that if the incidence of schizophrenia was increasing during the second half – and perhaps also during the first half – of the 19th century, there would have been an earlier time when it was a comparatively rare condition.[23] I think the commonly held view is that the incidence of schizophrenia has always been much the same: but that common opinion is certainly not based on historical evidence. In its acute stage, schizophrenia typically presents a striking clinical picture – of delusions, thought disorder and hallucinations in a young adult, with no sign of mental confusion or physical disease – but one may search in vain for any such description before the 19th century. There were many British writers in the latter part of the 18th century who set themselves to describe in detail the various types of madness and their associated signs and symptoms, but I have been unable to find there, even in the first edition of Haslam's *Observations on Insanity* (1798), any account indicative of what we would recognize as acute schizophrenia. Andrew Harper, in 1789, said it was well known "that young people are hardly ever liable to insanity and that the attack of this malady seldom happens before an advanced period of life", and in 1861 the Frenchman Renaudin remarked on the increasing number of cases where insanity had begun before the age of 20, adding that formerly, insanity of early age was a very rare exception. It was also Tuke's impression in 1886, with which Savage concurred, that "considerably more young people of both sexes break down mentally than there did formerly". This question – whether descriptions of a disorder corresponding to schizophrenia can be found in the older literature, and if not why not – is debatable and I will not discuss it further here, although it does seem to me that those who believe schizophrenic-like disorders have always been with us, and always with about the same incidence rate, have yet to make a convincing case on purely historical grounds.[24]

The view of schizophrenia as a perennial disease has been maintained on other grounds, and in particular it is implicit in the aetiological hypothesis put forward by Professor Manfred Bleuler (1978). On this hypothesis, schizophrenia is caused by the inheritance of an imbalance of normal genes, leading to the development of a type of schizoid personality which may later be tipped over into schizophrenia by the cumulative effect of traumatic psychological experiences. These experiences are

---

[23] In the discussion of Harrington Tuke's Address (1873), Dr Sibbald said, "the rate of increase thus represented (in Tuke's tables) is so startling that we are at once rendered doubtful as to its reality", for at that rate "we might expect . . . to reach back to a period when insanity may be said scarcely to have existed at all". So extravagant a conclusion was one which "we are fully justified in refusing to accept".

[24] The common presupposition that, apart from obvious epidemics the principal diseases of medicine have always been with us and in much the same form and severity as now, is perhaps a legacy from the 18th century, a time when diseases were considered to be like species and therefore immutable. Much of 20th-century epidemiology suggests the contrary. The lack of early descriptions of any schizophrenia-like condition is further discussed in Hare (1983).

non-specific and of a kind which will be unavoidable in the ordinary course of adult life. There are no important environmental causes of a purely physical kind. This is a hypothesis which can neatly explain many facts about schizophrenia which have proved hard to explain otherwise.

But my inclination to search for an alternative hypothesis lies primarily in the hope of finding one less pessimistic than Bleuler's. For although in Bleuler's view the symptoms of schizophrenia may be alleviated by treatment, his hypothesis holds out no prospect of our ever being able to prevent schizophrenia by the elimination of some specific environmental cause or even – in the long term – of the genetic load being reduced by natural selection.

On Bleuler's hypothesis, schizophrenia is not an illness and the patient has no physical disorder. An alternative hypothesis, which brings schizophrenia properly into the realm of medicine, is that there are specific environmental factors of a physical kind, which have yet to be found. I am the more emboldened to adopt this alternative in a Maudsley lecture because Maudsley himself was a firm believer in the physical origin of mental disorder.[25] Now once we think of schizophrenia as a disease with specific environmental causes, it becomes reasonable to accept that its manifestations and severity may have changed in the course of time and in response to changes in the prevalence or virulence of these causes and in the varying resistance to them which the prevailing conditions of human society permitted. The conclusion which I have drawn from my present study – that the incidence of schizophrenia increased in Britain during the 19th century – would come within the scope of such a causal hypothesis.

Dr Fuller Torrey (1980) was, I think, the first to put forward the idea that schizophrenia had been an uncommon disorder in Europe and America until towards the end of the 18th century, and that thereafter schizophrenia – or a particular type of it – became increasingly common. What I suggest now is that the lunacy statistics of Britain provide evidence in support of Torrey's idea. We then have the hypothesis of a slow epidemic of schizophrenia which in Europe, and perhaps also in the United States, began some 200 years ago and which can be attributed to the changing effect of some specific causal factor of a physical nature.

Conclusion

A hypothesis is useful insofar as it can explain a wide variety of observations and can point the way to further research. I should like to conclude by indicating some of the ways in which the 'slow epidemic' hypothesis provides a medical explanation of certain phenomena associated with schizophrenia which hitherto have received mainly psychological or sociological explanations.

A rapid increase in the incidence of schizophrenia, and therefore of 'insanity', at the end of the 18th century would very simply explain the abrupt development of

---

[25] "Mental diseases are neither more nor less than nervous diseases in which mental symptoms predominate, and their entire separation from other nervous diseases has been a sad hindrance to progress . . . So long as this is the case, we shall labour in vain to get exact scientific ideas about their causation, their pathology and their treatment." (Maudsley, 1873).

interest in mental disease and the publication of numerous books on the subject at that time. It would also account in a most straightforward way for the asylum era: the real increase in insanity made urgently necessary the establishment and increasing provision of a specialized system of care. An increasing need for asylums occurred at about the same time in Britain, France and America, and perhaps also (though I have not specially studied it) in Germany and Russia, and it is not easy to see how the sociological explanations of the need for asylums can cover countries which had such widely different social and political systems.

The hypothesis would also explain why there are no satisfactory descriptions – or none that I have so far been able to find – in the medical or general literature before the 19th century of a disorder resembling acute schizophrenia. It would also account for the remarks by medical writers, whom I have quoted, on the former rarity of insanity in young persons.

A phenomenon which has proved difficult to account for on purely genetic grounds – and which would also be difficult to explain sociologically – is the apparent persistence of schizophrenia in spite of the low fertility of schizophrenics. This difficulty disappears on the hypothesis that schizophrenia (at least in the form best known to the industrialized world) was an uncommon disorder until about 200 years ago.

The hypothesis that the incidence of schizophrenia increased because of some change in the effect of a specific environmental factor carries the implication that further changes in incidence will probably occur; and by analogy with the history of epidemic disorders we might expect a period of rapid increase in incidence to be followed by a more gradual decrease and by changes in the severity and manifestations of the disorder. The change in the mania : melancholia ratio might be so explained – it would certainly be hard to explain in sociological terms. There has been no clear evidence of any change in the incidence of schizophrenia during the present century, though any comparatively slight change would be hard to demonstrate because of the problem of diagnosis. However, there is good evidence for a decrease in severity, as shown by improvement in prognosis; and Professor Ødegård, in his Maudsley Lecture of 1966 (published 1967), concluded that this amelioration had become apparent in the 1930s, a time when it could not easily be attributed to advances in treatment. There is, of course, well-documented evidence of changes in the clinical manifestations of schizophrenia.

During the past decade or two a great deal of research has suggested an association of schizophrenia – or one type of it – with pathological changes in the brain; and two aetiological hypotheses of a strictly environmental kind have been put forward, one implicating a dietary factor and the other an infective (viral) factor. The historical evidence, which I have suggested indicates a change in the incidence of a schizophrenia-like disorder in Britain during the 19th century, is certainly compatible with a somatic cause and may, I think, be considered as lending support to these aetiological hypotheses, particularly the infective one.

I am aware that the ideas I have put to you may seem speculative. What is clear, I think, is that in Britain during the second half of the 19th century the incidence of insanity, as measured by the asylum admission rate, showed a remarkable increase. The question then arises, how far this increase is to be explained in sociological terms, as the increasing admission of milder cases, and how far in medical terms as an epidemic of a mental disorder. In this lecture I have wished only to suggest to you that a medical explanation of the asylum era is worth considering, as perhaps containing an element of truth. "Truth", said Maudsley (1917) in his old age, "is a pleasant abstraction, a visionary and ever-receding ideal to be pursued . . . We shall not capture it; the joy lies in the pursuit."

Acknowledgement

I am indebted to the late Dr Alexander Walk for his advice in the preparation of this paper.

References

Arlidge JT. (1859) Review of the Twelfth Report of the Commissioners in Lunacy. *J Ment Sci* 5: 245–257.
Arlidge JT. (1862) Review of the Sixteenth Report of the Commissioners in Lunacy. *J Ment Sci* 8, 417–429.
Arnold T. (1782) *Observations on the Nature of Insanity* (Vol I). Ireland: Leicester, p. 27.
Bleuler M. (1978) *The Schizophrenic Disorders: Long-term Patient and Family Studies*. Yale University Press: New Haven (translated from the German by Clemens SM: first German edition 1972).
Board of Control (1914) *First Annual Report, for the Year 1914*. HMSO: London, p. 33, Table VII.
Board of Control (1923) *Tenth Annual Report, for the Year 1923*. HMSO: London, p. 7.
Boyd R. (1871) Statistics of pauper insanity. *J Ment Sci* 17: 221–225.
Browne C. (1868) quoted by Robertson CL (1871) in: A further note on the alleged increase in lunacy. *J Ment Sci* 16: 473–497.
Brushfield TN. (1872) The alleged increase of insanity. *J Ment Sci* 16: 229.
Bucknill JC. (1855) Review of the Ninth Report of the Commissioners in Lunacy. *J Ment Sci* 2: 1–16.
Burrows GM. (1828) *Commentaries on the Causes, etc. of Insanity*. Underwood: London, p. 507.
Chapman TA. (1896) Insanity is decreasing: a statistical item suggesting that. *J Ment Sci* 40: 80–85.
Clouston TS. (1891) Asylum reports. *J Ment Sci* 37: 598–599.
Commissioners in Lunacy (1897) *Special Report on the Alleged Increase of Insanity*. HMSO: London.
Commissioners in Lunacy (1899) *Fifty-third Annual Report*. HMSO: London, p. 10.
Commissioners in Lunacy (1911) *Sixty-fifth Annual Report*. HMSO: London, Chart No. 4.
Conolly J. (1849) On some of the forms of insanity. *Lancet* ii: 2, 10.
Corbett WJ. (1893) On the increase of insanity. *Amer J Insan* 50: 224–238.
Cox JM. (1806) *Practical Observations on Insanity* (2nd edn). Murray: London, p. 8.
Crowther B. (1811) *Practical Remarks on Insanity*. Underwood: London, p. v.
Drapes T. (1894) On the alleged increase of insanity in Ireland. *J Ment Sci* 40: 519–561.
Duncan M. (1870) quoted by Robertson CL (1871) in: A further note on the alleged increase in lunacy. *J Ment Sci* 16: 473–497.
Dunham HW. (1971) Sociocultural studies in schizophrenia. *Arch Gen Psychiatry*, 24: 206–214.
Eames JA. (1885) Presidential address. *J Ment Sci* 31: 315–317.
Earle P. (1887) The curability of insanity. *Amer J Insan* 33: 483–533.
Eaton WW. (1980) *The Sociology of Mental Disorders*. Praeger: New York, p. 174 *et seq*.
Goldhamer H and Marshall AW. (1953) *Psychosis and Civilisation*. Free Press: New York.
Granville JM. (1877) *The Care and Cure of the Insane* (Vol 2). Hardwicke: London, p. 216.
Halliday Sir Andrew (1828) *A General View of the Present State of Lunatics*. Underwood: London, p. 15.
Halloran W. (1810) *An Enquiry into the Causes Producing the Extraordinary Addition to the Numbers of the Insane*. Edwards and Savage: Cork, pp 9, 11.
Hare EH. (1981) The two manias: a study of the evolution of the modern concept of mania. *Brit J Psychiatry* 138: 89–99. [This volume, Chap. 4].
Hare EH. (1983) Epidemiological evidence for a viral factor in the aetiology of the functional psychoses. In: Morozov PV (ed.) *Research on Viral Hypotheses of Mental Disorder*. Karger: Basel.

Harper A. (1789) *A Treatise on the Real Cause and Cure of Insanity.* Stalker: London, p. 23.

Haslam J. (1798) *Observations on Insanity.* Rivington: London.

Humphreys NA. (1890) Statistics of insanity in England, with special reference to its alleged increasing prevalence. *J Royal Stat Soc* **53**: 201–252.

Jamieson R. (1876) The increase of mental disease. *J Ment Sci* **21**: 138–141.

Jarvis E. (1852) On the supposed increase in insanity. *Amer J Insan* **8**: 333–364.

Jarvis E. (1871) Quoted by Corbett 1893.

Jones K. (1955) *Lunacy, Law and Conscience 1744–1845.* Routledge & Kegan Paul: London, pp 116, 149.

Jones R. (1906) The evolution of insanity. *J Ment Sci* **52**: 629–661.

Journal of Mental Science (1862) **7**: 534.

Journal of Mental Science (1869) **15**: 557.

Journal of Mental Science (1895) **41**: 498–512.

Journal of Mental Science (1904) **50**: 797.

Journal of Mental Science (1905) **51**: 733.

Journal of Mental Science (1909) **55**: 96–112.

Lancet (1866) Increase of insanity. **ii**: 675.

Lunier L. (1870) De l'augmentation progressive du chiffre des aliénés et de ses causes. *Annales Medico-Psychologiques*, **3** (5th series), 20–31.

MacCabe F. (1869) On the alleged increase of insanity. *J Ment Sci* **16**: 363–366.

Maudsley H. (1872) Is insanity on the increase? *BMJ* **i**: 36–39.

Maudsley H. (1873) *Body and Mind.* MacMillan: London, p. 41.

Maudsley H. (1877) The alleged increase of insanity. *J Ment Sci* **23**: 45–54.

Maudsley H. (1917) Optimism and pessimism. *J Ment Sci* **63**: 1–16.

Metropolitan Commissioners in Lunacy (1844) *Statistical Appendix to the Report of 1844.* HMSO: London

Mitchell A. (1879) Contribution to the study of death rates of persons in asylums. *J Ment Sci* **25**: 1–4.

Morrison A. (1826) *Outlines of Lectures on Mental Diseases* (2nd edn). Longman: London, pp 65, 68.

Ødegård Ø. (1967) Changes in the prognosis of functional psychoses since the days of Kraepelin. *Brit J Psychiatry* **113**: 813–822.

Pargeter W. (1792) *Observations on Maniacal Disorders.* Murray: London, p. 1.

Parry-Jones W. (1972) *The Trade in Lunacy.* Routledge & Kegan Paul: London, p. 328.

Perfect W. (1787) *Select Cases in the Different Species of Insanity, etc.* Rochester: London, p. 118.

Pierce B. (1919) Psychiatry 100 years ago: with comments on the problems today. *J Ment Sci* **65**: 219–235.

Prichard JC. (1835) *A Treatise on Insanity and other Disorders Affecting the Mind.* Sherwood: London, p. 350.

Renaudin E. (1861) Observations deduced from the statistics of the insane. *J Ment Sci* **7**: 534–546.

Robertson CL. (1869) The alleged increase of lunacy. *J Ment Sci* **15**: 1–23.

Robertson CL. (1871) A further note on the alleged increase in lunacy. *J Ment Sci* **16**: 473–497.

Robertson GM. (1926) The prevalence of insanity – a preliminary survey of the problem. *J Ment Sci* **72**: 455–491.

Rorie J. (1900) Statistics of six thousand cases of insane admitted to the Royal Dundee Asylum from 1st April 1890 to 2nd November 1898. *J Ment Sci* **46**: 205–207.

Sanborn FB. (1894) Is American insanity increasing? A study. *J Ment Sci* **40**: 214–219.

Savage GH. (1890) Discussion of Humphrey's paper. *J Royal Stat Soc* **53**: 201–252.

Scull AT. (1979) *Museums of Madness.* Lane: London, Chap 6.

Schwab JJ and Schwab ME. (1978) *Socio-cultural Roots of Mental Illness: an Epidemiological Survey.* Plenum: New York, p. 109.

Swift J. (1747) *A True Copy of the last Will and Testament of the Revd Dr Jonathan Swift.* Bate: Dublin.

Torrey EF. (1980) *Schizophrenia and Civilization.* Aronson: New York, Chap 2.

Tuke Harrington. (1873) Presidential address. *J Ment Sci* **19**: 327–340 and 479–485.

Tuke DH. (1886) The alleged increase of insanity. *J Ment Sci* **32**: 360–376.

Tuke DH. (1894) Alleged increase of insanity. *J Ment Sci* **40**: 219–231.

6

Schizophrenia as a recent disease

The hypothesis that schizophrenia is a recent disease can explain why descriptions of schizophrenia-like disorders were rare before 1800, why the prevalence of insanity in the Western world increased during the 19th but remained low in the non-Western world until the 20th century, and why schizophrenia has become milder in the West during recent decades. It also explains why schizophrenia has persisted in spite of its associated low fertility. The evidence for the hypothesis is somewhat frail, but perhaps not more so than that for alternative hypotheses.

It is generally agreed that few if any adequate descriptions of schizophrenia were written before the year 1800, and there is no doubt that during the 19th century the prevalence of insanity increased remarkably in many industrialised countries. Torrey (1980) suggested that both facts could be explained on the hypothesis that a new type of schizophrenia appeared – or that an old type abruptly became commoner – around 1800. The hypothesis offered a new explanation for the historical course of schizophrenia, and some of the strengths and weaknesses of this 'recency' hypothesis are considered here.

Schizophrenia before 1800

Schizophrenia has generally been considered to be of ancient origin. "The disease is probably extremely old", said Kraepelin (1913, p. 232). Nolan Lewis (1966), referring to passages in the *Rig-Veda*, Hippocrates, and Celsus, concluded that "some such disorder has probably always been recognised". And in the opinion of Strömgren (1982), "schizophrenia has probably existed as long as mankind".

The recency hypothesis is not incompatible with these views; but it asserts that some change of a biological kind occurred about 1800, such that a particular type of schizophrenia thereafter became much commoner. If such a new type of schizophrenia appeared, it is likely, I suggest, to have been of the type which was commonest at the end of the 19th century, then known as 'adolescent insanity'. The rarity of this type in the late 18th century is indicated by the observation of Harper (1789), who said it was "well known that young people are hardly ever liable to insanity, and that the attack of this malady seldom happens until an advanced period of life"; and its later frequency is indicated by Clouston's (1888) statement that "adolescent insanity ending in secondary dementia may be regarded as the typical form of mental disease". If this argument is accepted, then the recency hypothesis predicts that descriptions corresponding to adolescent insanity will hardly be found in pre-1800 records, and that schizophrenic disorders as a whole were rarer then than now.

Any attempt to test these predictions confronts the problem of diagnosis. Before modern diagnostic criteria became generally accepted, there was much difference of opinion on what signs and outcome were indicative of a schizophrenic illness. And what was a difficult decision in a clinical practice was likely to be more contentious in a historical setting, even where a detailed case history was available. Thus, in the case of Robert Schumann (who died in 1856), Slater and Meyer (1959) observe that "the very facts which led Möbius to a diagnosis of schizophrenia led Gruhle to a diagnosis of cyclothymia". Diagnostic criteria for schizophrenia have varied with time and place. There are likely to be few records before 1800 full enough to allow us to apply the criteria of DSM–III (American Psychiatric Association, 1980). In the only instance where such an attempt has been made – in the case of the 17th-century divine George Trosse (Jeste et al., 1985) – the attempt must be said to have failed (Hare, 1988a). But if criteria are not laid down in advance, agreement on diagnosis is unlikely.

There are other difficulties in attempting to discover schizophrenia in historical records. The clinical manifestations of schizophrenia seem to have been changing during the present century and so may have been different, and to an unknown extent, in earlier times. Many of the major signs of schizophrenia – thought disorder, flatness of affect, loss of initiative – are not only hard to assess, but in the absence of an accepted terminology would be hard to describe. And for descriptions made centuries ago in languages now dead or changed, the possibility of shifts in the meaning of words and of bias in modern translations (Torrey, 1980) must make tenuous any claim to diagnostic precision. For these reasons, the search for evidence of schizophrenia might best be concentrated on the records of recent centuries, for if the answer is (or is not) to be found within the period 1600–1800 (say), a more doubtful answer from earlier times becomes less important. Within this period, I shall now consider some of the evidence for and against the existence of schizophrenia.

Bark (1985) has pointed out that although in Shakespeare's King Lear (probably written 1605) Poor Tom imitated the behaviour of Toms o' Bedlam who themselves may often have been simulating madness, their simulation must have been based on real instances. This is a fair argument; but the popular idea of madness tends to be derived from particularly striking cases, and we do not know how common such cases may have been (nor, of course, how far these might have been symptomatic types of schizophrenia).

Statistical data on the prevalence of madness in the early 17th century are provided by the case records of Richard Napier; from a study of these, and of persons certified as lunatics by the Court of Wards, MacDonald (1981) concluded that 'extravagant' mental disorders were rare in southern England then. Over a period of nearly 40 years (1597–1634), such cases occurred at a rate of only six per year in a population estimated at 200 000. "Even if the real rate was three to four times that number, one would have to conclude that madness was not a common phenomenon" (p. 148). Ellard (1987) has suggested that some of Napier's cases described as 'mopish' and 'hallucinated' may have been less dramatic instances of schizophrenia, but their number would have been small.

Nolan Lewis (1966) has credited Sydenham with a description of schizophrenia. In his *Medical Observations* (1676), Sydenham distinguishes two types of madness: 'common madness'; and a type "that succeeds an intermittent of long standing and at length degenerates into idiotism" (p. 609). But from his discussion of intermittent fevers (p. 65), it seems evident that this "peculiar type of madness . . . terminating in a kind of folly for life" was a consequence of severe and long-standing fever ("especially of the quartan kind") – in other words, it had an organic basis. Of the common kind of madness which affects "strong and lively persons" and "young persons of a sanguine constitution", treatment is by bleeding and pills " 'till the disorder goes off" (p. 67). So far as I can find, these passages are all that Sydenham says about madness, and they hardly seem suggestive of schizophrenia.

Descriptions of schizophrenia have been found particularly in the writings of Thomas Willis. Thus Cranefield (1961) quoting Willis' description of 'foolishness', says that "in my opinion this passage may be regarded as a fairly good very early description of simple schizophrenia"; and his opinion is respected by Jeste *et al.* (1985). The relevant passage, in Pordage's contemporary translation of Willis' original Latin (1672), says that the foolish have a sound memory and apprehension but "by reason of a defect of judgement, they compose or divide their notions evilly, and very badly infer one thing from another; moreover, by their folly, and acting sinistrously and ridiculously, they move laughter in the by-standers" (chap. XIII). When this is translated into modern terms, says Cranefield, it means that "they have a loosening of association" – a translation which might be thought to beg the question. Willis himself does not appear to have made a distinction between foolishness and stupidity (his chapter is titled 'Of stupidity and foolishness'), but he says "there is commonly wont to be a distinction". An earlier passage in the chapter seems to imply that, whereas stupidity is inborn, foolishness results from some damage or malformation of the brain.

According to Lewis (1966), Willis recorded that a great number of young persons underwent mental deterioration even though they had been lively minded and even brilliant in their childhood, and that the deterioration was usually permanent. Lewis concludes that Willis described permanent deterioration of intellect in adolescence, and implies that this 'specific disease' must have been fairly common. Lewis' assertions are based (it must be presumed) on the passage which runs, "I have known many in their childhood very sagacious . . . who afterwards, becoming young men, were dull and heavy . . ." and which continues, "In like manner, it often happens on the contrary, that many at first indocile or unapt to learn . . . when they become young men . . . have had an excellent wit" (p. 211). The interpretation of this passage depends on how Pordage's English (or Willis' Latin) is translated into modern terms. One straightforward translation might be that bright children, when they grow up, do not always fulfil their early promise, while some dull children turn out better than expected.[1] But for Lewis, Pordage's 'many' becomes "a great number"; 'very sagacious' becomes "lively minded and even brilliant"; 'dull and heavy' becomes "deterioration"; and the fact that dull children may grow up to be bright is taken to mean that the deterioration is not always necessarily permanent.

Willis's observation, that "melancholy being a long time protracted passes oftentimes into stupidity or foolishness" (chap. XI, p. 193), has been taken by Altschule (1976) and others to indicate schizophrenia. This could be so, but we should note: (a) that melancholy of this kind may also bring 'convulsive distempers or a palsie or apoplexy', which suggests that some cases might be secondary to organic disease; (b) that of the two illustrative cases described by Willis, the one where recovery was incomplete was of a young man who became ill from 'the great heates' of a Spanish summer, his initial symptoms being of sweats and 'pricklings', passing to loss of appetite and sleep, and only thereafter to a melancholy – again a history which might suggest an organic basis; and (c) that in his discussion of madness (chap. XII), Willis says nothing to indicate that the course might be to mental deterioration.

If schizophrenia had been as common in the second half of the 18th century as it became during the 20th century in Britain (that is, a prevalence rate of about 1%), and if it had displayed the same range of clinical manifestations, we would surely expect to find recognisable descriptions in some of the many books written by British alienists then: particularly because alienists, in the latter part of the 18th century, under the influence of Linnaeus' system of classification, gave special attention to the varieties of mental disorder.[2] The argument would especially apply to adolescent insanity which, under its mid-19th century name of 'masturbatory insanity', was considered by Skae (1863) to form a class of insanity as clearly demarcated as those of idiocy or epilepsy, and was considered by Maudsley (1868) to form, from its characteristic features, 'a natural group or family'. Yet in none of the 18th-century books, so far as my reading

---

[1] That Willis (1672) is merely contrasting bright children who become dull with dull children who become bright is supported by two facts. (a) In the same passage, he draws a parallel between "very beautiful children" who grow up "not at all handsome" and children of "ill favour'd countenance" who grow up to "become beautiful". (b) Willis does not apply the terms stupidity or foolishness to the dullness of those who were bright as children; he uses the same term ('hebites') both for this group and for those who were "very dull in their first age".

[2] Linnaeus was himself a physician and in his *Genera Morborum* (1763), he classified diseases – including mental diseases – along the same lines as he had classified plants and animals. The method was adopted by such medical writers as de Sauvages and William Cullen – Cullen's book on nosology (1772) is subtitled "A systematic arrangement of diseases by classes, orders, genera and species". Like others of his time, Linnaeus believed in the fixity of species, and he seems to have taken the same view of diseases. If this was the general opinion of medical men, it would explain their apparent unwillingness to think that any of the diseases newly described during the 19th century – paralysis agitans, general paralysis, diphtheria, rheumatoid arthritis, multiple sclerosis – might really have been new. Even the theory of evolution did not mean any real change in the Linnaean view. "A morbid species", wrote Maudsley in 1908, "might perhaps be expected to be as stable as an organic species"; and while it was true that new diseases had been discovered, "it was pretty well certain that the newness was in the discoveries . . . not in the diseases" – an assertion which effectively maintained the close analogy between diseases and species.

But the discovery of bacterial mutation in the early 20th century, particularly of mutations from non-pathogenic to pathogenic forms, provided grounds for thinking that some infectious diseases might indeed be new. According to Adami (1918), diphtheria "gains its simplest explanation as being due to the acquirement within recent times of virulent properties by some previously harmless diphtheroid"; and Sir Humphrey Rolleston (1927) concurred. With recent experience of encephalitis lethargica and AIDS, and of toxicities from new industrial chemicals, medical men have no doubt become readier to accept that some diseases may really be new.   [Continued on next page]

goes, is there any such description. (See this volume, p. 146). It is perhaps noteworthy that, while descriptions of schizophrenia are now commonly accepted as recognisable in the second editions of books by Haslam (1809) and Pinel (1809), no such descriptions seem to have been remarked in their first editions (1798, 1801).

Some authors consider that, although there are no clear descriptions of schizophrenia before the 19th century, this does not mean it was absent, but rather that there are good reasons why it was not satisfactorily described. Thus, Altschule (1976) points to the underdeveloped state of clinical medicine and to prevailing beliefs about the objective nature of hallucinations. This is a reasonable view for records made many centuries ago, but becomes more debatable the closer we come to 1800. If one reason for not describing schizophrenia was that physicians thought in terms of symptoms rather than syndromes, then we might trace the history of one particular symptom – hallucinatory voices – which is characteristic of schizophrenia (particularly the early-onset type) but rare in other disorders. The subject has been briefly considered by Hare (1983a), but deserves a more thorough study. Present evidence suggests that although the hallucination of seeing a person and hearing him talk was often described, there is no clear record until the 19th century of a mentally disturbed person hearing voices in the absence of any visual hallucination. The earliest record I have found is that of Cox (1806), who said that many of the peculiar acts which accompany mental derangement seem to arise from "imaginations on the organ of hearing occasioning false perceptions" and that "fancied whisperings and distant voices are frequent symptoms".[3]

From the above, it might be concluded: (a) that the principal English language descriptions which have been taken to indicate the probable existence of schizophrenia before 1800 are doubtful, and that alternative explanations (mainly in terms of organic disease) are at least as probable; (b) that because such descriptions are uncommon and incidental, and because the only statistical evidence (that from Napier's records) indicates florid insanity to have been rare, the prevalence of schizophrenia was probably less than it is now – and may have been low enough to be accounted for solely in terms of symptomatic schizophrenia; and (c) that no satisfactory description has been found, before 1800, of a condition corresponding to the adolescent insanity of the 19th century, nor any indication of such a syndrome being recognised.

[Continued from previous page]

The epidemiology of schizophrenia has parallels with that of rheumatoid arthritis. Considering the evidence for the latter's being a 'new' disease, there appear to be no satisfactory descriptions of it, and no convincing anatomical evidence from skeletons, before about 1800 (Short, 1974; Scott, 1986; Rogers et al., 1987). Compared with its effect in Europeans, rheumatoid arthritis is rarer and milder in Arabs, Indians and Pakistanis (Hart, 1979). This difference is still more marked in the black population of rural South Africa (Beighton et al., 1975) but in city-dwellers there, rheumatoid arthritis is as common and severe in the black population as in the white (Solomon et al., 1975). The hypothesis of a viral factor in rheumatoid arthritis has been reviewed by Denham (1987). The evidence for a negative association between schizophrenia and rheumatoid arthritis (Spector and Silman, 1987) adds interest to this parallel.

[3] Cox (1806) also said that "sometimes madness subsides into incurable melancholy . . . but the most hopeless sequel is of disordered intellect ending in idiotism". Six of the 21 cases described by Cox were of adolescent age, but it is unclear how far these were instances of such a sequel. However, Cox's belief that "the baneful and detestable habit of monkish seclusion" was a prolific source of diseased intellect suggests he was describing the condition which came to be called masturbatory insanity and, later, adolescent insanity.

Schizophrenia in the 19th century

To determine how far the recency hypothesis can explain the increasing prevalence of insanity throughout the 19th century, we need first to consider how far this increase could have been due to an increase in incidence. Modern studies of 19th-century insanity have been mainly made by sociologists, almost all of whom have attributed the increased prevalence to social factors and have not considered the possibility of increased incidence. Scull (1979, chap. 7), however, did not conclude that the incidence had increased, but attributed this to a gradual widening of the definition of insanity – by which he implied (1984) that a type of case admitted to asylums towards the end of the century (and therefore classed as insane) would not have been admitted earlier, either because there was then no pressure for their admission or no place available. Thus he did not accept any increase in the incidence of insanity in the sense postulated by the recency hypothesis.

Cooper and Sartorius (1977) suggested that the increased prevalence of insanity was not due to any increase in incidence, but to an increase in the proportion of acute cases that became chronic. Industrialism led to improvements in health and medical care, which meant that frail children who would formerly have died young survived; if they later developed schizophrenia, their frail constitutions tended to make the disorder chronic. Industrialism also led to the growth of large towns, where the population pressure was such that chronic schizophrenic sufferers could no longer be absorbed into the community, as had been possible before, but had to be cared for in special institutions – the asylums. An association between early constitutional damage and schizophrenia is now well documented, although recent studies (McNeil, 1988; Murray et al., 1988) do not suggest that such damage generally leads to the chronic rather than the acute form. In addition, it is not easy to explain on this hypothesis such comments as those of Prichard (1835, p. 336): "the fact that insanity prevails so much in agricultural districts indicates that its development is favoured by some of the conditions connected with the condition of agricultural life", or Hood (1862): "there is no doubt that the general voice of experience is in favour of the idea that insanity is less likely to originate in large towns than in the country"; nor why in Ireland, where there was little industrialisation and few large towns during the 19th century, the reported prevalence of insanity rose even more sharply than in England (MacCabe, 1869; Drapes, 1894).

In England (although perhaps less so in Scotland and Ireland), the social effects of the industrial revolution no doubt played an important part in the increasing prevalence of reported insanity. But this cannot be closely measured, nor, I think, can the possibility of a real increase in incidence be excluded (Hare, 1983b). If this possibility is accepted, then, to examine the prediction of the recency hypothesis, we need to estimate what proportion of reported insanity was of the kind later called schizophrenia, and how much this accounted for the increased prevalence of insanity.

Kraepelin (1913, p. 232) states that many of the cases he called dementia praecox had previously been classed as mania or melancholia; and we may assume that almost all cases classed as 'ordinary dementia' would have been schizophrenia.[4] The first report of the Board of Control (1914) gives a detailed diagnostic table, with age groups, for insanity in England and Wales during the period 1909–1913 (Table 1). This allows us to form a group of the functional psychoses derived from pre-Kraepelin diagnoses, a group which, in Kraepelin terms, would be comprised principally of schizophrenia (dementia praecox) and manic-depressive psychosis. This group (constituted as in Table 1) represents 69% of all admissions (and 70% of all 'first attacks' – Table XVII of the Board's report).

Unfortunately, the reports of the Board of Control do not provide any diagnostic tables that would allow us to compare, in terms of numbers, the pre- and post-Kraepelin classifications. But one such comparison may be had from Lang's (1931) data for admission to the University Clinic for Psychiatry in Munich. If, from Table 2, we take the functional psychoses to comprise schizophrenia and manic-depressive psychosis, then schizophrenia formed 68% of these.[5] A rough check on this figure can be made from the in-patient statistics, for England and Wales, of the Mental Health Enquiry during the years 1970–1979. There were 40 421 first-ever admissions for functional psychoses and the proportion of these receiving a diagnosis of schizophrenia was 55% (66% for males, 46% for females). The Munich data show that about two-thirds of the functional psychoses were schizophrenia; and insofar as this proportion holds for the English data of 1909–1913, we can conclude that the proportion of schizophrenia patients among all those admitted to asylums during that period was about 69% of 68% (i.e. about 46%).

Table 1 Yearly average number of direct admissions to all lunatic asylums in England and Wales for the years 1909–1913 (data from Board of Control (1914), Table XVI

Diagnosis	Number
Congenital insanity	1426
Insanity with epilepsy	1035
General paralysis	1603
Functional psychoses[a]	15 150
Senile dementia	1270
Confusional insanity	926
All others	422
Total	21 832

[a] Comprising stupor (196), primary dementia (617), secondary dementia (459), mania (6005), melancholia (5886), alternating insanity (56), and delusional insanity (1931).

[4] Ordinary' dementia comprised the two forms later distinguished as primary and secondary. Primary (or acute) dementia was "the form which occurs more especially in young persons of feeble mental development", and secondary dementia was the form "that follows acute attacks of insanity, maniacal or melancholic" (Tuke, 1882) – the form which Clouston considered to be the typical form of insanity.

Although in Jablensky's (1986) opinion we are "guessing" if we equate ordinary dementia with schizophrenia, it seems to me that a close relationship between the two may be asserted with confidence. With Kraepelin, it was 'dementia' which particularly distinguished dementia praecox from manic-depressive insanity; the age-incidence curve of primary dementia corresponds closely to that of schizophrenia (Board of Control, 1914) and a reading of Clouston's presidential address (1888) will surely convince a doubter.

[5] Jablensky (1986) found the proportion of in-patients diagnosed schizophrenic at the Munich University Clinic in 1908 to be only about 8%, and this led him to suggest the most significant increase in schizophrenia occurred during the early 20th century. But Lang's data (see this volume, Table 2, p. 121) show that the average proportion of patients diagnosed schizophrenic at the clinic during the first quarter of the century was 23%. If the proportion of schizophrenic patients had risen gradually from 8%, then the proportion in later years would have been a good deal higher that 23% – perhaps as high as 35% – and that would be very high for a clinic admitting all types of psychiatric disorder.

Between 1859 and 1909. the prevalence rate of reported insanity in England and Wales nearly doubled, the rate of increase being higher in the earlier decades (Table 3). If we accept that, in 1909, 46% of all cases of insanity were of schizophrenia, a prevalence rate (per 10 000 of the population) of 16.5 for schizophrenia and 19.3 for all other diagnostic groups is obtained. On the recency hypothesis, the prevalence of schizophrenia increased throughout the 19th century, and we could assume that midway through the century its prevalence would have been about half that at the end of the century. Taking the proportion of instances of schizophrenia in 1859 to be 23% of all cases of insanity, the prevalence of schizophrenia at that time would have been 4.3, and that of all other groups, 14.2. Between 1859 and 1909, the schizophrenia rate would have increased be 12.2, and the rate for other groups be 5.1. Taking a 'worst case', and supposing that all the increase in the non-schizophrenic groups was due to social factors and that this increase applied to schizophrenia in the same degree, the prevalence rate of schizophrenia still increased by 7.1 (i.e. 12.2 minus 5.1) above that of other groups. Between 1859 and 1909, the total increase in the rate of insanity was 17.3 (35.8 minus 18.5); and of this, 7.1 (41%) was due to the increase in schizophrenia over and above that attributable to causes acting to increase the rate of all types of insanity. Thus, the postulated increase in the incidence of schizophrenia can account for at least 40% of the increased prevalence of insanity between 1859 and 1909.

There are a number of assumptions in this argument, and sounder calculations could be made if the proportion of schizophrenia in the group of functional psychoses could be estimated more surely, and at different times. A greater increase in the prevalence rate of schizophrenia than of other categories can, of course, be explained in two ways – either in terms of an increase in its incidence (the postulate of the recency hypothesis), or in terms of the hypothesis of Cooper and Sartorius (1977).

Table 2 Numbers of patients admitted to the University Psychiatric, Clinic, Munich, up to 1927 (data from Lang, 1931)

Diagnosis	Number	Percentage
Schizophrenia	3976	22.9
Manic-depressive psychosis	1879	10.8
General paralysis	1720	9.9
Psychotherapy	2692	15.5
Hysteria	1089	6.3
Senile and arteriosclerotic dementia	1011	5.8
Others	5024	28.9
Total	17 391	100.1

Schizophrenia in non-industrialised countries

The testimony of travellers in distant lands, said Tuke (1878), "suffices to prove that insanity is rare among uncivilised tribes. The evidence is so uniform that we cannot but allow it great weight". This conclusion could not be doubted (he said) even when "a very great allowance" was made for the possibility that cases might escape a traveller's notice. Reports on the rarity of psychoses (and of schizophrenia) in societies untouched by industrialism continued to appear during the 19th century, and for the first four decades of the 20th century (reviewed by Torrey 1980, 1987). Since then, however, more formal studies have found schizophrenia to occur in most countries, and a general conclusion has been reached that the prevalence rate of schizophrenia is much the same everywhere. The question then arises: was schizophrenia formerly rare in the non-Western world – as the earlier evidence indicates – or is this evidence to be discounted as unreliable? Torrey considered the early evidence reliable enough to suggest that schizophrenia is a disease of civilisation.

Table 3 Numbers of reported lunatics, idiots and persons of unsound mind in England and Wales on 1 January in various years (data from Board of Control 1914, Table II)

Year	Population $(\times 10^{-3})$	Number	Rate per 10 000 population
1859	19 687	36 480	18.5
1869	22 223	52 545	23.6
1879	25 371	68 585	27.0
1889	28 448	82 684	29.1
1899	31 881	103 247	32.4
1909	35 424	126 791	35.8

Eaton *et al.* (1988), on the other hand, found the evidence "not highly credible because there had been no attempt to use epidemiological methods".[6]

Changes in the prevalence of a disease with changes in the circumstances of a society have often been described, and have been attributed to the introduction of a causal agent to which the society had not previously been exposed. Where the nature of the causal agent is known, the observations on prevalence are easily credible. Thus gout is said to have been rare among the Maoris in the 19th century, but is now common because of the introduction of "abundant proteinaceous food and alcoholic drinks" (Hart, 1979). But where the prevalence of a disorder is found to be low at one time and higher at a later time, and no clear reason for this is apparent, caution will suggest the likeliest explanation to be an error in the earlier estimate. Thus the prevalence of insanity in England and Wales was found to be a good deal lower in the first half of the 19th century than in the second, and this was then attributed to defects in the earlier methods of ascertainment. Yet a modern sociologist, examining these early statistics, has concluded there is no good reason to doubt their accuracy (Scull, 1979, chap. 7).

In this respect, the history of general paresis provides a curious parallel to that of schizophrenia. General paresis was first described in Paris in 1818. It was not recognised in North America until after 1840, and not in Brazil until the 1880s. Its prevalence in Asian countries was reported to be very low in the early 20th century. Later, when its prevalence in the non-West was found to be comparable to that in the West,

---

[6] Their reasoning may lead us to wonder how far the credibility of historical evidence should be related to the use of a technique poorly understood or inapplicable at the time. The 1929 study of mental illness in Astrakhan by Skliar and Starikova (as summarised by Ackerknecht, 1959) is not easily discounted; and a clinician might think the personal observations of Fortes and Mayer (1969) to be at least as convincing as an epidemiological investigation. It is curious that, while the large body of evidence consistent with the former rarity of insanity in the non-Western world may be dismissed for not having met the standards of a modern test, the sparse and vague descriptions in the pre-1800 literature of the Western world continue to be accepted, despite the fact that not one of them meets modern diagnostic criteria, as satisfactory evidence for schizophrenia having been as common then as it is now.

the discrepancy was commonly explained on the lines that the 'legend' (of paresis having been rare or absent in certain societies) was being disproved by 'advancing knowledge' (Hare, 1959). Yet Kraepelin (1927, p. 1147) records that when he was in Java in 1904, he could not find a single case of paresis among the natives, although syphilis was common; and that 20 years later, paresis appeared to have increased in frequency there (Kraepelin, 1926). From this and similar instances, he concluded that the changes in prevalence were real and must be attributed to changes in an environmental factor.[7] (See also this volume, Chapter 3, especially pp 59–60).

If we accept the evidence that insanity (and therefore schizophrenia) was rare in non-Western societies during the 19th and early 20th centuries and has only lately become common there, the most simple explanation of the increase is environmental change. The recency hypothesis then identifies the environmental change as the event which, around the year 1800, led to the appearance (or increased incidence) of a type of schizophrenia that spread rapidly in the Western world during the 19th century, but only later, and more slowly, to the non-Western world.

The persistence problem

The fertility of schizophrenic patients has been widely studied, and it is now generally accepted, from studies made over the past five or six decades, that life-time fertility is much reduced (to between 30 and 80% of that of the general population). If schizophrenia has been present for thousands of years, and if genetic factors are important in its transmission, why has it not been eliminated by natural selection? This persistence problem remains unanswered, but three types of explanation have been offered: 1. Schizophrenia is not a genetic disorder; 2. The losses are replaced by mutation or through heterozygous advantage and 3. The fertility rate in the past has varied with varying environmental factors.

---

[7] Kraepelin never expressed the opinion that paresis had been a new disease in the early 1800s. But he concluded that "we may take it as very probable that (it) was formerly uncommon, then underwent a progressively rapid increases from the beginning of the last century and for some time now has been gradually diminishing" (Kraepelin, 1927, p. 1145).

In 1959, I argued the case for paresis having been a new disease (see p. 67), and in 1965, the traditional view was reaffirmed by Jacobowsky. So far as I know, the matter has rested there. The basis of Jacobowsky's opinion is that before the 19th century the development of paresis was suppressed by the effect of fevers, particularly of smallpox, whose high incidence only began to diminish with the introduction of vaccination. But against this view, the following points may be urged: (a) fevers could hardly have prevented every case of paresis, yet there are no satisfactory descriptions of this dramatic disease before 1800; (b) vaccination originated in England but paresis, which rapidly became common in northern France from 1815, was relatively rare in England before 1830 (Prichard, 1835, p. 108); (c) paresis' prevalence in France increased explosively, but a diminution of fevers would have been a gradual process; (d) the traditional view does not account for the different prevalence rates among different groups of the same society, e.g. Kraepelin's (1926) reference to the 'remarkable fact' that general paresis was reported to be extremely rare in North American Negroes 40–50 years back but had now become equal to that among the Whites; (e) nor does it account for the changes in clinical manifestations during the 19th and early 20th centuries – the lessening proportion of the grandiose type, the increasing proportion of the depressed and simple types, and the changes in sex ratio (discussed by Kraepelin, 1927, p. 1150, who concluded that "there can be no doubt about the overall increase in the danger to the female sex").

1. In Bleuler's opinion (1972), no genetic explanation can account for the persistence of schizophrenia. He concludes that schizophrenia is not a genetic disorder in the ordinary sense, but is the result of an unfavourable mix of normal genes, leading to a personality particularly sensitive to normal environmental stresses. This accounts for persistence, but implies that, since schizophrenia is not a biological disorder but a statistical misfortune, it will continue to persist among mankind, and there is no likely way of preventing it.

2. The generally accepted figure for the mutation rate of a human gene is too low to explain the persistence of schizophrenia as due to genetic mutation. Thus the problem is not easily solved in terms of a single-gene hypothesis. Polygenetic hypotheses, implying either a genetic or a clinical heterogeneity of the schizophrenic syndrome, allow for a lower rate of mutation; but it might seem that the number of such genes, each individually causing a type of schizophrenia, would need to be uncomfortably large. Crow (1987), in his virogene hypothesis of schizophrenia, postulates that an element of the gene is located at a 'hot spot' in the genome, i.e. at a position where transpositions, equivalent to mutations, may occur at a relatively high rate.

   Heterozygous advantage is most simply explained in terms of an increase in the number of fertile off-spring of relatives of the propositi. But the weight of evidence is against any such increase either in the parents or in the siblings (Vogel, 1979). Kidd (1975) pointed out that small reproductive advantages in more distant relatives could maintain schizophrenia. But this suggestion will not be easy to test; studies made on the survival rates of offspring of nieces and nephews of schizophrenic people were inconclusive because of the unreliability of the data (Kay and Lindelius, 1970; Buck et al., 1977).

   There is evidence of high ability or special gifts among the relatives of schizophrenic people (Heston, 1966; Karlsson, 1984). Crow (1987), postulating a genetic continuum from affective psychosis to schizophrenia, suggests that the well-documented high ability common in persons with affective psychosis (and in their relatives) may, through an increased fertility, ensure the persistence of the virogene, and so, schizophrenia. Haverkamp et al. (1982), however, have argued that, in a disorder where the inheritance does not follow a clear Mendelian pattern, the concept of heterozygous advantage may not be applicable.

3. All the above explanations presuppose that the incidence of schizophrenia has remained unchanged throughout history. But if there are specific environmental causes of schizophrenia, its incidence may have varied. Because schizophrenia appears to occur only in humans, Kuttner and Lorincz (1966) considered any heterozygous advantage to be likely to be of a social rather than a biological kind. Eisenberg (1968) suggested that if schizophrenia appeared only after the development of human culture (say 50 000 years ago), then culture might have protected persons of a schizoid nature – in the role of priests, for instance. Buck et al. (1975) suggested that the diminished fertility might be quite a recent

phenomenon related to a culturally delayed age of marriage, although there is evidence that low fertility is due as much to the pre-morbid personality as to the illness (Stevens, 1969). Rosenthal (1970) suggested that the loss from low fertility might be balanced by an increase in the strength of environmental causes – such causes becoming more common as societies became more complex and indus-trialised. He also suggested that the incidence of schizophrenia might be falling in some areas and rising in others, and that differential migration could keep the total incidence steady.

The recency hypothesis provides an explanation which is comparable to the suggestions of Rosenthal, i.e. based on the idea of a change in incidence rate due to change in an environmental cause. The particular type of schizophrenia which (on this hypothesis) became common about 200 years ago, and which is the type mainly responsible for the 20th-century incidence rate of schizophrenia, has been present for too short a period for the genetic effects of its low fertility to be ap-parent. In the absence of other factors, the recency hypothesis predicts a long-term decrease in the incidence rate of this type.

Changing manifestations of schizophrenia

The difficulties of assessing the outcome of schizophrenia, and of comparing out-come in different places and times, have been stressed by Wing (1987). Nevertheless, there is much evidence to support the view that the course and clinical manifes-tations of schizophrenia have been changing during the 20th century. Clinicians have recorded their personal experience of change towards a milder type of illness (Grinker, 1973; Romano, 1977; Ellard, 1987). The catatonic and hebephrenic subtypes are diagnosed less now than formerly, while paranoid, intermediate, and un-differentiated types are diagnosed more often (Hare, 1988b). Changes in the out-come of schizophrenia have been reviewed by Bourgeois et al. (1987), and by Westermeyer and Harrow (1988), who conclude that the recovery rate is better now than in Kraepelin's time.

How far are such changes attributable to changes in diagnostic practice and to advances in treatment? One problem is that if schizophrenia is becoming a milder disease for reasons unrelated to medicine (as scarlet fever became milder during the 19th century), the effect would be to make any new therapy appear more effective and might well lead to shifts in the diagnosis of subtypes. There is evidence to suggest that not all the changes in schizophrenia can be attributed to new treat-ments. In Sweden, improvement in prognosis was recorded during the period 1904–1929 (Evenson, 1936), and, in Norway, Ødegård (1967) found a 'dramatic' improvement in prognosis about the year 1936. Bleuler (1972, p. 415) considered that the catastrophic type of schizophrenia had become steadily rarer during the years 1920–1970. Improvements in the course of schizophrenia were found in comparisons of two periods that were before the introduction of phenothiazines (Kuriansky et al., 1974) or after (Romano, 1977). The incidence of schizophrenia will not be influenced by treatment, but a recent decline in its incidence has been reported (Eagles *et al.*, 1988; Joyce, 1987) from Denmark, Scotland and New Zealand.[8]

Whether the recency hypothesis can offer an explanation for such changes depends on the nature of the postulated event that occurred about the year 1800. As Crow has pointed out (1987), the epidemiological facts about schizophrenia – particularly its world-wide distribution – seem incompatible with such environmental factors as trauma, toxins and dietary deficiencies, leaving infection and immunity as the most probable causes. Syphilis, diphtheria, encephalitis and AIDS are examples of diseases likely to have owed their origin to the mutation of infectious organisms, and the presumption would be that if the early-onset type of schizophrenia was a new disease in 1800, it was due to a new type of infection. If so, that could explain, by analogy with the history of other new infectious diseases, the changing manifestations in the present century. This would be supported by many of the changes – the diminution in catatonia and hebephrenia, and a lesser degree of mental deterioration – being particularly associated with schizophrenia of the early-onset type. In the history of infectious disease, changes to a milder type of illness have been attributed to increased host resistance or to the emergence of milder strains of the organism. In Europe, such changes occurred in syphilis after its appearance in the late 15th century, in bubonic plague in the 17th century (McEvedy, 1988), in tuberculosis, measles and scarlet fever in the 19th century (McKeown, 1979), and perhaps in erysipelas and puerperal fever in the 20th (Loudon, 1987). Although the course of such change in infectious diseases has not always been towards a continued mildness, the recency hypothesis would predict that, given a continuance of health standards at the present level, the trend towards a milder type of schizophrenia is likely to continue.

An assessment of the evidence

The evidence bearing on the acceptability of the recency hypothesis may be summed as follows:

1. The hypothesis implies that there should be no records before 1800 corresponding to the 19th century concept of adolescent insanity, and that the incidence of schizophrenia was substantially less than now. The traditional view is that schizophrenia has always been present; and this view has also implied (I think) that the subtypes and incidence rate have not varied much. The historical evidence available to us is meagre, and it remains possible that schizophrenia occurred but was unrecorded. Yet present evidence might seem, on balance, to favour the recency hypothesis here.

2. On the recency hypothesis, the early-onset type of schizophrenia increased during the 19th century and would account, at least in part, for the increase in diagnosed

---

[8] Hogarty (1977) reviewing studies of the prognosis of schizophrenia, concluded that not all the improvement could be put down to treatment. This led him to 'fantasize' that schizophrenia might disappear by the 21st century. His fantasy may be compared with that of a commentator a century earlier who observed that, if the course of increasing insanity were to be traced backwards, one would be forced to the 'extravagant' conclusion that there was a time in the past when insanity must have been quite rare (Tuke, 1878).

insanity. An estimate can be made, for asylums in England and Wales in the early 20th century, of the proportion of admissions that were likely to have been for schizophrenia. This estimated proportion is about 45%, high enough to allow the possibility that an increasing incidence of schizophrenia could account for a substantial part of the increase in insanity. The case is not firm, but it may be questioned whether the alternative explanation, in terms of purely sociological causes, is any firmer.

3. Whether insanity was rarer in non-Western countries during the 19th and early 20th centuries than it is now, or whether it was always equally prevalent but inadequately recognised, is not easily determined. Argument from analogy – the changing incidence in time or place of syphilis, general paresis, appendicitis, carcinoma of the lung, etc. – is hazardous, but here perhaps it would favour the prediction of the recency hypothesis.

4. The 'persistence' problem derives from the presupposition that schizophrenia has occurred in human societies for a long time and with the same incidence rate as now. No satisfactory explanation has been found; and the fact that the recency hypothesis allows this problem to be avoided must be considered a point in its favour.

5. Although the hypothesis does not postulate the nature of the biological event supposed to have caused the change in schizophrenia in 1800, the mutation of an infectious agent would seem to provide a plausible explanation. In that case, the recency hypothesis becomes a particular aspect of the more general viral hypothesis of schizophrenia.

6. Evidence that the manifestations of schizophrenia have changed over recent decades is strong, and there are some reasons, although not compelling ones, for thinking that the changes cannot all be attributed to diagnostic changes or advances in care and treatment. If there was a non-medical cause of the changes, the hypothesis of a biological event occurring about the year 1800 – either a viral mutation or a changed immunological reaction to existing infections – allows an explanation based on analogy with the changing manifestations observed in the course of known infectious diseases.

Conclusion

The recency hypothesis rests on flimsy evidence, although the evidence which supports alternative hypotheses might seem equally flimsy. What is chiefly in its favour, perhaps, is that it provides a straightforward and consistent explanation for all the major aspects of the history and epidemiology of schizophrenia, while, in the more traditional view, a different type of explanation is needed for each of these. It also provides two testable predictions: that schizophrenia will continue to become milder and probably decrease in incidence; and that these changes will be principally apparent in the schizophrenias of early onset.

References

Ackerknecht EH (1959) *A Short History of Psychiatry* (trans. Wolff S, pp 5–6). Hafner: London.

Adami JG (1918) *Medical Contributions to the Study of Evolution.* Duckworth: London, p. 42.

Altschule M (1976) Historical perspective – evolution of the concept of schizophrenia. In: Wolff S and Berle BB (eds) *The Biology of the Schizophrenic Process.* Plenum Press: New York, chap. 1.

Bark NM (1985) Did Shakespeare know schizophrenia? The case of Poor Mad Tom in *King Lear. Brit J Psychiatr* **146**: 436–438.

Beighton P, Solomon L and Valkenberg HA (1975) Rheumatoid arthritis in a rural South African negro population. *Annals of Rheum Dis* **34**: 136–141.

Bleuler M (1972) *Die Schizophrenen Geistesstörungen im Lichte langjähriger Kranken – und Familien- geschichten.* Translated by Clemens SM (1978) as *The Schizophrenic Disorders: Long-term Patient and Family Studies.* Yale University Press: London, chap. 8.

Board of Control (1914) *First Annual Report for the Year 1914.* HMSO: London.

Bourgeois M, Etchepare JJ, Degeilh B, Rager P and Peyre F (1987) L'évolution des Schizophrénies. Problèmes méthodologiques et revue de la littérature. *Annals médico-psychologique* **145**: 608–620.

Buck C, Hobbs GE, Simpson H and Wanklin JM (1975) Fertility of the sibs of psychiatric patients. *Brit J Psychiatr* **127**: 235–239.

Buck C, Simpson H and Wanklin JM (1977) Survival of nieces and nephews of schizophrenic patients. *Brit J Psychiatr* **130**: 506–508.

Clouston TS (1888) Presidential address. *J Ment Sci* **34**: 325–348.

Cooper JE and Sartorius N (1977) Cultural and temporal variations in schizophrenia: a speculation on the importance of industrialisation. *Brit J Psychiatr* **130**: 50–55.

Cox JM (1806) *Practical Observations on Insanity* (2nd edn). Baldwin and Murray: London, pp 8, 14.

Cranefield PF (1961) A seventeenth century view of mental deficiency and schizophrenia: Thomas Willis on 'Stupidity and Foolishness'. *Bull Hist Med* **35**: 291–316.

Crow TJ (1987) Two syndromes of schizophrenia as one pole of the continuum of psychosis: A con- cept of the nature of the pathogen and its genomic locus. In: Henn FA and DeLisi IE (eds) *Handbook of Schizophrenia, vol. 2. Neurochemistry and Neuropharmacology of Schizophrenia.* Elsevier: Amsterdam, chap. 2.

Cullen W (1772) *Synopsis Nosologiae Methodica.* English translation (1800) *Nosology; or, a Systematic Arrangement* (etc.). Creech: Edinburgh.

Denham AM (1987) The viral aetiology of arthritis. *Reports on Rheumatic Diseases (Series 2): Topical Reviews 7.* The Arthritis and Rheumatism Council: London.

Drapes T (1894) On the alleged increase of insanity in Ireland. *J Ment Sci* **40**: 519–561.

Eagles JM, Hunter D and McCance C (1988) Decline in diagnosis of schizophrenia among first contacts with psychiatric services in north-east Scotland, 1969–1984. *Brit J Psychiatr* **152**: 793–798.

Eaton WW, Day R and Kramer M (1988) The use of epidemiology for risk factor research in schizo- phrenia: an overview and methodologic critique. In: Tsuang MT and Simpson JC (eds) *Handbook of Schizophrenia, vol. 3. Nosology, Epidemiology and Genetics of Schizophrenia.* Elsevier: Amsterdam, chap. 9.

Eisenberg L (1968) The interaction of biological and experimental factors in schizophrenia. In: Rosenthal D and Kety SS (eds) *The Transmission of Schizophrenia.* Pergamon Press: London, pp 403–409.

Ellard J (1987) Did schizophrenia exist before the eighteenth century? *Aust and NZ J Psychiatr* **21**: 306–314.

Evenson H (1936) Recherches faites après la sortie sur environ 800 cas de démence précoce. *Sixth Congress of Scandinavian Psychiatrists* Copenhagen, pp 799–816. Quoted by Ødegård (1967).

Fortes M and Mayer DY (1969) Psychosis and social change among the Tallensi of Northern Ghana. In: Foulkes SH and Prince GS (eds) *Psychiatry in a Changing Society.* Tavistock: London, chap. 3.

Grinker RR (1973) Changing styles in psychoses and borderline states. *Amer J Psychiatr* **130**: 151–155.

Hare EH (1959) The origin and spread of dementia paralytica. *J Ment Sci* **105**: 594–626. [See this volume, p. 36]

Hare EH (1983a) Epidemiological evidence for a viral factor in the aetiology of the functional psychoses. In: Morozov PV (ed.) *Research on the Viral Hypothesis of Mental Disorders.* Karger: Basel, pp 52–75.

Hare EH (1983b) Was insanity on the increase? *Brit J Psychiatr* **142** 439–455. [See this volume, p. 88]

Hare EH (1988a) Schizophrenia before 1800? The case of the Revd George Trosse. *Psychol Med* **18**: 279–285.

Hare EH (1988b) Temporal factors and trends, including birth seasonality and the viral hypothesis. In: Tsuang MT and Simpson JC (eds) *Handbook of Schizophrenia, vol. 3. Nosology, Epidemiology and Genetics of Schizophrenia.* Elsevier: Amsterdam, chap. 15.

Harper A (1789) *A Treatise on the Real Cause and Cure of Insanity.* Stalker: London, p. 23.

Hart FD (1979) Arthritis as a world-wide problem. *Curr Med Res and Opinion* **6** (Suppl. 2): 3–8.

Haslam J (1798) *Observations on Insanity.* Rivington: London.

Haslam J (1809) *Observations on Melancholy and Madness.* Callow: London.

Haverkamp F, Propping P and Hilger T (1982) Is there an increase of reproductive rates in schizophrenics? *Archiv für Psychiatrie und Nervenkrankheiten* **232**: 439–450.

Heston LL (1966) Psychiatric disorders in foster home reared children of schizophrenic mothers. *Brit J Psychiatr* **112**: 819–825.

Hogarty GE (1977) Treatment and the course of schizophrenia. *Schizophren Bull* **3**: 587–599.

Hood WC (1862) *Statistics of Insanity.* Batten: London, p. 52.

Jablensky A (1986) Epidemiology of schizophrenia: a European perspective. *Schizophren Bull* **12**: 52–73.

Jacobowsky B (1965) General paresis and civilisation. *Acta Psychiatr Scand* **41**: 267–273.

Jeste DV, Carman R, Lohr JB and Wyatt RJ (1985) Did schizophrenia exist before the eighteenth century? *Comp Psychiatr* **26**: 493–503.

Joyce PR (1987) Changing trends in first admissions and re-admissions of mania and schizophrenia in New Zealand 1974–1984. *Aust and NZ J Psychiatr* **21**: 82–86.

Karlsson JL (1984) Creative intelligence in relatives of mental patients. *Hereditas* **100**: 83–86.

Kay DWK and Lindelius R (1970) In: Lindelius R (ed.) *A Study of Schizophrenia: a Clinical, Prognostic and Family Investigation.* Munkgaard: Copenhagen (*Acta Psychiatr Scand* suppl. 216).

Kidd KK (1975) On the possible magnitudes of selective forces maintaining schizophrenia. In: Fieve RR, Rosenthal D and Brill H (eds) *Genetic Research in Psychiatry.* Johns Hopkins University Press: London, chap. 10.

Kraepelin E (1913) *Psychiatrie* (8th edn) Translated by Barclay RM (1919) from vol 3, part 2 as *Dementia Praecox and Paraphrenia.* Livingstone: Edinburgh.

Kraepelin E (1926) The problems presented by general paresis. *J Nerv and Ment Dis* **63**: 209–218.

Kraepelin E (1927) *Psychiatrie* (9th edn), vol. II, chap. VI. Barth: Leipzig.

Kuriansky JB, Deming E and Gurland BJ (1974) On trends in the diagnosis of schizophrenia. *Amer J Psychiatr* **131**: 402–408.

Kuttner RE and Lorincz AB (1966) Schizophrenia and evolution. *Eugen Q* **13**: 355–356.

Lang T (1931) Zur Frage: Geisteskrankheit und Geburtsmonat. *Archives der Rassen-biologie* **25**: 42–57.

Lewis NDC (1966) History of the nosology and the evolution of the concepts of schizophrenia. In: Hoch PH and Zubin J (eds) *Psychopathology of Schizophrenia.* Grune and Stratton: London, p. 1.

Linnaeus C (1763) *Genera Morborum.* Uppsala. English translation in Cullen (1800).

Loudon I (1987) Puerperal fever, streptococcus and the sulphonamides, 1911–1945. *BMJ* **295**: 485–490.

MacCabe F (1869) On the alleged increase of insanity. *J Ment Sci* **16**: 363–366.

MacDonald M (1981) *Mystical Bedlam. Madness, Anxiety and Healing in Seventeenth Century England.* Cambridge University Press: Cambridge, p. 148.

Maudsley H (1868) Illustrations of a variety of insanity. *J Ment Sci* **14**: 149–162.

Maudsley H (1908) *Hereditary Variation and Genius.* Bale: London, p. 199.

McEvedy C (1988) The bubonic plague. *Scient Amer* **258**: 74–79.

McKeown T (1979) *The Role of Medicine: Dream, Mirage or Nemesis?* Blackwell: Oxford, pp 51, 92.

McNeil TF (1988) Obstetric factors and perinatal injuries. In: Tsuang MT and Simpson JC (eds) *Handbook of Schizophrenia, vol. 3. Nosology, Epidemiology and Genetics of Schizophrenia.* Elsevier: Amsterdam, chap. 14.

Murray RM, Reveley AM and Lewis SW (1988) Family history, obstetric complications and cerebral abnormality in schizophrenia. In: Tsuang MT and Simpson JC (eds) *Handbook of Schizophrenia, vol. 3. Nosology, Epidemiology and Genetics of Schizophrenia.* Elsevier: Amsterdam, chap. 24.

Ødegård Ø (1967) Changes in the prognosis of functional psychoses since the days of Kraepelin. *Brit J Psychiatr* **113**: 813–822.

Pinel P (1801) *Traité médico-philosophique sur l'aliénation mentale* Translated by Davis DD (1827) as *A Treatise on Insanity.* Cadell and Davis: Sheffield (facsimile edition by Hafner, New York, 1962).

Pinel P (1809) *Traité médico-philosophique sur l'aliénation mentale* (2nd edn). JA Brosson: Paris.

Prichard JC (1835) *A Treatise on Insanity and other Disorders Affecting the Mind.* Sherwood: London.

Rogers J, Waldron T, Dieppe P and Watt I (1987) Arthropathies in palaeopathology: the basis of classification according to most probable cause. *J Archael Sci* **14**: 179–193.

Rolleston H (1927) Changes in the clinical aspects of disease. *BMJ* i: 87–95.

Romano J (1977) On the nature of schizophrenia: changes in the observer as well as the observed (1937–1977). *Schizophren Bull* **3**: 532–559.

Rosenthal D (1970) *Genetic Theory and Abnormal Behaviour.* McGraw Hill: New York, p. 181.

Scott JT (ed) (1986) *Copeman's Textbook of Rheumatic Diseases* (6th edn). Churchill Livingstone: London, p. 12.

Scull AT (1979) *Museums of Madness.* Lane: London.

Scull AT (1984) Was insanity increasing? A response to Edward Hare. *Brit J Psychiatr* **144**: 432–436.

Short CL (1974) The antiquity of rheumatoid arthritis. *Arthrit and Rheum* **17**: 193–205.

Skae D (1863) A rational and practical classification of insanity. *J Ment Sci* **9**: 309–319.

Skliar N and Starikova K (1929) Zur Vergleichenden Psychiatrie. *Archiv für Psychiatrie und Nervenkrankheiten* **88**: 554–585.

Slater E and Meyer A (1959) Contributions to the pathology of the musicians. 1. Robert Schumann. *Confinia Psychiatrica* **2**: 65–94.

Solomon L, Robin G and Valkenberg HA (1975) Rheumatoid arthritis in an urban South African negro population. *Annals Rheum Dis* **34**: 128–135.

Spector TD and Silman AJ (1987) Does the negative association between rheumatoid arthritis and schizophrenia provide clues to the aetiology of rheumatoid arthritis? *Brit J Rheum* **26**: 307–310.

Stevens B (1969) *Marriage and Fertility of Women Suffering form Schizophrenia and Affective Disorders.* Maudsley Monograph No. 19. Oxford University Press: London.

Strömgren E (1982) Developments of concepts of schizophrenia. In: Wing JK and Wing L (eds) *Handbook of Psychiatry 3: Psychoses of Uncertain Aetiology.* Cambridge University Press: Cambridge, p. 17.

Sydenham T (1676) *Observationes Medicae.* Translated by Swan J (1742) as *The Entire Works of Thomas Sydenham.* Cave: London.

Torrey EF (1980) *Schizophrenia and Civilization.* Aronson: London, chap 2.

Torrey EF (1987) Prevalence studies in schizophrenia. *Brit J Psychiatr* **150**: 598–608.

Tuke DH (1878) *Insanity in Ancient and Modern Life.* Macmillan: London, pp 15–16.

Tuke DH (1892) *Dictionary of Psychological Medicine.* Churchill: London.

Tuke H (1873) Presidential address. *J Ment Sci* **19**: 327–340 and 479–485.

Vogel HP (1979) Fertility and sibship size in a psychiatric patient population. *Acta Psychiatr Scand* **60**: 483–503.

Westermeyer JF and Harrow M (1988) Course and outcome in schizophrenia. In: Tsuang MT and Simpson JC (eds) *Handbook of Schizophrenia, vol. 3. Nosology, Epidemiology and Genetics of Schizophrenia.* Elsevier: Amsterdam, chap. 10.

Willis T (1672) *De Anima Brutorum.* Translated by Pordage S (1684) as *Dr. Willis' Practice of Physick, Part II. Concerning the souls of the Brutes.* Davis: Oxford.

Wing JK (1987) Has the outcome of schizophrenia changed? *Brit Med Bull* **43**: 741–753.

7

Some physical problems in asylums

This paper describes some minor medical disorders or problems which affected patients in British asylums and mental hospitals during a period of about a hundred years (from 1850–1950) and which, to all intents and purposes, are no longer seen today. The most rapid change in British psychiatry during these hundred years occurred, I think, soon after the Second World War, in the decade centred on 1950. It was then that many of the old asylum disorders, which had long been declining, finally disappeared. The present generation of psychiatrists will hardly have known them. But the distress they occasioned to patients, and the worry they caused the staff, will still be clear in the memories of those who, like myself, were working in mental hospitals throughout the critical post-war decade.

Asylum pellagra

A condition which began to cause concern in British asylums just before the First World War was pellagra. Pellagra is characterised by redness and roughness of the exposed skin, by diarrhoea and loss of weight, by paralysis and by mental disturbance. The condition was first recognised in Spain about 1740, and by the early 19th century was a frequent cause of admissions to the asylums in northern Italy. For an early, and for a recent, historical review, see Peacock (1863) and Roe (1973)

By the mid-19th century, pellagra (or a condition like it) was being found in southern France. An asylum officer there, Billod (1859), reported 66 cases of a disorder which he described as 'very like pellagra' and for which he proposed the name 'asylum pellagra'. Pellagrous insanity was found in the asylums of the southern United States soon after 1900, and the number of cases there grew rapidly until the researches of Goldberger and his colleagues (Terris, 1964) led to an improvement in asylum diet.

In Britain, if we exclude one or two isolated reports (see the review of Stannus and Gibson, 1934) the first case series was reported by Sambon and Chalmers in 1912 and included two asylum cases from Scotland. This was followed by a spate of reports in the *British Medical Journal* and the *Lancet*, including 11 cases from Napsbury asylum (Blandby, 1913) and three from Holloway Sanatorium (Johnson, 1913). Whether these represented a new phenomenon here or whether by the accounts given in British journals, attention had been alerted to the increasing problem of pellagra in the United States, is uncertain. But during the next ten years, 66 deaths from pellagra were reported in the asylums of England and Wales; and although the mortality declined thereafter, pellagra continued to figure in the Reports of the Board of Control and the Ministry of Health right up to 1952 – the last year in which such statistics were published – when there were four cases with one death. In 1948 I myself saw a mental hospital case, diagnosed by a dermatologist as 'probably pellagra', but I doubt if any cases have been reported in mental hospitals here during the last 30 years.

Many authorities considered asylum pellagra to be a syndrome rather that a specific disease; and it would seem that the classical pellagra associated with a diet of maize may have differed in some ways from the British asylum pellagra, where maize was not a factor, where the diet seems to have been adequate, and where vitamin supplements apparently did not necessarily effect a cure (White and Taylor, 1932). Of asylum pellagra it was often asked (see for example, Parfitt, 1939), which came first, the pellagra or the insanity? But the question was never really answered. Thus in 1924 McCowan described four cases of pellagra at Cane Hill asylum. The patients had all been malnourished, from their refusal to eat enough, before signs of pellagra appeared; but whether their refusal was due to an unrelated mental illness, or to the early stages of pellagra, could not be said.

The type of mental disorder associated with pellagra was variously reported. McCowan perhaps voiced a common opinion in saying that 'pellagra may be the exciting cause of most of the recognized forms of insanity'. But at the St Hans Hospital in Copenhagen (Guttman, 1936), schizophrenia was the psychosis most often associated with pellagra; and, in a smaller series, the same was found by Leigh (1952). It was of course the clinical association of these two disorders which played a part in the hypothesis that a deficiency of nicotinic acid was a factor in the cause of schizophrenia. That hypothesis would have had a stronger basis if asylum pellagra could have been equated with maize-diet pellagra. But, at least in Britain, the nature and causes of asylum pellagra, like the reasons for its appearance and disappearance, remain unclear.

Erysipelas

There was another asylum condition where the skin of the patient presented the most obvious sign of disease – erysipelas. Erysipelas, the word simply means red skin, has been known to medicine for centuries. It was called St Anthony's fire, and was a frightening condition because the associated toxaemia carried a high mortality – Charles Lamb died from erysipelas.

During the second half of the 19th century, epidemics of erysipelas began to occur in the asylums of this country. Such outbreaks might involve up to 50 cases, and the death rate from erysipelas in asylums was ten times that in the general population. A typical case is described by Symes in the *Journal of Mental Science* of 1858 from the Dorsetshire Asylum.

A female patient aged 49, who had been washing clothes, rubbed with her wet hand a small boil on her forehead. The next morning she complained of headache, and stiffness over the eyes, with a sense of itching. On the third day, erysipelas appeared all over her scalp, eyes and face, of great severity, and rapidly extended downward to the throat. She speedily got worse and died on the ninth day after the appearance of the inflammation.

From the Reports of the Commissioners in Lunacy, we learn that outbreaks occurred in about half of all asylums and that the disease was more than twice as common in females as in males.

There was much argument about the cause. Dirty floors were at one time held to blame, but the best way to keep them clean posed a problem. For, said John Bucknill in 1859, when the floors were 'dry-rubbed' there was dysentery, but when 'in the attempt to preserve extreme cleanliness' the floors were frequently scoured, erysipelas appeared. This led Bucknill to observe that 'dysentery and erysipelas are the Scylla and Charybdis of ward management'.

Another theory, upheld by Dr Phillimore in 1877 of the Nottinghamshire County Asylum, blamed the many post-mortem examinations made in asylums. He drew a parallel between erysipelas and puerperal fever and showed that epidemics of erysipelas had become common only since the Lunacy Commissioners had stressed the importance of post-mortems. But the preferred view sprang from the observation that outbreaks of erysipelas tended to occur in the same hospitals as outbreaks of diarrhoea. Dr McDowall, of the South Yorkshire Asylum, wrote to the *Journal of Mental Science* in 1878 that all medical men, 'with the exception of Dr Phillimore', agree that erysipelas, typhoid and dysentery 'are due to over-crowding, sewage gas, deficient and impure water supply, and like causes'.

Until the bacterial cause of erysipelas was established, the sewer gas theory was firmly held both by doctors and also, it seems, by the public. At the inquest on a female patient in the Somerset and Bath Asylum in 1879 (Commissioners in Lunacy, 1880), the coroner's verdict was that she "died from erysipelas, caused by sewer-gas emerging from the water closets of the infirmary"; and the jury added a rider that "they were unanimous in their conviction of the absolute necessity of immediate and thorough inspection, by a competent man, of the sewerage and ventilation of the Asylum". The inspection was made and various defects remedied. But the erysipelas continued, and the Commissioners concluded that the inspection could not have been sufficiently thorough, for (they said in their Report) "we are strongly of opinion that defective drains permitting the escape of sewer gas will be found to be the cause", and they recommended that the services of a sanitary engineer of eminence and practical experience should, without delay, be secured. Perhaps the hospital authorities were reluctant to incur further expense; for "it then appeared that at this asylum there was no general plan of the whole of the drains"; and the Commissioners had to content themselves with the barbed remark that, in the absence of such a plan, they "could express no opinion as to the probable efficacy of the means proposed".

Elsewhere however, such measure might be rewarded. Outbreaks of erysipelas had occurred at the Midlothian and Peebles Asylum; and on examining the drains, wrote the Superintendent, Dr Mitchell in 1892, "it was found that a water closet, abolished a good many years ago, had had its soil pipe led into a branch drain near the windows of the north east wing, and that this pipe had never been disconnected or sealed. It contained a large quantity of foul matter, and it appears most probable that this was the cause of the epidemic. The defect was thoroughly remedied by our own workmen, and since then the health of the inmates has remained good".

There are no references to erysipelas in the *Journal of Mental Science* later than 1902, but it continued to be a cause of morbidity and death in mental hospitals until quite recently. From the Reports of the Board of Control, we learn (for example) that there were 179 cases during 1925, with 16 deaths – and a further three deaths among the nursing staff. It was not until after the Second World War that the yearly number of deaths from erysipelas fell below 20; and non-fatal cases continued to figure in the reports of the Ministry of Health up until 1952. Even at the time, when most young doctors would have regarded an attack of erysipelas as a relatively trivial matter, older staff remembered it as an epidemic disease and one likely to be taken as reflecting adversely on nursing efficiency, and they might still feel a sense of anxiety and alarm when a case of ERY was discovered.

We do not know why erysipelas became an asylum disease in the 1850s. Over-crowding, by increasing the chance of cross-infection, may have played a part; but 90 years later, during the Second World War, when the over-crowding was probably worse, erysipelas was less common and much less severe. We do not know why it became a milder disease, rarely seen in mental hospitals after 1940. The virulence of the infecting organism may have declined – as has been supposed in the parallel case of scarlet fever. But there was probably another factor. During much of the last century, the general state of health of patients admitted to Bethlem Hospital was recorded – and it should be noted that because of its policy of taking recoverable cases, patients admitted to Bethlem were likely to be in better health than those admitted to county asylums. Of 200 patients admitted to Bethlem Hospital in 1854 and 1874, the physical health on admission was described as weak, feeble or bad in 25%, and as indifferent in a further 12%. That certainly could not be said of present day admissions, and this evidence supports that view that, during the past 100 years, the general health of mental hospital patients improved greatly – and with it, presumably, their resistance to infection.

Insane ear

I now describe a condition which came and went long before my time. *Haematoma auris* was a relatively minor ailment. Because it was almost confined to asylum patients it was commonly called 'insane ear'. The ear was affected by a blood-stained effusion, often developing rapidly over a day or two. In the acute stage, the swelling was red, tense and painful. But in the course of a few weeks, the fluid was replaced by granulation tissue which then became fibrosed, leaving the ear thickened, scarred and misshapen. For a historical view, see Robertson (1896).

Insane ear was first reported in 1833 from an asylum in Germany, and one of the earliest British accounts was that of Stiff in 1857. The condition was commoner in the left ear and in males, and particularly affected patients with mania or with general paralysis.

Several writers were able to collect series of more that a 100 cases a year, and in the average asylum during the mid-19th century there might be three or four cases a year. Gradually, however, the numbers diminished. In 1896, Mickle observed that the condition was rarer than formerly, and there are no references to *haematoma auris* in the *Journal of Mental Science* after the year 1907.

Although it was never very common and although it was relatively trivial in its effects, insane ear was a subject of considerable medical attention – five whole pages are devoted to it in Hack Tuke's *Dictionary of Psychological Medicine* (1892) – and this was because of the belief that it was caused by trauma and in particular by a blow from an attendant or nurse. Why did the condition occur only in the insane? Because (said those who held this belief) the insane cannot protect themselves from assault. Why did it occur more in men? Because men are more likely to be struck, and because women are protected by their hair and their caps. Why did it occur more in the left ear? Because that ear would be struck by a right-handed person facing the patient. And according to the superintendent of a German asylum, when the attendants were held responsible and appropriately disciplined, the condition practically disappeared.

But not everyone thought the attendants were to blame. One superintendent reported that insane ear continued to occur even after the attendants had been warned; and others (Stiff, 1863) pointed out that the patient's ear might have been struck by another patient rather than an attendant, or might have been injured in a fall. And there were arguments against any idea of trauma (Hun, 1870). Thus insane ear was rare in epileptics who had frequent falls; it might occur spontaneously in quiet and docile patients; an actual blow on the ear led to an entirely different sequence of events; and most significantly, insane ear was a bad prognostic sign for it occurred only in cases which proved to be incurable – as Maudsley (1867) characteristically remarked, it was "ever of evil augury". The most commonly held theory was of poor local nutrition. This, it was supposed, led to degenerative changes in the cartilage of the ear and so to a cyst which became lined with fragile blood vessels; these then ruptured either spontaneously or from a minor trauma. Treatment – which does not seem to have influenced the course of the disorder – was by incision or blistering.

So insane ear came – and went. The question of trauma was never really resolved; and as late as the 1880s one authority (Pieterson, 1892) maintained that asylum officers played down the role of trauma from fear that they or their staff might be censured for ill treatment in the Reports of the Lunacy Commissioners. We do not know whether it was a new condition when it was first described; we do not know what really caused it, and we do not know why it went away when it did.

Insane ear seems to have been commonest in general paralytics; and its disappearance – from the literature at least – coincided with the decline of general paralysis. Yet general paralysis continued to be a common disorder for decades after insane ear had apparently gone.

Fractured ribs

The concern of asylum staff, and of the public, that insane ear might be the result of ill treatment, was as nothing compared with the furore over fractured ribs. The death of an asylum patient, where post-mortem examination revealed fractured bones or any other sign suggestive of violence, was a matter of particular concern to the Commissioners in Lunacy, that body of independent asylum inspectors, set up by Parliament under the Lunatics' Act of 1845. For 40 years under the Chairmanship of the great Lord Shaftesbury, the Commissioners were untiring in their determination to detect and expose instances of harshness, mismanagement or neglect. Lord Shaftesbury was certainly a great man: but he was also an eccentric one. Florence Nightingale said of him that "he would have been *in* a lunatic asylum if he had not devoted himself to reforming lunatic asylums" (Smith, 1950).

In August 1861, a patient with advance general paralysis was admitted to the Durham County Asylum. He died the following January, and the Medical Officer gave the cause of death as pleuro-pneumonia. But at the inquest it was revealed that the post-mortem examination had shown fractures of 16 or 17 ribs and a rupture of the bladder. An attendant, Metcalfe, was implicated by the coroner, but the jury acquitted him of manslaughter and found the cause of death to be pleuro-pneumonia. On learning of these events, the Commissioners in Lunacy (1863) set up their own enquiry (they were empowered to take evidence on oath). It transpired that about two weeks before the death, Metcalfe had had a personal altercation with the patient in the airing court, and they fell together, Metcalfe uppermost, and that the latter – as it is believed – to extricate himself from the patient's grasp, knelt upon his chest. For this, and for certain other instances of harshness, Metcalfe was dismissed. The Commissioners then instituted proceedings against the Medical Officer for he, in certifying the cause of death, had omitted all mention of the post-mortem results. But the Justices of the Petty Sessions dismissed the case, and the Commissioners, who wished to appeal, found themselves frustrated by a legal technicality.

Between about 1850 and 1890, the yearly reports of the Lunacy Commissioners are replete with such cases. Strangely – as it might seem – the Commissioners often found themselves at variance with the hospital's Committee of Visitors and with the local justices: where the Commissioners sought to prosecute, the justices tended to block proceedings and the Visitors were often content with a dismissal or simply a censure. But sometimes the Commissioners gained their point. A notorious case occurred at Lancaster Asylum in 1869 (Commissioners in Lunacy, 1870). On the death of a patient with general paralysis, post-mortem revealed 12 broken ribs, three of them broken in two places. Two attendants were implicated but both denied the charge. They were convicted however on the sole evidence of another patient, and were each sentenced to seven years penal servitude. It was this case which established the admissibility of evidence by a lunatic.

Such stories naturally got into the newspapers and caused public concern. The novelist Charles Reade wrote to the *Pall Mall Gazette*, denouncing the brutalities of asylum practice (See Sankey, 1870). And yet, as time went on, the clamour died down and the accusations became rarer. One reason for this was the growing evidence that factors other than violence might be responsible. Sankey, in 1870, observed that cases of fractured rib were too common, and the numbers of ribs fractured were too many, for it to be likely that the blame always lay with the attendants. Nor could the fractures be caused simply by falls, since epileptic patients often fell but did not frac-ture their ribs. Fractured ribs occurred most commonly in patients with general par-alysis; and the cause, Sankey suggested, was the furious behaviour of such patients together with a lack of reflex muscular protection. Another idea was that the ribs of general paralytics were unusually brittle – a suggestion which some saw simply as an attempt to excuse the asylum staff. In a paper to the *Lancet* of 1870, the Superintendent of the Sussex Asylum, Williams, described two cases of fractured ribs where neither patient had at any time been violent. Although in each case the coroner's verdict was that death had been due to natural causes and to disease of the bone, Williams commented that, for his part, he "could not for a moment subscribe to the absurd hypothesis that lunatics' ribs are more brittle than other people's".

Yet it was this 'absurd' hypothesis that gained ground. In 1873, post-mortem examination of a manic patient showed fractures of 12 ribs, some of them fractured in two or three places, together with a transverse fracture of the breast bone, though no wound of the pleura or lungs was detected. There was evidence of a struggle, but the Hospital Visitors found that if the attendants did in fact inflict the injury, they did not intend to do so, and that the fatal result was entirely owing to the abnormal condition of the patient. The Lunacy Commissioners (1874) reported without com-ment that the ribs of this patient were stated to be unnaturally brittle. Another patient, dying from general paralysis in 1890, was found at post-mortem to have four frac-tured ribs. This patient had never been excited and had never required coercion, and the post-mortem report stated that the bones were in a very fragile state. The coroner's jury concluded that 'how the said ribs were fractured there is no evidence to show'; and the Commissioners (1891) said only that 'no doubt it was due to a fall, probably from the edge of his bed'.

By the early years of the present century it seems to have become accepted that patients with general paralysis were very liable to fractured bones and that this was due, not to muscular weakness or inadequate reflexes, but to the bones (with the ex-ception of the cranial bones) being porous, light and fragile.

Although the evidence strongly suggests that in general paralysis the rib bones were unduly fragile, we have no satisfactory explanation of the cause. The subject attracted little attention after 1900, and I cannot determine how long fractured ribs continued to occur. In the 1940s, I dealt with many cases of general paralysis, but I never met one with fractured ribs and I do not recall reading or being told that this was a complication to be looked for. It seems likely then that at some stage patients with general paralysis ceased to have fragile ribs, just as they ceased to have insane ears. But if so, we do not know why that was.

I think this story of fractured ribs has an enduring relevance for psychiatry. To the Commissioners in Lunacy, humanely concerned to expose mal-treatment in asylums, it was obvious in the 1860s that fractured ribs meant violence. As a result, a number of medical officers were severely censured and a number of attendants dismissed and prosecuted; and if those numbers were not as many as the Commissioners wanted, this was because the Hospital Visitors and local justices, closer to the grass roots of the matter, sensed that things were not always as bad as they might seem. Even so, in all probability some asylum staff were wrongly censured and wrongly dismissed. There is a deeply-rooted tendency in human nature to believe that unexplained misfortunes are the result of someone's sins. In just the same way as it was believed that dementia praecox was due to the patient's masturbatory habits (Hare 1962), and general paralysis to his sexual excesses (Hare, 1959), so it was believed that erysipelas was due to the carelessness, and insane ear and fractured ribs to the wickedness, of the asylum staff. We now know that all these beliefs were almost certainly incorrect; but the story may remind us that one may be over-zealous in the search for evil, and that where illness, and particularly where mental illness is concerned, cause and effect may not be as simple as they seem.

Physiognomy

Physiognomy is the art of judging character and disposition from the features of the face or (more generally) of the body form. This is something we do all the time, but in the 19th century it was considered an important diagnostic aid. "There is no class of diseases," wrote Alexander Morison in 1840, "in which the study of physiognomy is so necessary, as that of mental disease. It not only enables us to distinguish the characteristic features of different varieties, but also gives warning of the approach of the disease . . . as well as confirms our opinion of convalescence." John Bucknill, in 1856, considered that no physician could practise his art satisfactorily or successfully unless he were a good physiognomist. "In a great number of cases," he wrote, "a remarkable peculiarity is observable in the physiognomy of the insane." In chronic mania, for example, "the hair becomes harsh and bristling"; and in secondary dementia, it is the varying enfeeblement of the mental faculties which "renders the facial expression of so many chronic lunatics at once stupid and vicious".

But during the second half of the century, these abnormalities of feature seemed to fade away. In 1874 Bucknill and Tuke wrote that the peculiarity in the physiognomy of secondary dementia "is infinitely less frequent and less pronounced than we remember to have seen it, from 10 and 15 years ago; or than is delineated in the engravings of Morison or Esquirol, and to a still greater extent in the paintings of Hogarth and Fuseli." And Cibber, whose "well-known state of Dementia . . . reported to have been copied from the actual condition of a lunatic in the wards of Bethlem, a man who had been Oliver Cromwell's porter, . . . would not at the present day find it easy to procure such a model, faithfully and painfully expressing not only the effects of disease but those of cruel and brutal treatment" (see Appendix).

Psychiatric interest in physiognomy waned rapidly during the 1890s and has not been revived. If we ask why the interest arose and why it declined, there are, broadly, two different answers.

One answer comes from the fact that psychiatry is a branch of medicine largely dependent on subjective assessment and is always emotionally loaded. Before photography, portrayal of the features of madmen or criminals had to be made by a drawing, sculpture or written description, and so carried the risk that the portrayer would exaggerate for the sake of dramatic effect or, from the same motive, would search for specially striking examples. Now as Bucknill and Tuke (1874) remarked, "the idea entertained of a madman by the public is more frequently taken from such descriptions than from personal observation"; and from such descriptions, just as from textbook descriptions, observers may be biased into distorting what they actually see into what they believe they ought to be seeing, and it may take many years for such distortion to yield to commonsense or new techniques. One such new technique was photography; and the decline in physiognomy was doubtless due in part to the objective and permanent record provided by a photograph. Another technique, perhaps, was that of statistical comparison: the old idea that ears of abnormal shape indicated an insane or criminal tendency was countered by Professor Schwalbe of Strasbourg (1895), who compared the ears of 467 criminals, 800 lunatics and 25 000 normal persons.

But we ought not to suppose that experienced men such as Bucknill and Tuke (1874) would have been liable to much subjective distortion. They had been in no doubt there was a characteristic physiognomy in the insane; and they also had no doubts of why this was becoming less marked. "The most undubitable testimony with which we are acquainted, of the immense change which has taken place in the condition of lunatics, is afforded in the entirely different facial expression of lunatics as they are painted and described by our forefathers and as they are observed by ourselves." And the change, they believed, was due to improvements in care and treatment for "the old treatment converted the insane patient into a ferocious, malevolent and repulsive being," but "under the humane and judicious treatment which now prevails in lunatic asylums" these exaggerated passions no longer occurred.

With regard to the changes in physiognomy, we do not know the truth of the matter. It seems reasonable to suppose, on the evidence, that many chronic asylum patients did show characteristic peculiarities of appearance during the first half of the 19th century, and that these gradually became less marked. But as to the cause of the change, I think there is no simple answer. It is an understandable prejudice of medical men to suppose that any improvement in the outcome of a disease is due to improvements in medical treatment. But the supposition is not necessarily true. Treatments change of course, but so do diseases; and it may not be easy, over a short span of time, to say which change came first.

Incontinence

There are two conditions which were not strictly disorders but which caused difficult ethical problems of mental hospital management right up until the 1950s, though I think they are much rarer nowadays. These are incontinence and destructive behaviour.

Incontinence of urine and faeces seems to have been common in asylum patients in the last century. Where the patient suffered from an evident organic disorder, such as general paralysis, no doubt it was accepted that he could not be held responsible. But where there was no such evidence, as in cases of what we would now call chronic schizophrenia, the patient's responsibility was harder to assess. An incontinent patient was a source of unpleasantness on the ward and of trouble to the attendants. Was there a treatment for incontinence?

The cold shower, or douche, had been introduced as a purely medical treatment. "It is used," said Hack Tuke, "in the form of a continued stream of cold or iced water poured on the head from a sponge or hand shower-bath, for from 2 to 6 minutes, as a revulsive in cases of congestion of the brain;" and he added that "the pain attending its application beyond a certain time is severe and becomes intense if prolonged."

In 1857, a notorious case of misuse, which resulted in the death of a patient at the Surrey County asylum, led the Lunacy Commissioners to make a general enquiry of its value among medical superintendents; and, as might be expected, the replies were diverse. "I prescribe the douche," said Dr Sutherland of St Luke's Hospital, "in cases of acute dementia, the effects of which are something marvellous. *Before* the douche, the patient is like a statue; he never speaks, he is apparently unconscious of all that passes around him, his movements are automatic, the limbs fixed in catalepsy in the position in which they are placed . . . *After* the douche, the patient's energies of mind and body are roused into activity. He appears like someone waking out of sleep." Mr Millar, of Buckinghamshire Asylum, employed the cold shower "as a remedial agent in its moral character . . . As a last resort with patients of excited, mischievous, destructive, dirty or immoral habits, I have used the bath for the purpose of stimulating the power of self control, which I believe them to possess but which, from indolence or perversion of the moral feeling, they are unwilling of their own account to exert;" and at two Licenced Houses, the cold bath was used particularly "in the cases of patients who are dirty in their habits." With regard to the duration or number of such treatments, Dr Palmer of the Lincolnshire County Asylum found that in the majority of cases one or two showers were sufficient; "but still, with reference to time, I think they should always be given *ad effectum*, on the same principle as jalap, opium or any other therapeutic agent employed."

Others were more guarded or more sceptical. "The utmost caution is needed," said Mr Hill of the North East Riding Asylum, "to avoid the semblance of punishment, and great pains are invariably taken to explain the nature of the remedy before its application so as to prevent the recipient from suspecting foul play." And according to Dr Burnett of Westbrook House, "the use of such baths does not apply to the insane; and my impression is that their application in a cold state to the bodies of the insane is quite as cruel as the most objectionable form of mechanical restraint."

The Commissioners caustically summed up the supposed medical virtues of the shower-bath. "It is stated to act," they said, "according to the mode of its administration, as a stimulant in cases of cerebral inaction and depressed nervous power, invigorating and giving tone to the system generally; and as a sedative in cases of maniacal excitement . . . relieving congestion of the circulation, and producing sleep." And they concluded that "an agent which is always regarded by the patient, and admits of being used as, a punishment should be administered only in the presence of the Medical Officer – a full record being inserted by him into the case book." Yet the Commissioners' strictures did not lead to the total demise of the cold shower. As late as 1920, the Board of Control (which, by comparison with the old Lunacy

Commissioners, were very restrained in their comments) reported undesirable practices at an asylum where, on medical orders, the cold douche had been given as a correctional treatment to certain patients who exhibited filthy and destructive habits and were believed to know better. The Report adds that whereas the Board "entirely deprecate any form of correctional treatment," they "of course entirely approve of the considered use of hot and cold baths or douches as purely medical treatment."

The cold shower or cold plunge was an example of those 'shocking' treatments which are common in the history of psychiatry, and which reflect the widespread belief that a sudden shock may bring a deranged person to his senses. Then, as now, the Medical Officer faced a dilemma in the prescription of such treatment. If he believed in its efficacy but gave too much – or gave it *ad effectum* – he might be accused of using it as a punishment. If he was sceptical and gave too little – or none at all – he might be accused of failing to provide treatment or stimulation for his patients, with the consequence, as one Commissioner put it, of their 'drifting pleasantly into dementia'. Granville, (1877) who agreed with this Commissioner, observed that Conolly's system of non-restraint had been followed not merely by the absence of any improvement in outcome but on the contrary by a diminution in the proportion of cures. He favoured the use of shocking treatments such as the cold pack, even if these carried the risk of abuse, and he deplored the fact that public outcry had led to their being used less often – "the penalty we have to pay for the unreasonable, and I fear unreasoning, criticism sometimes hurled at medical superintendents by censors less familiar with the phenomena of insanity than skilled in the art of fine and fierce writing." In fact, the prognosis of insanity seemed to worsen during much of the second half of the 19th century, in America as well as Britain (Hare, 1982); and in so far as this was so, it was probably quite unrelated to any method of management or treatment then available.

Destructive behaviour

Another problem of management in asylums was presented by habits of destructiveness. The patient, usually a woman, would persist in tearing, or tearing off, her own clothing; and during the 19th century the attempt to control such behaviour was commonly by the use of the canvas dress (or strong clothes). A canvas dress was made of heavy, coarse, untearable material, often in one piece like combinations, fastening at the back and sometimes with blind sleeves so that the patient could not use her fingers. We learn about the ethics of its use from the Reports of the Lunacy Commissioners. Their statutory visit to Coney Hatch Asylum in 1873 led them to censure its Superintendent, Dr Sheppard, for the degree of mechanical restraint and particularly for the free use of canvas dresses. The Superintendent defended his practice. Canvas dresses, he said, are "as pinafores for children". "If a patient persistently undresses himself, or destroys ordinary clothing, I should be no more justified in *withholding* from him a canvas suit, than in *giving* a knife to a suicidal patient. It is an utter misuse of terms," he went on, "to call any treatment humane and philanthropic which violates the first principles of decency and safety."

The Commissioners disagreed. Canvas dresses, they said, were unsightly and must be uncomfortable to wear; but they "are mainly objectionable because they lead to the permanent degradation of the patient, by tending to confirm bad habits and by accepting such habits as incurable, instead of attempting their improvement by correction." "Experience has shown," they concluded, "that good results follow the persistent efforts of treating or curing, patients of a destructive or dirty character" (Commissioners, 1873).

The ethical problems – the distinctions between medical treatment, moral treatment and correctional treatment – were very difficult. The use of a canvas dress could be seen as too degrading to justify its undoubted practical value; but it could also be seen as a form of moral treatment, rather like a dunce's cap. And as for the persistent efforts at treatment which the Commissioners recommended, the Superintendent at Coney Hatch might have replied that such efforts had already been made in the case of incontinence – by the use of the cold shower – without marked success.

The habit of tearing clothes, and the use of canvas dresses, certainly continued, though with diminishing frequency. I can remember seeing a patient in a canvas dress at Brentwood Mental Hospital in 1947, but I am sure it is never used now. One reason for the change seems probable enough. "The fact," said the Board of Control in its Report of 1932, "that women commissioners can now take part in statutory visits has resulted in greater attention being paid to the clothing of female patients;" and I expect it was a woman commissioner who made the sensible comments that, "clothing which no sane person would ever wear except under compulsion ought not to be inflicted on convalescent or other well behaved persons;" and that such patients should wear attractive clothes, not only because in these days such clothes can be produced very cheaply, but also because anything which helps to restore the patient's self-respect is an aid to recovery. Even the men benefited, for "though the use of pyjamas (wrote the Board in 1933) cannot be encouraged since the cords might offer too great a temptation in suicidal cases, it is satisfactory to note the increasing adoption of night shirts for male patients." And one may further presume that once patients were in a position to wear their own clothes, that constituted a powerful reason for not tearing them.

The use of the cold shower, whether for medical or correctional purposes, was abandoned at least 50 years ago. What then replaced it, as a means of treating incontinence, I am not sure. But when I joined the staff of Warlingham Park Hospital in 1955, there was still a special ward for incontinent male patients, where treatment was by a mixture of methods which would now be known as token therapy or behavioural therapy. The scheme had worked well, and the numbers of such patients diminished until a special ward was no longer needed – and all this was substantially before the introduction of neuroleptic drugs. Nowadays, as far as I know, patients are very rarely incontinent simply from chronic schizophrenia, just as they very rarely display persistent destructiveness. But it remains a matter of opinion how far these changes were the result of new drugs, or of the kind of moral treatment practised at Warlingham, or of an amelioration in the schizophrenic process (in the sense that schizophrenia in this country does not now progress to the profound dementia which Kraepelin thought to be characteristic).

Conclusion

I have said nothing of the major disorders of asylum patients, the disorders which were the principal causes of death and morbidity during most of the years 1850–1950 and which have now disappeared or greatly decreased – dysentery, tuberculosis, Bright's disease, epilepsy. Most notable of all, perhaps, has been the disappearance of general paralysis. It was probably this disease, above all others, which contributed to the popular fear of asylums and to a sense of pessimism among asylum staff. General paralysis was a mental disorder which, in the words of Maudsley (1867) selects "those who seem to be buoyant in health and at the height of their energy." Its course was almost invariable: progressive dementia, with death in a very few years. During most of the second half of the 19th century, it was responsible for about one in seven male admissions and for some 1500 asylum deaths a year. Its cause was then quite unknown and there was no useful treatment. General paralysis was first described around 1820, and its prevalence seems steadily to have increased throughout the 19th century, but began to decline from about 1900. The causes of this increase and decline, and the question whether the disorder was present before 1820 but unrecognized, are still matters of opinion (Hare, 1959; Jacobowsky, 1965 and Martin, 1972).

When a disease appears abruptly and then disappears within a few years (as happened with encephalitis lethargica) it will be thought of as a passing epidemic. But once a chronic disease has been recognized for a century or more (like general paralysis) it is apt to be thought of as one which must always have afflicted mankind and which will continue to do so until conquered by the advance of medical science. Yet it seems to me more reasonable to suppose that all diseases are continually changing, more or less rapidly, in their manifestations, prevalence and severity, and that new diseases continually appear and old ones disappear in response to changing environments, mutations or (rarely) prevention.

The present account of some relatively minor disorders which have now practically disappeared from British mental hospitals may illustrate this theme of change in the pattern of disease. And two further points may be noted. In most cases we do not know what caused the changes; and the medical and ethical problems presented by the management of the disorders were never solved – the problems simply disappeared when the disorders themselves disappeared.

We should not forget, though, that during a hundred years when the nature of asylum insanity was continually changing and when the various attempts at curative treatment were at best unavailing (and at worst, of a kind which later generations, faced with quite different problems, too easily see as having been harmful to the cause of medicine), one thing remained constant – the need to provide care and comfort for the patients. The manner in which the services of mental hospital staff have been acknowledged has varied with the times. In 1858, Dr Forbes Winslow concluded his Presidential Address to the Medico-Psychological Association with words which might raise a smile today. "Oh! what a holy, honourable and sacred occupation," he said, "is that in which we have the privilege to be engaged. The angels in Heaven might well envy us the nobling and exalted pleasures incidental to our mission of love and charity." The mode of expression has changed, but the sentiment, I think, has not. Thirty years after Winslow, the Commissioners in Lunacy (1891) – always grudging in these matters – observed that the work of the asylum staff was wearing and not free from danger and that it called for the exercise of qualities of intelligence, tact and patience which are by no means too common. Later still, in the Report of the Royal Commission on Lunacy (Board of Control, 1926), its members took the opportunity of paying tribute "to the skill, devotion and self-sacrifice of the nursing staff who, in circumstances peculiarly exacting, are rendering great service to suffering humanity." And those are words which today we might still accept unchanged.

Appendix

Cibber's Statue of 'Dementia'

The two well-known statues by Cibber (1630–1700), originally on the gates of the 17th century Bethlem at Moorfields and now in the museum of Bethlem Hospital at Beckenham, Kent, have generally been held to represent Raving Madness and Melancholy Madness. Morison (1840), however, considered that the statue of Melancholy Madness properly represented Dementia because the features displayed a 'total absence of mind' and 'a want of emotion'; and of the statue of Raving Madness (which he considered to represent Mania) he says: 'This is supposed to represent the porter of Oliver Cromwell, who, it is said, was a patient in the Bethlem Hospital of his time'. Bucknill and Tuke, in using Morison's title of Dementia, seem mistakenly to have applied it to the statue of Raving Madness.

We should note that Thomas Arnold, in his *Observations on Insanity* of 1806, refers to a patient Daniel, a porter of Oliver Cromwell, "whose brain was supposed to have turned by his plodding in mystical books of divinity", and who was confined for many years in Bethlem. But his treatment there is particularly noted to have been humane, and he was permitted to continue his preaching from a window, below which his audience "would often sit for many hours . . . with great signs of devotion". The possibility that Daniel was the same patient as Cibber's model must raise a doubt about Bucknill and Tuke's belief that the patient's ferocious appearance, as reflected in the statue, was the consequence of brutal treatment.

References

Arnold T. (1806) *Observations on the Nature, Kinds, Causes and Prevention of Insanity, Lunacy or Madness* (2nd edn). Robinson and Cadell: Leicester, p. 224.
Billod E. (1859) D'une variété de pellagre propre aux aliénés. *Annales Medico-psychologiques* 5: 161–216.
Blandby GS. (1913) Contribution to the study of pellagra in England. *Lancet* 2: 713–717.
Board of Control. *7th Report (for the year 1920)*. HMSO: London, p. 17.
Board of Control. *13th Report (for the year 1926)*. HMSO: London, p. 1.
Board of Control. *19th Report (for the year 1932)*. HMSO: London, p. 8.
Board of Control. *20th Report (for the year 1933)*. HMSO: London, p. 17.
Bucknill JC. (1856) The diagnosis of insanity. *J Ment Sci* 2: 433–455.
Bucknill JC. (1859) Reports of lunatic asylums. *J Ment Sci* 5: 166.
Bucknill JC and Tuke DH. (1874) *A Manual of Psychological Medicine* (3rd edn). Churchill: London, pp 411–421.
Commissioners In Lunacy. *11th Report (for the year 1857)*. HMSO: London, pp 24–33, 119.
Commissioners In Lunacy. *17th Report (for the year 1863)*. HMSO: London, p. 32.
Commissioners In Lunacy. *24th Report (for the year 1870)*. HMSO: London, p. 17.
Commissioners In Lunacy. *27th Report (for the year 1873)*. HMSO: London, p. 1.
Commissioners In Lunacy. *28th Report (for the year 1874)*. HMSO: London, p. 30.
Commissioners In Lunacy. *34th Report (for the year 1880)*. HMSO: London, p. 85.
Commissioners In Lunacy. *45th Report (for the year 1891)*. HMSO: London, pp 39, 61.

Granville JM. (1877) *The Care and Cure of the Insane* Vol. 2. Hardwicke and Bogue: London, pp 131, 210, 221.

Guttmann E. (1936) Review of Pellagroide Dermatosen an Geisteskranken (by Reiter PL and Jakobsen JJ. Levin and Munksgaard: Copenhagen, 1935). *J Ment Sci* **82**: 74.

Hare EH. (1959) The origin and spread of dementia paralytica. *J Ment Sci* **105**: 594–626. [See this volume, Chap. 3, p. 36]

Hare EH. (1962) Masturbatory insanity: the history of an idea. *J Ment Sci* **108**: 1–25. [See this volume, Chap. 8, p. 146]

Hare EH. (1982) Was insanity on the increase? *Br J Psychiatry* **142**: 439–455. [See this volume, Chap. 5, p. 88]

Hun ER. (1870) Haematoma auris. *Am J Insanity* **27**: 13–28.

Jacobowsky B. (1965) General paralysis and civilization. *Acta Psychiatr Scand* **41**: 267–273.

Johnson EM. (1913) Note on a case of pellagra. *Lancet* **2**: 1114.

Leigh D. (1952) Pellagra and the nutritional neuropathies: a neuro-pathological review. *J Ment Sci* **98**: 130–142.

Martin J. (1972) The conquest of general paralysis. *BMJ* **3**: 159–160.

Maudsley H. (1867) *The Physiology and Pathology of the Mind*. Macmillan: London, pp 349, 360.

McCowan PK. (1924) Pellagra. A report of 4 cases. *J Ment Sci* **70**: 410–422.

McDowall J. (1878) *J Ment Sci* **24**: 328–333.

Mickle WJ. (1896) Haematoma auris. *J Ment Sci* **42**: 888.

Mitchell RB. (1892) Asylum reports. *J Ment Sci* **38**: 289.

Morison A. (1840) *The Physiognomy of Mental Diseases* (2nd edn, no publisher): London.

Parfitt DN. (1939) Pellagra in recent psychoses. *J Ment Sci* **82**: 440–444.

Peacock TB. (1863) Notes on hospitals in northern Italy and on pellagra. *Medico-chirurgical Review* **31**: 210–224.

Phillimore WP. (1877) Post-mortem examinations in lunatic asylums. *BMJ* **2**: 908–909.

Phillimore WP. (1878) Erysipelas in county asylums. *J Ment Sci* **24**: 506–508.

Pieterson JFC. (1892) In: Tuke DH. *Dictionary of Psychological Medicine*. Churchill: London, p. 561.

Robertson WF. (1896) On morbid changes in the ear-cartilages, with special reference to the pathology of haematoma auris. *Edinburgh Hospital Reports* **4**: 407–422.

Roe D. (1973) *A Plague of Corn: The Social History of Pellagra*. Cornell University Press: London.

Sambon LW and Chalmers AJ. (1912) Pellagra in the British Isles. *BMJ* **2**: 1093–1096.

Sankey WHO. (1870) Ribs fractured in asylums. *J Ment Sci* **16**: 135–142.

Schwalbe G. (1895) Zur Methodik statisticher Untersuchungen über die Ohrformen von Geisteskranken und Verbrechern. *Archiv für Psychiatrie* 633–644 (reviewed in *J Ment Sci* 1896; **42**: 401–402).

Smith WC. (1950) *Florence Nightingale*. Constable: London, p. 589.

Stannus HS and Gibson CR. (1934) Pellagra in Great Britain. *Quart J Med* **27**: 211–236.

Stiff WP. (1857) On simple sanguineous cyst of the ear in lunatics. *British and Foreign Medico-chirurgical Review* **21**: 222–227.

Stiff WP. (1863) Notes on haematoma of the external ear in the insane. *BMJ* **2**: 115.

Symes JG. (1858) Treatment of erysipelas. *J Ment Sci* **4**: 587–588.

Terris M. (1964) *Goldberger on Pellagra*. Louisiana State University Press: Baton Rouge.

Tuke DH. (1892) *Dictionary of Psychological Medicine*. Article on Haematoma auris. Churchill: London, p. 557.

White EB and Taylor AL. (1932) A case of pellagra at the Bristol Mental Hospitals. *J Ment Sci* **78**: 929–934.

Williams SWD. (1870) Ribs fractured in the insane. *Lancet* **2**: 323–324.

Winslow F. (1858) Presidential address. *J Ment Sci* **4**: 4–16.

8

Masturbatory insanity: the history of an idea

A hundred years ago it was generally believed by the medical profession, and particularly by alienists, that masturbation was an important and frequent cause of mental disorder. Today no one believes this; and the masturbatory hypothesis (as we may call it) has in all probability been finally abandoned. If we enquire into the history of this change we find, somewhat surprisingly, that medical references to the harmfulness of masturbation are vanishingly rare before the 18th century. For practical purposes, the whole history of the masturbatory hypothesis is contained within the last 250 years. This history is not one in which the present-day psychiatrist is apt to feel much pride. Yet it is worth studying, not only for its own sake (the history of psychiatric ideas is a much neglected subject), but also for the light it throws on the peculiar difficulty of refuting causal hypotheses in psychiatry. The aim of the present essay is, first, to give a short history of the idea that masturbation is an important cause of mental disorder and, second, to examine some of the reasons for the rise and fall of this idea and why it persisted for so long.[1]

The 18th century

Men have no doubt always been aware that frequent repetition of the sexual act is often followed by a feeling of lethargy; and from the time of Hippocrates, physicians have recorded their belief that over-indulgence in sexual activity is harmful to health. This was still the authoritative medical view at the start of the 18th century. Boerhaave, for example, in his *Institutes of Medicine* (1708) says, "The semen discharged too lavishly occasions a weariness, weakness, indisposition of motion, convulsions, leanness, dryness, heats and pains in the membranes of the brain, with a dulness of the senses, more especially of the sight, a *tabes dorsalis*, foolishness and disorders of the like kind." However, none of the classical writers appears to make specific reference to the ill-effects of masturbation; and from the absence of such

---

[1] As is indicated by the innumerable references in the literature of the past two centuries, the effect of masturbation on health is a subject on which almost every medical writer has felt competent to express an opinion. Of these references, I do not pretend to have studied more than a fraction. On the other hand, there seem to be relatively few accounts that deal with the historical aspects of the subject and none at all that deals specifically with the history of masturbation in relation to mental disorder. My most useful sources of general reference and criticism have been Christian (1881), Ellis (1936), Spitz (1952) and Kinsey *et al.* (1948, 1953), but I have as far as practicable consulted the appropriate originals. There are several much quoted books that I have been unable to consult; these include Pouillet's second treatise (1883) and Rohleder's *Die Masturbation* (1899).

passages[2] we may reasonably assume that, although masturbation was perhaps included in the terms 'sexual activity' and 'loss of semen', yet there was no general belief before the 18th century that masturbation was specifically harmful to health or that it was more harmful than an equivalent indulgence in sexual intercourse.

We can scarcely imagine a sudden change in the climate of opinion, yet all writers on the subject are agreed that the medical dangers of masturbation first became widely popularized throughout Europe as the result of the publication in London, early in the 18th century, of a book entitled *Onania, or the Heinous Sin of Self-Pollution*.[3] There is some reason to think that its anonymous author was a clergyman turned quack. Certainly he was not a reputable physician. His book is more concerned with the sin than the harm of masturbation; his medical knowledge is slight and shaky; and he advertises a secret remedy, efficacious not only against the evils of masturbation but against impotence and sterility as well, at half a sovereign a box. It would be superfluous to enumerate the very varied bodily diseases which, according to this author, await the masturbator; among the 'spiritual' consequences of masturbation he notes "the troubles and agonies of a wounded conscience", the vapours, and "lying, forswearing, perhaps murder". Although masturbators "sometimes fall into a slight madness", serious mental disorders are surprisingly absent from his catalogue of woes, but we find here what must be one of the earliest statements of the view so widely held throughout the 19th century that masturbation (as opposed to sexual intercourse) is a common cause of epilepsy. The assertions of the *Onania* did not go unchallenged[4] but that the book was very widely read we may presume from the fact that it had reached its 15th edition by 1730 and, at the time when Voltaire was writing

---

[2] The well-read Tissot could find nothing on the subject, and he is reduced (1766, p. 4) to allowing his readers to suppose that Hippocrates, Celsus and Actius, in referring to the dire effects of the abuse of amorous pleasure, included masturbation as one of the forms of abuse; but there is no positive evidence at all for this. Celsus (*De Medicina*, Bk. VII, Chap. 25) may be referring to masturbation when he says, "Some have made a practice of infibulating boys, sometimes on account of their health"; but he adds that for this purpose the operation "is more frequently needless than necessary" (Grieves, 1756).

[3] This at least is the title of the 4th edition (undated, but usually assigned to the year 1726), which is the earliest edition still generally available. The identity of the author and the year of first publication have been the subject of some controversy. Tissot (1766, p. 20) says, though without giving any reasons, that "Dr Bekkers at London must necessarily be the author". I cannot discover any more about this Dr Bekkers but from internal evidence and in the opinion of a contemporary critic ('Philo-Castitatus'), the author of the *Onania* was probably not a medical man. Pouillet (1876, p. 4) attributed the work to the German Boerner; but, as Christian (1881) supposes, Boerner was probably only its German translator. Several writers (for example Kinsey *et al.*, 1953) refer to the author as Crouch but it is clear from the 15th edition (1730, p. 46) that Mr Crouch was only the bookseller who undertook to forward readers' letters to the author.

As to the date of the 1st edition, we know it must have been before 1723, for in that year 'Philo-Castitatus' published his criticism of the *Onania*, in which he refers to it as "a book which has so long made so much noise in the world". In the 4th edition of the *Onania* there are reproduced letters received by the author from grateful or perplexed readers of earlier editions; and the earliest of these letters is dated 5.6.1717 (p. 66). We may conclude that the 1st edition was published shortly before this date, i.e. probably in 1716 or early in 1717.

[4] The 'extreme' views of the *Onania*, viz. that masturbation is a universal practice in both sexes and that it is more harmful than sexual intercourse, were challenged in the *Onania Examined and Detected; or the Ignorance, Error, Impertinence and Contradiction of a Book call'd Onania, Discovered and Exposed* (1723). Its author, who wrote under the pseudonym 'Philo-Castitatus', claimed to be, and probably was, a medical man. His book may have had a temporary restraining effect, but later it was forgotten. I have not found a single reference to it and it is not mentioned in the Catalogue of the Surgeon General of the United States Navy (1889, 1905). There is a copy in the library of the Royal Society of Medicine, London.

about onanism in his *Dictionnaire Philosophique* (1784), it was in its 80th edition (though, as Voltaire suggests, this high figure might represent only a bookseller's method of enticing new readers). Moreover, the use of the word 'onanism', which the author of the *Onania* was first to use as synonymous with the terms 'masturbation' and 'self-abuse', became widespread and indeed ousted the older terms during the next century and a half, in spite of the fact that Onan's sin had nothing to do with masturbation.[5] Nevertheless, reputable English physicians did not refer to the book, and it seems probable that the *Onania* would now be forgotten but for the fact that its name and its assertions were both adopted by the celebrated Swiss physician, Tissot.

Coming from an unimpeachable medical authority, Tissot's book, *Onania, or a Treatise upon the Disorders produced by Masturbation*, first published at Lausanne in 1758, had a profound effect on medical thought. Schwartz (1815), who agreed with it, said it "made a tremendous sensation", as also did the anti-clerical Lallemand (1838, p. 313), who disapproved of its exaggerations. The scholarly Christian (1881), who thought it all rubbish, observes that it went through "innumerable" reprintings and adds, "we are hard put to explain the prodigious influence of this work not only on the public but still more on the physicians of his time". Havelock Ellis (1901) says that this book "raised masturbation to the position of a colossal bogey", and accuses Tissot of combining his reputation as a physician with the fanaticism of a devout believer. Briefly, Tissot's teachings were that the author of the English *Onania* is right and that sexual excess of all types, but masturbation in particular, can cause a whole host of serious disorders both bodily and mental. Bodily illnesses result from loss of semen, which occasions general debility and so opens the way to consumption,[6] deterioration of eyesight, disorders of digestion, impotence and so on. In both sexes, however, the more serious effects are on the nervous system and this is due to the sexual act causing an increased flow of blood to the brain. "This increase of blood explains how these excesses produce insanity. The quantity of blood distending the nerves weakens them; and they are less able to resist impressions, whereby they are enfeebled" (1766, p. 61).

---

[5] In his preface, the author of the *Onania* says he has decided to use the term "onania" to refer to self-pollution in both sexes "because I cannot think of any other word which would so well put the reader in mind both of the sin and its punishment at once, as this". There is some evidence that the words 'onanism' and 'onanist' were already in use at this date, but all authorities are agreed that the author of the *Onania* was the first to give these words their modern sense. In medical literature, the use of 'onanism' was generally preferred to that of 'masturbation' until towards the end of the 19th century.

There is little doubt that, etymologically, 'onanism' is a bad substitute for 'masturbation'. From the social point of view Onan's sin was his refusal to comply with the Hebrew custom of the levirate (see Jeffreys, 1951); and clerical and medical writers are in general agreement that the physiological aspect of the sin was coitus interruptus. Onan's punishment was, of course, death – "the thing which he did displeased the Lord; wherefore he slew him" (Genesis, 38: 9).

We may note in passing that the word 'masturbation' occurs in the *Onania* of 1726 (for example on p. 18), although the Oxford English Dictionary does not mention its appearance in English literature before 1766 (when Hume's translation of Tissot's book was published). Eighteenth-century medical writers were in no doubt that the word was a corruption – *via* 'mastupration' (used by Burton, 1621) – of 'manustupration' or 'manual stupration' (Latin, *stuprare*, to defile); but according to the OED the origin of the word 'masturbation' is obscure, its variants being only etymologizing forms.

[6] The general quality of Tissot's style and reasoning may be gathered from a typical case history: "Whilst I was studying philosophy at Geneva, a time which will be ever dear to me the rest of my days, one of my fellow-students had arrived at such a horrid pitch in the practice of these abominations (i.e. masturbation) that he was incapable of abstaining from them, even at the time of his receiving his lessons: he did not long await his chastisement; he died miserably of consumption at the end of two years" (p. 77).

Eight reasons are given why masturbation is more pernicious than excesses committed with women, the last reason being "the shame and shocking remorse" which must follow masturbation "when illness has opened the criminal's eyes to his crimes and dangers". "Although exhausted by perpetual fatigue, they (masturbators) are seized with all the disorders incident to the brain, melancholy, catalepsy, imbecility, loss of sensation, weakness of the nervous system and a variety of similar disorders" (p. 75). Like so many later physicians, Tissot was incapable of dealing dispassionately with his subject. His book abounds in moral censure; the "flagrant crime" of masturbation reduces its victim to a state "which more justly entitles him to the contempt than pity of his fellow creatures" (p. 76); and his punishment by disease in this world is only a prelude to his punishment by eternal fire in the next (p. 152).

Between the publication of the English *Onania* in about 1716 and that of Tissot's book in 1758, there appear to be very few medical references on the effects of masturbation[7] and it is not until after the appearance of Tissot's book that writings about masturbation become numerous (see the references given by Fournier and Régis, 1819). We may accept Lallemand's view (1838, p. 313) that these later 18th century works did no more than reiterate the opinions of Tissot; but from their very number and from the whole tone of the early 19th century writings (see below), we may reasonably conclude that by the end of the 18th century the masturbatory hypothesis was widely accepted throughout Europe and America. The Church had always taught the sinfulness of masturbation; its harmfulness was now asserted by a considerable, perhaps a major, part of the medical profession; and if a sceptic was unmoved by these two sources of authority, he might yet tremble to read the strictures of Voltaire and Rousseau on the subject.[8]

"Insanity ex Onania"

The vague and all-embracing doctrines of Stahl and John Brown, and later of Broussais, provided a climate of opinion in which the masturbatory hypothesis could be applied with equal facility to every kind of bodily and mental disorder. But by the beginning of the 19th century the idea that masturbation could cause specific structural disease must have come to appear fanciful when laid alongside the

---

[7] According to Tissot (p. 14), the English physician Lewis took a serious view of the effects of masturbation in his book, *A Practical Essay upon the Tabes Dorsalis* (3rd edn, 1749). Tissot quotes Lewis as saying, "All the ills that are occasioned by excesses with women, more quickly follow in youth the abominable practice of seminal pollution, and it would be difficult to paint in colours so glaring as they merit the practice to which youths devote themselves, without being acquainted with the enormity of the crime and all the ills which are its physical consequences. The soul is sensible to all bodily disorders but particularly to those which arise from this cause". I have been unable to find a copy of Lewis' book.

[8] Voltaire (1784) accepted the views of the English 'Onania' and of Tissot on the effects of onanism, which he refers to as "a shameful and disastrous habit". Observing that Tissot also quotes cases of illness due to sexual continence, he asks, "What then ought we to do with the precious liquor that nature has made for the propagation of the species? Released incautiously, it may kill you; retained, it may also kill you". He concludes that, in healthy people, both masturbation and rash vows of continence are a sacrilege against the Creator.

Rousseau warns against a too youthful gratification of sexual desires, but if Emile's temperament demands an outlet then "je t'arracherai plus aisément aux femmes qu'à toi" (*Emile*, 1762, Book IV).

anatomical and pathological observations of such men as Morgagni, the Hunters and Laennec. Whether for this reason or not, we find that the emphasis on masturbation as a cause of bodily disease gradually fades out during the early decades of the 19th century.[9] The new attitude is clearly seen in the three-volume work, *Involuntary Seminal Losses*, by Claude-François Lallemand (1842), Professor of Medicine at Montpellier. Lallemand taught that all discharge of semen was weakening to the body and therefore dangerous to health, but he held that masturbation was a relatively unimportant cause of such discharge when compared with local inflammation, gonorrhoea and rectal disorders (Vol. 3, p. 200). Although not doubting that seminal loss may lead to mental disturbances of all sorts, he denies that dorsal consumption or indeed any other disease associated with pathological change can be directly due to this cause. "All observers agree", he says, "that mental illness is very commonly provoked by self-abuse or venereal excess" (p. 198); but "the symptoms produced by abuse, by excess or by involuntary pollutions are purely nervous; they do not call for any of the treatments applicable to organs which are functioning pathologically" (p. 215). Lallemand believed that masturbation was a menace to the future of civilization (p. 479) but he does not lard his prose with moral epithets and he reasonably restricts the consequences of masturbation to those nervous disorders of unknown aetiology. His approach is altogether more sensible and objective than that of Tissot, and the ridicule in which his work was often held towards the end of the century was to a large extent undeserved.

Thus from the early 19th century, medical interest in the effects of masturbation becomes increasingly confined to the realm of mental and nervous disorders, and the views of those medical men who made a special study of these disorders – the alienists – assume a greater importance in our history. However, when we examine the writings of the early alienists we do not immediately find any reference to masturbation as a cause of insanity. It is impossible to suppose that they were unaware of the hypothesis, but whether their silence was due to disbelief or to their sense of decorum we do not know.[10] Pinel does not mention masturbation in the first edition of his *Traité* (1801), and although he discusses the subject in the second edition (1809, Secs. 79, 81) he does not state or imply that masturbation may be the cause of mental disorder.[11] The earliest definite statement by an alienist that I have been able to find is in the

---

[9] I have found only a few exceptions to this rule in the English literature. The surgeon Allnatt (1843) wrote confidently to the *Lancet* of a case of testicular atrophy due to excessive masturbation; Hagenbach (1879) supposed that masturbation was "in some way" the cause of many urethral strictures; Stanley Hall (1904) thought that Basedow's disease was "perhaps" among the consequences of masturbation. Bloch (1908, p. 424) quotes H. Cohn as having "proved by investigations that the eye suffers manifold injuries" from this habit.

[10] Among English authors it was probably for the latter reason. Many of them wrote for the general public and would not wish to shock their readers. I have not found any reference to masturbation in the principal works of Harper, Fawcett, Haslam, Arnold, Black, Crowther, Hallaran or Knight. Even as late as 1839, Sir William Ellis, in his *Treatise on Insanity*, felt it necessary to apologize for introducing "this painful subject", the details of which, being "not exactly suited to the eye of the general reader", he relegates to an appendix.

[11] The habit of onanism, says Pinel, is common in states of mania, and usually disappears during convalescence; but "the condition may become so ingrained that some patients fall into a stupid and fatuous state or into extreme emaciation and a true consumption".

Medical Inquiries and Observations upon Diseases of the Mind by Benjamin Rush (1812), Professor of Medicine at Philadelphia. In this, the first textbook of psychiatry by an American, Rush mentions onanism as among the causes which induce madness. "Four cases of madness occurred, in my practice, from this cause between the years 1804 and 1807. It is induced more frequently by this cause in young men than is commonly supposed by parents and physicians." Four cases in as many years does not sound too serious, but "the morbid effects of intemperance in sexual intercourse with women are feeble and of a transient nature compared with the train of physical and moral evils which this solitary vice fixes upon the body and mind" (p. 33), and onanism (excessive or not) "produces seminal weakness, impotence, dysury, tabes dorsalis, pulmonary consumption, dyspepsia, dimness of sight, vertigo, epilepsy, hypochondriasis, loss of memory, manalgia, fatuity and death" (p. 347).

It was a melancholy fact, in the opinion of Havelock Ellis, that the great Esquirol gave his authority to the belief that masturbation caused insanity. Yet Esquirol only affirmed what was already very generally believed. In 1816 he wrote, "Masturbation is recognized in all countries as a common cause of insanity"; and in 1822, "onanism is a grave symptom in mania; unless it stops at once it is an insurmountable obstacle to cure. By lowering the powers of resistance it reduces the patients to a state of stupidity, to phthisis, marasmus and death".[12] These views are repeated and extended in his textbook, *Des Maladies Mentales* (1838): "it (masturbation) may be a forerunner of mania, of dementia and even of senile dementia; it leads to melancholy and suicide; its consequences are more serious in men than in women; it is a grave obstacle to cure in those of the insane who frequently resort to it during their illness" (I, p. 68). He also asserts that onanism predisposes to epilepsy and may be its exciting cause, even in infancy (I, p. 300). Esquirol did not elaborate any theory about how masturbation acts as a cause of insanity, but contented himself with the brief observation that its effect is similar to the abuse of alcoholic drinks – "these two exhaust the faculties and lead to apathy and hopelessness" (I, p. 591).

Some of Esquirol's ablest pupils (Calmeil and Georget, for example) do not appear to mention masturbation in their books, and it may be that their silence represents a respectful disagreement with their teacher's opinions. In Britain, however, Esquirol's views were probably decisive. The first reference to masturbation by a British alienist that I can discover is that of Burrows (1828, p. 96) who, in the middle of a learned and critical discussion on the physical causes of insanity, inserts a single paragraph on the subject of masturbation, which begins, "The lamentable vice of masturbation is a frequent and formidable cause of insanity"; but which ends with the observation that, according to Pinel, masturbation is sometimes the result rather than the cause of the disorder. Prichard (1835) says (and it is his only observation on the subject), "Sensual vices are frequently causes of insanity, as the tables of M. Esquirol sufficiently

---

[12] Reference is often made to Esquirol's remark that insanity associated with paralysis is incurable. We do not hear so much of his similar remark about insanity complicated by masturbation. The first observation was true if, as seems certain, it referred to cases of dementia paralytica; and if, as seems reasonable, the second observation referred principally to cases of hebephrenic schizophrenia, then this also was true in the main.

illustrate." A few years later (1839), Sir William Ellis, then Superintendent of Hanwell Asylum, takes the extreme view that "by far the most frequent cause of fatuity is debility of the brain and nervous system . . . in consequence of the pernicious habit of masturbation" (p. 336). But unlike Tissot, who thought masturbation caused madness by congestion of the brain, Ellis believed the damage was due to the cerebrum being deprived of its proper share of blood, for during the act of masturbation this blood was diverted to an unusual degree through other portions of the body. Early 19th-century British views on the masturbatory hypothesis are summed up in the article on 'Insanity' in Copland's *Dictionary of Practical Medicine* (1844). Here the general opinion is expressed that "whatever greatly exhausts organic nervous power both predisposes to, and directly occasions, insanity". The three great exhausting factors are masturbation, libertinism and intoxicating stimulants; but libertinism causes insanity "neither so frequently nor so certainly" as does masturbation.

German alienists began to write on masturbation during the 1830s.[13] With some exceptions (for example, Ellinger, 1845), they seem to have taken a much more moderate view than the French or English. Thus Flemming (1838) feared that his mild opinions might expose him to attack by moralists and found it advisable to say, "I hope I shall not be accused of having written an apologia for self-abuse; my object has simply been to question the correctness of the view that self-abuse is so very often the only or the principal cause of mental disorder." He admits that "against my view there can be brought the almost innumerable cases of insanity, of both sexes, which are collected in asylums under the rubric *ex onania*", but he adds – and this must be almost the earliest instance of rational argument on the subject – that, because so little is known of the aetiology of insanity, we are apt to suspect as causal what may in fact be only a consequence or a symptom of the illness.[14] Nevertheless, Flemming believed that masturbation led to "all those bodily and psychical manifestations which Tissot and his school have so excellently described", though these, he thought, developed only slowly into insanity "unless the onanism has been very excessive or unless there are other factors determining the evolution of the illness, such as suppressed haemorrhoidal flow".[15] The authoritative views of Griesinger (1861) are on the whole still milder than those of Flemming, though the somewhat muddled and contradictory

---

[13] Griesinger (1861, p. 173) refers to an article by Jacobi and Nasse in 1835 on 'Self-abuse as the Cause of Insanity', but I have been unable to consult this.

[14] In addition, Flemming gives three sound reasons why masturbation cannot be the cause of dementia paralytica; the disease is more common among married people (who presumably masturbate less than the unmarried); among unmarried people it is more common in the sexually promiscuous; and it does not occur in chronic asylum patients, who masturbate excessively. This reasoning should, we might think, have been sufficient to settle the matter. But years later the Belgian Guislain (1852), the Englishman Blandford (1871), the Frenchman Pouillet (1876) and the American Spitzka (1887) continued to assert the fact or maintain the probability that masturbation was a causal factor in dementia paralytica.

[15] The belief that insanity might be caused by suppression of the flow of menstruation, milk, epistaxis, etc., had an astonishing vitality. Not being a subject for moralizing, it did not claim the same attention as the masturbatory hypothesis, but it appears to have been at least as widely held. Even as late as 1904, Clouston discusses it and still believes it to be true "in some few cases" (p. 527). Its particular origin may perhaps be traced to Stahl's theories (1708) on *Vollblütigkeit*; but more generally it may be seen as a logical consequence of the belief that the discharge of coarse fluids from the body (by bleeding, purging, sweating, blistering and so on) was beneficial to health.

nature of his remarks suggests that even the clearest-sighted alienist of his time had difficulty in penetrating the mists of prevailing opinion. "Onanism", he says (p. 173), "is an important and frequent cause of insanity as of all other physical and moral degradation." But having offered this sop to Cerberus, he goes on to express his belief that by far the most harmful effects of masturbation are due to the shame and distress caused by inability to resist the desire; and he says further that the increase in sexual excitement often shown by patients at the beginning of insanity is a symptom and not a cause of the disease. A similar note of hesitancy may be seen in other Continental writers of the mid-19th century. Thus Guislain (1852) can say that "the habit of solitary vice gives rise to a host of evils" among which are hysterical attacks, asthma, epilepsy, melancholia, mania, suicide, dementia, and "above all dementia with paralysis"; yet in his own experience he could suspect masturbation as a cause of insanity in no more than three or four cases per year[16] and he observes that, although masturbation is certainly very common among asylum patients, yet "many of them contract the habit only after they become ill". Morel, in his *Traité des Maladies Mentales* (1860), takes much the same view. He thinks Ellis and Ellinger overstated the case, yet at the same time he feels it important to contradict the opinions of those who belittle the dangers of masturbation. He quotes Guislain with approval, adding that in the treatment of hysteria it is "extremely important" for the physician "to direct his attention to the vice of onanism"; but he also adds that it is not always easy to be sure who masturbates and who does not.

These incipient doubts and general softening of views which had occurred among Continental alienists by the mid-19th century were not yet paralleled in the English-speaking world. In Britain, partly perhaps from bigotry but more from acuteness of observation, the hypothesis that masturbation caused insanity was taken one stage

---

[16] Statistics on the frequency of insanity due to masturbation are sparsely scattered through the literature. As may be seen from the table below, the proportion of cases assigned to this cause ranged from 2–20%. Christian (1881) used this wide variation to sustain his argument that there was no such entity as masturbatory insanity, but a similar argument might be used to deny the existence of schizophrenia.

Author	Place	Type of case	Number due to masturbation	% Due to masturbation
Esquirol (1822)	Bicêtre	Mania due to physical causes:		
		Males	6 of 26	–
		Females	2 of 51	4.0
Esquirol (Prichard, 1835)	Charenton	Male admissions due to physical causes, 1826–1828	23 of 254	9.0
Jacobi (Prichard, 1835)	–	Melancholia	6 of 165	3.5
Ellinger (Guislain, 1852)	Wurtemburg	Males	83 of 383	22.0
Bucknill and Tuke (1874)	York Asylum	Males	15 of 603	2.5
Hagenbach (1879)	Illinois	Males	49 of 800	6.1
Burr (Spitzka, 1887)	Pontiac	Males	158 of 1474	10.7
Spitzka (1887)	Private practice	Males	41 of 362	11.3
		Females	8 of 401	2.0
Barrus (1896)	Middletown	Females	10 of 121	8.3

further before it finally collapsed towards the end of the century. This stage we must now examine.

Masturbatory insanity

Some of the earlier 19th century alienists thought that the insanity due to masturbation had certain characteristic features. Thus Esquirol (1838, I, p. 391) held that when insanity is caused by onanism or coitus it "had a bad prognosis and quickly passes into dementia". Ellis (1839), as we have seen, attributed most cases of 'fatuity' to this cause. In America, Luther Bell and Ray (1844) described the insanity of masturbation as a form of moral insanity, its particular features being "a tendency to dementia, loss of self-respect, a mischievous and dangerous disposition, and an irritable, depressed state of mind". Griesinger (1861) says, "the mental disorders which originate under the influence of onanism have no constant specific character, but in the majority of cases they betray themselves by profound dulness of sentiment and mental exhaustion, by hallucinations of hearing, by a religious character of the delusions, by a rapid transition to dementia and a consequent frequent incurability".

However, the first person to maintain that there was a particular and specific type of insanity due to masturbation was probably the Scottish physician David Skae. In his paper of 1868, Skae lays down the principle that mental disorders should be classified according to their natural history rather than by their associated symptoms. For example, a patient should be assigned to the group of puerperal mania or general paralysis according to the history and progress of the disease and irrespective of whether the symptoms are of dementia, monomania or melancholia. In such a classification, idiocy and epilepsy are the first two natural groups. "The *third* natural family I would assign to the *masturbators*. Although I designate this family by the cause only which originates the insanity, yet I think it cannot be denied that that vice produces a group of symptoms which are quite characteristic and easily recognized, and give to the cases a special natural history: the peculiar imbecility and shy habits of the very youthful victim; the suspicion and fear and dread and suicidal impulses and scared look and feeble body of the older offenders, passing gradually into Dementia or Fatuity." Later, in his Morisonian lectures (1874), Skae tells his audience that he thinks they can hardly fail to admit that he has made out a good case for there being a distinct type of 'insanity of masturbation'. But he has now broadened his concept and is somewhat less gloomy about the prognosis: "If these cases are put under proper care and treatment before the mind has become too impaired to exert self-control when reasoned with, they generally recover. But when dementia has begun to show itself in impaired memory and energy, silly vanity and self-satisfaction, the cases assume a very hopeless aspect with a tendency to gradually increasing dementia if the vice is persevered in."

Skae's views do not seem to have influenced the Continental outlook, but in Britain and America they were adopted by many of the most eminent specialists. They are repeated, for example, by Blandford (1871), by Bucknill and Tuke (1874) and by Clouston (1883). Clouston, however, was to change his opinion. In his Presidential

Address to the Medico-Psychological Association (1888) he asks the plain question, "Does the habit of masturbation cause dementia?"; he observes that although "no doubt in certain adolescent cases . . . constant masturbation tends strongly towards brain exhaustion and stupor and these conditions may end in dementia", yet dementia may occur without masturbation and excessive masturbation may not end in dementia; and he concludes that masturbation and dementia "cannot be put as cause and effect".[17]

This evolution from certainty to doubt and disbelief may be seen still more clearly in the writings of Maudsley. In 1867, discussing the effects of excessive sexual indulgence and of continued self-abuse, he says: "Nothing is more certain than that either of these causes will produce an enervation of nervous element which, if the exhausting vice be continued, passes by a further declension into degeneration and actual destruction thereof. The habit of self-abuse notably gives rise to a particular and disagreeable form of insanity, characterized by intense self-feeling and conceit, extreme perversion of feeling and corresponding derangement of thought, in the earlier stages, and later by failure of intelligence, nocturnal hallucinations, and suicidal or homicidal propensities." His article of 1868 is devoted entirely to "that kind of insanity which is brought on by self-abuse"; "the interest of these cases does not lie in what we can do for them by medical treatment, but in the characteristic features which they present, so that they form a natural *group* or family having certain definite characteristics".[18] Under the heading "Insanity of Self-abuse", these views are repeated in the first edition of Maudsley's *Pathology of Mind* (1879, p. 452), but there is now less moral censure and in other parts of the work (pp 276 and 280) he suggests that the precocious feelings which lead to self-abuse are commonly the result of an inherited trait. By 1895, when the second edition was published, Maudsley's views are further modified. The heading 'Insanity of self-abuse' now reads 'Insanity and self-abuse' (p. 399); "mental disorder due to self-abuse is not always to be distinguished from simple adolescent insanity, for the early symptoms of both are the same and are due to the processes of adolescence and not to the particular vice"; and even where there has been positive evidence of masturbation, one cannot be sure that masturbation is not really more a symptom than a cause.

On the American continent, the belief in a characteristic form of 'masturbatic insanity' was upheld notably by Spitzka, Professor of Medical Jurisprudence in New York. According to Spitzka (1887) the typical age of onset of masturbatic insanity is between 13 and 20 years; it is at least five times as common in males as in females because of the greater rarity of masturbation in females; in the majority of cases there is a rapid decline into agitated dementia, but where deterioration is less rapid

---

[17] The opinion expressed in the 1st edition of Clouston's Textbook (1883, p. 485), that "there is a form of mental disorder in which masturbation is the chief cause of the malady", is repeated unchanged in the 6th edition (1904). But we should regard this repetition as an oversight rather than a relapse.

[18] This article is not one on which admirers of Maudsley could wish to dwell, but it may profitably be read as a warning example of that besetting sin of psychiatrists – a tendency to confuse the rules of mental health with those of morality. In the life of the chronic masturbator, says Maudsley, "nothing can be so reasonably desired as the end of it", and "the sooner he sinks to his degraded rest, the better for himself and the better for the world, which is well rid of him".

"the obtrusive selfishness, cunning, deception, maliciousness and cruelty of such patients" is such that "the most kindhearted and philosophical alienist may find it impossible to reconcile himself to regarding them as anything else than repulsive eye-sores and a source of contamination to other patients, physically and morally". Although, compared with hebephrenia, this type of insanity shows more day-to-day variability and more mental ruin, yet in general "hebephrenia is very difficult to differentiate from true masturbational insanity".[19] Spitzka also discusses the question of whether a similar form of insanity could be caused by excessive sexual intercourse during adolescence, but concludes that this is improbable.

From such descriptions, from the case histories accompanying them and from the observations of later writers,[20] it is clear that the name masturbatory insanity stood for the same syndrome which later became known as the hebephrenic type of dementia praecox or of schizophrenia. Nor is it difficult, from our present standpoint, to see how this came about. Masturbation is most commonly and most frequently practised during adolescence and therefore most likely to be observed when mental disease insidiously deprives an adolescent of his normal social inhibitions. It is to Skae's credit that he recognized adolescent insanity as the last and most strongly defensible bastion of the general hypothesis that masturbation caused insanity; and had it not been for his unlucky choice of nomenclature he might be remembered today as having given one of the earliest descriptions of the syndrome which Hecker, in 1871, first designated 'hebephrenia'.[21]

The careful study of the supposed effects of masturbation had another consequence; it led to the delineation of a cluster of signs thought to be indicative of the masturbator. Youths who developed an insanity associated with masturbation were observed to have often displayed characteristic personality traits before they became frankly disordered,[22] and these traits were held to be the early effects of the habit of masturbation which, if it were continued long enough, would lead to their exaggeration into insanity. Thus Flemming (1838) says that masturbation at first causes a downcast or vacant appearance, pallor, easy blushing and so on, to be followed later by a tendency to solitariness, marked vacuity, loss of attention, and a frequent absorption in thought "as though brooding about something". Lallemand (1842, p. 133) emphasizes the cold and callous qualities of the masturbator: "He has no other interests; he loves no one; he is attached to no one; he shows no emotion

---

[19] On account of the moral reprobation associated with the one, but not with the other, of these diseases, differential diagnosis must have presented a problem of some delicacy.

[20] Kraepelin (1896), for example, referring to "that type of insanity which hitherto has been thought to be the particular result of onanism", says, "we see there without any difficulty the picture of dementia praecox, the insanity of adolescence" (p. 51).

[21] Unlike Hecker and unlike Kahlbaum (who in 1869 gave the name 'catatonia' to a syndrome which he believed was chiefly caused by prolonged and excessive masturbation), Skae made the mistake of giving his new syndrome an aetiological instead of a descriptive name. Asher (1959) has reminded us of the dangers of this mistake.

[22] This sequence of observations, from the type of insanity to the nature of the premorbid personality, might have been made in the reverse order. But I have been unable to find any descriptions in the 18th century writers of that cluster of traits which became accepted as indicating the early effects of masturbation.

before the grandeur of nature or the beauties of art; still less is he capable of any generous impulse or act of loyalty; he is dead to the call of his family, his country, or of humanity." When a patient of Allnatt's (1843) "entered the room with a timid and suspicious air and appeared to quail like an irresolute maniac when the eye was fixed steadily upon him", that surgeon was left in no doubt of the cause of his patient's complaint (and the patient, "on being directly charged with masturbating", immediately admitted it). Pouillet (1876), in his essay on onanism in females, held that although no single sign was pathognomic of masturbation, yet there were a number of signs which, taken together, "create a strong, even an almost certain, presumption of this vice, in spite of denials"; these signs included an unsteady and peevish disposition tending towards anger, an exaggerated timidity in the presence of parents and a surly attitude towards strangers, profound idleness, a tendency to lying and "finally, a certain aspect, a *je ne sais quoi*, easier to recognize than to express in words" (p. 25).

In this group of signs, by which the 19th century writers thought the masturbator could be detected, it is not difficult to recognize what we now call the schizoid constitution; and the observation that such signs were common in adolescents who later developed 'masturbatory insanity' was, we may fairly concede, a perfectly correct one.[23]

Masturbation and neurosis

During the last 15 years of the 19th century, there was a great decline in the belief that masturbation could cause insanity and epilepsy. The belief still lingered in the writings of some older psychiatrists: Clouston (1904) and Savage and Goodall (1907) in England, Stanley Hall (1904) in America, Bianchi (1906) in Italy, for example; but these were vestiges, and by the beginning of the 20th century the majority of writers had adopted the view of Kraepelin (1896) that insanity "is never caused by onanism". This decline, together with the renewed interest in the neuroses aroused by the writings of Beard, Charcot and Janet, raised into prominence the second aspect of the masturbatory hypothesis, the belief that masturbation was a common cause of neurotic disorders.

The change of emphasis is apparent in the later writings of Maudsley. By 1895, Maudsley had practically abandoned his earlier views on masturbatory insanity, but he is now of the opinion that there is another class of chronic disorders due to masturbation which "present certain tolerably distinctive features", these features being obsessional thoughts, compulsions, ruminations, *folie de doute* and phobias (pp 407, 413). Havelock Ellis (1901) summarizes (but does not analyse) the general state of opinion at the turn of the century. Masturbation as a cause of insanity is a subject which no longer claims serious attention, but authorities are divided on the importance of masturbation in neurasthenia. Its causal importance is emphasized by

---

[23] The belief that masturbation leads to characteristic personality traits persisted until quite recently. See, for example, the descriptions given by Yellowlees (1892), Stanley Hall (1904), Meagher (1924, 1936) and Stern (1930). Huhner's contribution (1944) – he lists separately for each sex the signs and symptoms of masturbation – is perhaps the last outlier of this range.

Krafft-Ebing, Freud, Erb and Rohleder; denied by Charcot and his school, by Gilles de la Tourette and by Binswanger, Ellis himself adopts what he considers to be a middle view: "We must steer clearly between the opposite errors of those, on the one hand, who assert that heredity is the sole cause of functional nervous disorders, and those, on the other hand, who consider that the incident that may call out the disorder is itself a sole sufficient cause" (p. 259). In the constitutionally disposed, however, masturbation may lead (says Ellis) not only to neurasthenia but to *ejaculatio praecox*, impotence and aversion to coitus – the latter helping to "furnish a soil on which the inverted impulse may develop" (p. 261). Krafft-Ebing, Moreau and Bloch were also among those who believed that masturbation might lead to homosexuality.

Many of the most prominent members of the psychoanalytic school held opinions similar to those of Ellis. Ernest Jones, for example, wrote in 1918 that "true neurasthenia . . . will be found to depend on excessive onanism or involuntary seminal emissions"; and "persistence of clitoris masturbation is one of the most important agents leading to (sexual) anaesthesia because it means fixation on the infantile, male form of sexuality". The views expressed by Freud himself in 1912 are recalled and affirmed by Stern (1930); and that these views were still taken very seriously between the wars is evident from the summaries of contemporary opinion presented by Menzies (1919) and Meagher (1924, 1936). The masturbatory hypothesis still finds a place in the psychiatric textbooks of the 1930s, though the bold assertions of earlier decades are now emasculated and become coupled with the opinion that the harmful effects of masturbation are not due to the act itself but to worry over exaggerated opinions of its consequences.[24]

By the irony of history, this view – that masturbation is harmful only if, from ignorance or misinformation, the patient worries about it – is all that now survives of the masturbatory hypothesis. Two centuries of indoctrination have taught the public a lesson which it can forget less quickly than can its teachers; and today the principal concern of medical writers on the subject is to persuade the public that its fears of the consequences of masturbation are groundless.

The prevention of masturbation

To the physician who accepted the truth of the masturbatory hypothesis, the prevention of masturbation was clearly a matter of importance. It was important in the

---

[24] See, for example, Henderson and Gillespie (1936) and Rosanoff (1938). In one of the few attempts (indeed, as far as my reading goes, the only real attempt) at a scientific study of the masturbatory hypothesis, Malamud and Palmer (1932) found masturbation to be apparently the most important cause of disorder in 22 of 500 patients consecutively admitted to the Iowa State Psychopathic Hospital. The majority of these 22 were 'misinformed' about the effects of masturbation and there was no definite temporal relation between the masturbation and the illness. The authors concluded that it was the mental conflict engendered by masturbation rather than the habit itself which led to the illness, and they believed this conclusion to be supported by the efficacy of psychotherapy directed towards readjusting the patient's ideas about masturbation. Yet the fact that 15 of the 22 patients suffered from depression must raise doubts about the validity even of this temperate conclusion, for the depressed patient is not only prone to blame himself for neglect of what he believes to be the rules of health, but also tends to recover from his illness whether treated by psychotherapy or not.

treatment of patients with mental disorder because of the belief (dating from Pinel and Esquirol) that the disorder would worsen if the patient continued to masturbate;[25] and it was also important as a straightforward measure of hygiene in children and adolescents.

The 18th century writers on masturbation concerned themselves mainly with the treatment of physical and neurotic ailments in adults. They seem to have taken the view that their patients would stop their bad habit once they were apprised of its dangers; or, if they did not stop, then they had only themselves to blame. At all events, we do not find any particular account of preventive measures other than a call to repentance and to abstinence. A simple regimen is prescribed, one which we should still agree is well suited to the needs of a neurasthenic patient or indeed to anyone anxious to lead a healthy life. Thus the author of the *Onania* (*c.* 1716) advises a spare and cooling diet, the avoidance of salt meat, "pretty much exercise (though not too violent)", and "proper medicines". Tissot (1766) is in the same vein and adds cold baths, fresh air, not too much sleep, and the avoidance of boredom.

But in the early 19th century, physicians became concerned with the prevention of masturbation by other means than moral exhortation. I cannot find that Esquirol discusses this, but medical methods of prevention must have been common in his day. Schwarz (1815, p. 31) says that the local application of camphor is recognized as the most effective anti-aphrodisiac and he also recommends the operation of infibulation.[26] Sir William Ellis (1839, p. 339) thought (strangely enough) that "tincture of cantharides is the most efficacious means of cure" but he mentions a surgeon of Paris who "informs me that he has discovered an effectual mechanical preventive".

By the second half of the 19th century the use of surgical and pharmacological methods of preventing masturbation was certainly widespread. The London surgeon, Baker Brown, in the belief that hysteria, epilepsy, and cognate disorders in the female were due to and maintained by masturbation, drew the rational but unfortunate conclusion that these disorders would be cured by clitoridectomy, an operation he introduced in 1858. But the results "were by no means satisfactory" and both the operation and its originator fell into disfavour during the next decade.[27] Alexander Robertson

---

[25] Although this particular belief was very widely held, it was not of course a necessary consequence of the masturbatory hypothesis, for masturbation may be conceived as inducing an insanity associated with irreversible changes. This possibility was recognized by Gowers (1881).

[26] Infibulation was the procedure of placing wires through the prepuce in such a manner as to prevent its retraction behind the glans penis. Celsus, who describes the operation in his *De Medicina*, says that its main use is where a person chooses, 'for the sake of decency', to have his glans covered (Bk. 7, Chap. 25). It was also performed in boys 'on account of their voices' (Grieves, 1756), presumably in the hope that the breaking of a chorister's voice would be delayed if he were prevented from masturbating.

[27] Isaac Baker Brown (1812–1873) achieved fame as an ovariotomist and was elected president of the Medical Society of London in 1865. He grew unduly enthusiastic about the benefits of clitoridectomy and was expelled from the Obstetric Society after the publication (in 1866) of his book on the subject. He defended himself on the grounds that it was "more honest to attempt a radical cure than to accept fees for an attendance confessedly useless"; but against this it was urged that, of his alleged cures, a very large number were not permanent. See a correspondence in the *Lancet* (1866) and his obituary notice in the *Medical Times and Gazette* (1873).

Clitoridectomy also had some vogue in America (for example, Eyer, 1894) and was particularly adopted by the disreputable school of 'orificial surgery', whose quackery is ridiculed by Meagher (1923).

(1869) reported that, in one American asylum, bromide of potassium had become the treatment of choice for patients who masturbated; the superintendent "had formerly tried the effect of a silver ring through the prepuce to prevent its retraction, but in their efforts to continue the vile practice it had been torn out".[28] Bucknill and Tuke (1874, p. 760), however, found potassium bromide of only temporary value because it soon led to weakness and emaciation; faradization of the spine, blistering of the prepuce, or "a constant attendant by day with mechanical restraint by night" were also only temporary in their effects. They regretfully concluded that no satisfactory means of prevention had yet been devised and they doubt whether more radical measures are appropriate: "if it could be supposed", they say, "that any great mind likely to be of use to the human race was in danger of being destroyed and lost through this habit, the question might fairly arise whether an effectual operation was justifiable; but those miserable helots of sensation who are the usual victims of this despicable vice are not worth the responsibility even of such a thought". Castration, ovariotomy and section of the pudendal nerves were certainly urged and sometimes performed,[29] but in any case, as Yellowlees (1892) noted, "sexual desires are not destroyed and their prurient indulgence will not be prevented" by these measures. The recognition that no method achieved lasting success led many who believed in the masturbatory hypothesis (Maudsley, Blandford and Clouston, for example) to condemn all forms of local interference.

Spitz (1952) has enlarged upon the "extremely cruel persecution of the masturbator" which developed in the mid-19th century and which continued, though with decreasing severity, until the outbreak of the second world war. But this is a wrong, or at least a sentimental, view. Treatments are justified not by their harmlessness but by their efficacy; and only when we are sure that there is no appreciable difference in the efficacy – or inefficacy – of two treatments, should we necessarily be ready to adopt the shorter, safer and less painful one. A believer in the truth of the masturbatory hypothesis was bound to take very serious steps to prevent masturbation, and the development of anaesthesia and the increased safety of surgical operations in the second half of the 19th century permitted him a wider range of experiment than had hitherto been available. With radical procedures such as clitoridectomy or

---

[28] In Scotland, however, Yellowlees was using silver wire with success in 1876. He had completed 12 cases and "the sensation among the patients themselves was extraordinary". He was struck with the conscience-stricken way in which they submitted to the operation upon their penises. He meant to try it on a large scale and go on wiring all masturbators. In 1892 he still considered wiring the best method of prevention.

[29] Burrows (1828, p. 279) observes that castration had been advised as a cure for insanity on the grounds that violent sexual irritation has been the cause; "but", he continues, "how much afflicting instances are there of self-emasculation and yet the mental delusion which impelled it has remained the same!" This sound argument did not have the decisive influence it should have had, and in 1891 Hutchinson, a president of the Royal College of Surgeons, was still able to avow his conviction "that measures more radical than circumcision would, if public opinion permitted their adoption, be a true kindness to many patients of both sexes".

Spratling (1895) considered that for the treatment of masturbation among insane males "complete section of the dorsal nerves of the penis is a rational procedure but rather too radical for constant routine practice"; for females, however, "nothing short of ovariotomy will be found to deserve even the term palliative". Clark and Clark (1899) cut the pudendal nerves in an insane man of 48 so as to prevent sensation and erection of the penis, and "the mental result in this case justified the operation".

castration, it was quickly realized that the results were not commensurate with the damage and suffering caused by the treatment. Nor can it be urged that the search for lesser (though still harsh) measures of prevention should have been dropped as soon as it was evident that those tried were without benefit to the patient; for these measures did not effectively prevent masturbation and so their failure did not necessarily indicate that the masturbatory hypothesis was untrue. The only moral we can draw properly is that where an apparently rational method of treatment proves both inconvenient and of uncertain value, we should return to a closer consideration of the validity of the hypothesis on which it is based.

The rise of the masturbatory hypothesis

It is easy to understand why the masturbatory hypothesis (that is, the idea that masturbation is a cause of mental disorder) should have been proposed. Many mentally disordered patients masturbate openly and frequently, whereas in sane persons the act of masturbation is rarely observed. There is an obvious association between masturbation and mental disorder and, as Flemming (1838) pointed out, we tend to suppose as causal of a disease any associated activity which is itself thought to be harmful.

When we enquire why the masturbatory hypothesis should first have become widely accepted towards the end of the 18th century, we can distinguish a number of probable reasons. Firstly, the old ideas that madness was due to possession by evil spirits or to witchcraft had by then fallen into disrepute (in England, the penal laws against witchcraft were repealed in 1736), and no satisfactory hypothesis had replaced them. Even the belief that lunatics were affected by the moon was effectively discredited by Pinel and Haslam.[30] Secondly, the great advances in pathological anatomy made during the 18th century led to increased interest in the effect of bodily disturbances on the mind, and prepared the way for the acceptance of a physical theory of the cause of madness.[31] Thirdly, asylums for the insane became common in Europe only towards the end of the 18th century, and certainly it was under the conditions of asylum care that the association between masturbation and insanity would be most clearly manifested.

We are on less sure ground when we come to consider why medical interest in masturbation first arose in the early 18th century. The problem has intrigued many

---

[30] "To ascertain how far this opinion (that lunatics are affected by the moon) was founded in fact, I kept, during more than 2 years, an exact register, but without finding in any instance that the aberration of the human intellect corresponded with, or was influenced by, the vicissitudes of this luminary" (Haslam, 1809, p. 216).

[31] In his book, *A New System of the Spleen, Vapours and Hypochondriack Melancholy* (1729), Nicholas Robinson attributes all "disorders of the fancy" to an "irregular motion of the nerves", and asserts that these ailments should be treated by mechanical means and drugs rather than by discussion and advice. One of his patients, a sufferer from the spleen, believed himself a hobby horse and "all the philosophy I was master of could not dispossess him of this conceit; 'till, by the application of generous medicines, I restor'd the disconcerted nerves to their regular motions and, by this means, gave him a sight of his error". Here, perhaps, we see an early example of the conflict between the organic and the psychological approach to the therapy of mental disorders.

writers, and one of the commonest suggestions is that the practice of masturbation must formerly have been rare and only become widespread during the late 17th century. To Lallemand (1842, p. 477), this was evident from the fact that "the ancients did not mention this scourge and it is only during the last century that physicians have been thoroughly concerned with it"; and he attributes the increased prevalence of masturbation "to the absence of regular and vigorous physical exercise, to the greater strictness of morals, to the increase of contagious disease, etc.". Havelock Ellis (1901, p. 277) also argued that masturbation must have been comparatively rare in classical times because of the freer scope for heterosexual and homosexual activities. Christian (1881) disagreed with this view on the rather inadequate grounds that the 18th century was no more vicious an age than the 15th and 16th centuries (when the vices most inveighed against were sodomy and bestiality); and that masturbation must always have been common because sexual depravity has always been common. We are unlikely to reach any certainty in this matter, but when we bear in mind these considerations: that very few, if any, medical writers before the 18th century refer to masturbation as harmful;[32] that the fear of venereal disease must, after the 15th century, have driven many people to seek sexual relief by other means than sexual intercourse; that the rise of Puritanism in England and of the bourgoisie in France was accompanied by an increased moral strictness; and that there are many countries today where masturbation is uncommon and is certainly not regarded as harmful;[33] then it is not unreasonable to accept the probability that the prevalence of masturbation increased markedly in Europe during the 17th and 18th centuries. Spitz (1952) has attributed the shift from religious to secular interest in masturbation to the spread of Protestantism and to the Protestant's difficulty in distinguishing a venial from a mortal sin; but this would scarcely account for the fact that by the end of the 18th century the consequences of masturbation were as much feared by the Catholic as by the Protestant physicians of Europe.

Its fall

Belief in the idea that masturbation could cause insanity declined rapidly during the years 1885–1900. It was replaced by the belief that masturbation could cause neurotic disorders, and this in turn declined over the next 40 years. The reasons for these periods of decline are not discernible in any straightforward way, for, as Malamud and Palmer (1932) pointed out and as is evident from Havelock Ellis' discussion (1901), most authorities were content to state opinions rather than facts, and I have not been able to find any critical assessment of the evidence for and against the

---

[32] Galen (quoted by Christian, 1881) records that Diogenes and many of his contemporaries used to masturbate in public. They did this, however, "not from pleasure but that they might be preserved from harm". Their belief that sexual intercourse was harmful evidently did not extent to masturbation.

[33] Havelock Ellis (1901) observes that Mohammedan theologians regard masturbation as a Christian vice and that there is little reprobation against masturbation in Islam. I am assured by physicians who know the countries well that masturbation is uncommon and uncensored in rural Ghana and in Ceylon.

masturbatory hypothesis at a particular time. From a study of the literature, however, I suggest that the fall of the masturbatory hypothesis may be attributed to four general reasons. These reasons were sufficient to erode both the 19th century view that masturbation caused insanity and the 20th century view that it caused neurosis; but their effect was more obvious on the former view and this would account for the fact that it succumbed the more rapidly.

The first reason, and the one which had the most effect during the 19th century, sprang from the argument that masturbation might be a symptom rather than a cause of mental disorder. This possibility was always recognized, but it did not necessarily lead to doubt or to a closer examination of the problem. The phrenologist Gall, for example, was content to state in his *Fonctions du Cerveau* (1825) that mental weakness is the cause and not the result of excessive masturbation. With equal but opposite dogmatism, many writers asserted that masturbation was often the result and not the cause. Thus Griesinger (1861, p. 173) says that at the beginning of insanity, patients often show an increase in the sexual instinct and this is due to the mental disease; and Sankey, in the first edition of his *Lectures on Mental Diseases* (1866), makes a similar statement – "onanism is often supposed to be the cause of the pale and emaciated looks and feeble health of a patient whereas in some at least the irritability and debility has induced the onanism". In his second edition (1884) however, Sankey puts the case objectively: "that the habit of masturbation is found to a great degree in the insane cannot be denied . . . but it leaves the question of masturbation as a cause of insanity entirely unproved".

The attempt to distinguish cases of insanity caused by masturbation from those in which masturbation was merely a symptom led Skae and his followers to delineate the syndrome of 'masturbatory insanity'. But still closer investigation showed that the distinction between masturbatory insanity and hebephrenia (or adolescent insanity) was an artificial one, and that the same clinical picture might or might not be accompanied by masturbation. As we have seen, this was the view that Clouston had reached by 1888, and Kraepelin summed up the situation when he said (1896), "there are many confirmed onanists who never become hebephrenic and *vice versa* there are hebephrenics, especially females, who seldom or never masturbate in spite of strong sexual excitement". Precisely the same argument was later used (for example by Stekel, 1951) to maintain that masturbation could not be the cause of neurosis.

There was another aspect of the cause-*versus*-symptom controversy. From the time of Pinel the belief prevailed that where insanity was associated with masturbation the disorder would become more severe if the patient continued to masturbate and would remit or be ameliorated if he ceased to do so. The strength of this belief is reflected in the vigorous and often drastic measures proposed during the 19th century for the prevention of masturbation among the insane. But increasingly careful observation would have failed to confirm this postulated co-variance and, although I can find no references to such observations in the 19th century, yet Bleuler was presumably voicing a widespread opinion when he wrote on the subject in 1911. "It is certainly true", he says, "that most of our patients masturbate or have masturbated. However, if one looks at the matter a little more closely, one can find no relationship with the course of the disease. Very excessive masturbators, who masturbate almost continuously, can and do recover from their acute episodes or may remain on the same level of deterioration for years."

The second, and ultimately the most decisive, reason sprang from the researches which showed that masturbation was a very common habit among healthy people. The author of the *Onania* (*c.* 1717) had blandly stated that masturbation was a universal practice in both sexes, a bare assertion which others (for example Philo-Castitatus) had as blandly denied. What is curious, however, is the fact that until late in the 19th century no writer seems to have asked the question, How prevalent is masturbation in the community? – and very few seem to have appreciated that the answer to this question might have a bearing on the validity of the masturbatory hypothesis.[34] One of the earliest to appreciate it was Sir James Paget (1879) who, in his lecture on *Sexual Hypochondriasis*, delivered in 1870, remarked on the numbers of sensualists and drunkards who do not go mad and concluded that "to determine the influence of excesses in producing insanity you must count not only the insane, but the sane who have committed excesses and retained their mental power". The argument was reiterated by Sankey (1884): masturbation, he says, "is a habit of which no one can say when it exists nor in whom it exists; and whether it is more common among one class than another is an undiscovered fact: we have therefore no data on which to make a comparison or conclusion".

We must presume it was statements like these which led to studies on the prevalence of masturbation in normal people. In 1884, Dukes, physician to Rugby School, stated that in his experience 90–95% of boarding-school boys masturbated. Moraglia (1897) found that 60% of lower-class Italian women admitted masturbation. Later surveys in Europe and North America, made with increasing thoroughness (and, we may suspect, with increasing frankness from the participants), reached essentially similar conclusions.[35] Such findings did not, however, deal an immediate death-blow to the masturbatory hypothesis. The additional postulates were made that masturbation was only dangerous in persons of weak constitution or only when practised to excess, and these sufficed to bolster for several decades the view that masturbation could cause neurotic disturbances. However, it seems gradually to have become accepted that many normal persons masturbated to excess; that there was anyhow no satisfactory definition of 'excess'; that the definition of 'weak constitution' in this context was a circular one; that many persons who were inadequate,

---

[34] John Hunter (1786) was one of the few. Discussing sexual impotence, he says, "the complaint is by many laid to the charge of onanism at an early age; but how far this is just it will in many cases be difficult to determine; for upon a strict review of this subject, it appears to me to be by far too rare to originate from a practice so general".

[35] We may note the surveys of Rohleder (1899), Davis (1925), Haire (1952) and of course Kinsey *et al.* (1948, 1953); and also of Berne (1944). The inference to be drawn from these epidemiological studies was supported by at least one clinical study. In 1897, the American McClanahan published case histories of 12 persons who admitted to very frequent and prolonged masturbation but who had all been healthily successful both in their careers and in their married lives; the composure of two had been temporarily shaken on their learning that masturbation was supposed to be dangerous. These 12 cases are, of course, just as strong an argument against the masturbatory hypothesis as the publication of 12 cases of insanity associated with masturbation would be for the hypothesis; but the latter type of publication was as common as the former was rare.

neurasthenic, frigid or impotent, masturbated infrequently or not at all; and finally, that the hypothesis of innately different strengths of sexual drive would account for the facts better than the masturbatory hypothesis.

A third argument against the masturbatory hypothesis was the difficulty of being sure whether a patient had masturbated or not. For a long time, this difficulty was solved on the principle of Morton's fork: those who admitted masturbation were believed, those who denied it were disbelieved. Thus, case histories of patients who attributed their wretched state to the effects of masturbation are frequently quoted (by the author of the *Onania*, Tissot, and Rush, for example), and the confessions are used as evidence for the correctness of the writer's views. But the melancholic's tendency to exaggerate or to invent sins in order to account for his present misery is a circumstance which has been more often neglected than remembered in the history of psychiatry,[36] and it was not until towards the end of the 19th century that the unsatisfactory nature of such evidence was clearly pointed out. Clouston (1883, p. 492), for example, says, "Do not believe all melancholic patients who attribute their bad symptoms to the former practice of this vice in youth. It is a common self-accusation." Kraepelin (1896) is characteristically more emphatic.

In a similar way, patients who denied masturbation got short shrift if they were considered to be suffering from insanity due to that vice. "There is no faith to be put in their most solemn assertions," says Maudsley (1868), "their moral nature being thoroughly vitiated." "We must take care", says Schroeder van der Kolk (1870), "not to be put off the right scent by audacious denial".[37] While it was no doubt true that many of those who denied masturbation were lying, yet, as other evidence accumulated against the masturbatory hypothesis, its support by assertions which the patient denied and for which there was no objective evidence must have come to appear increasingly unsatisfactory.

A fourth weakness of the masturbatory hypothesis was its continued inability to provide a satisfactory physiological explanation of the mode of action of masturbation in causing insanity. By itself, this weakness was not a serious one, for there are many undoubted causal factors in medicine where the mode of action remains obscure. But it raised the awkward question: is masturbation more harmful than sexual intercourse, and if so, why? Of the many early writers who discuss this question, I have found only one – John Hunter (1786) – who could "affirm that this act itself (i.e. masturbation) does less harm to the constitution in general than the natural". Only a few, until towards the end of the 19th century, believed that masturbation and sexual intercourse were equally harmful. Philo-Castitatus (1723), Lallemand (1842) and Paget (1879) were of this number, Paget putting the case in these words: "I believe you may teach positively that masturbation does neither

---

[36] The fact was recognized, of course, by those who in earlier centuries had believed the self-accused witch to be a lunatic (see Field, 1955).

[37] Not all patients denied masturbation. Discussing masturbatory insanity, Maudsley (1868) found it "a curious thing that to such a state of moral degradation have patients of this class come, that they will actually defend their vice on some pretense or other".

more nor less harm than sexual intercourse practised with the same frequency . . . Practised by the very young, that is, at any time before or at the beginning of puberty, masturbation is very likely to produce exhaustion, effeminacy, over-sensitiveness and nervousness; just as equally frequent copulation at the same age would probably produce them." The great majority of those who held to the mas-turbatory hypothesis, however, believed that masturbation was more harmful than sexual intercourse. To explain why this should be so, when there was no obvious physiological difference between the acts, two reasons were advanced. The first, and earlier, reason was that masturbation is accompanied by a sense of secret shame and guilt which, by depressing the mental faculties, increases the physically debili-tating effects of the orgasm. The inadequacy of this explanation as a cause of in-sanity lay in the obvious fact that many insane patients masturbated without any sense of shame; and, as a cause of neurosis, in the fact that many normal persons who masturbated with shame did not become ill. The second and much the more commonly expressed reason was that masturbation, being an 'unnatural' act, was associated with inadequate gratification and so caused a greater strain on, or a less complete detensioning of, the nervous system.[38] In as far as this was a physiological explanation, it received no experimental support and it could hardly survive in an age where understanding of pathological processes in the nervous system had greatly increased.

In this discussion, I have made no reference to the studies of Kinsey *et al.* (1948, 1953) on the masturbatory habits of normal people. The masturbatory hypothesis, which was still flickering feebly in the 1930s, appears to have burnt itself out during the second world war; but if there had still remained any glowing embers, they must have been extinguished by the Kinsey reports, in which we have by far the largest and most thorough study that has been made of the natural history of masturbation.

Reasons for its persistence

Viewed from the vantage point of history, the surprising thing about the mastur-batory hypothesis is that it lasted so long. Its fall was not brought about by fresh discoveries or new techniques. The evidence which destroyed it could, in principle, have been obtained in the time of Pinel. Indeed, except for the prevalence surveys, the evidence had always been there for the taking. We are left wondering why the fall was so long delayed, and our interest in this problem may perhaps be heightened when we recollect that for many decades the masturbatory hypothesis called forth 'rational' measures of prevention and therapy which seem strange to us now and which left, and still leave, a legacy of fear and distress in the minds of unsophisti-cated people. The reasons why the masturbatory hypothesis proved so resistant to

---

[38] This reason was being put forward as late as 1936, when Meagher wrote, "Though legitimate orgasm in coitus lowers physical tension, this is not so in cases of masturbation, where feelings are pent up, there being no emotional outlet" (p. 43). Similarly, William Brown, of Oxford, wrote in 1934. "In masturbation there is incomplete stimulation followed by a complete reaction, in *coitus interruptus* there is a complete and normal stimulation followed by incomplete reaction. In both cases the strain set up in the nervous system is apt to produce an anxiety-neurosis."

overthrow may, I think, be grouped under three general headings: (1) conservatism, (2) the poverty of scepticism, and (3) certain fallacies of reasoning. Of these, the first two belong to unchanging aspects of human nature and of medicine, but the third concerns the application of scientific method to medicine, and this is a field in which we may claim some, and hope for further, progress.

1. Conservatism exerted its influence under the guises of authority and morality. In an underdeveloped branch of medicine, a hypothesis is more likely to be accepted on authority than on evidence, and between 1800 and 1880 the masturbatory hypothesis was very widely accepted on the authority of such men as Esquirol, Luther Bell, Griesinger and Maudsley. There was need for a bold man to express his doubts in print and to rely on 'the candour of cultivated minds'; and in fact it was not until 1881 that the Frenchman Christian became the first (as far as I can determine) to deny the hypothesis *in toto* – and he was much ahead of his time. Before this, there were many partial doubters, but none who attempted any critical assessment of the evidence or who made any controlled test in the way that Haslam, for example, had tested the hypothesis that lunatics were affected by the moon. We can scarcely doubt that one of the reasons for the lack of such criticism or experiment lay in the relation between the masturbatory hypothesis and the moral law. To a pious mind, the moral conviction that masturbation was wicked must have seemed an adequate justification for the medical belief that it was harmful; and the physician who criticized the masturbatory hypothesis exposed himself to the retort that he was attacking morality – a retort against which the earlier sceptics had had to be at pains to defend themselves.

2. The poverty of scepticism (as we may call it) reflects the circumstance that in medicine any hypothesis is better than none. A scientist is apt to find this circumstance distressing, but it nevertheless accounts for the fact that, at least until very recently, medicine has been concerned less with the search for effective treatment than with the performance of traditional ritual. We read that Harvey's practice declined after the publication of the *De Motu Cordis*, and the fact that a practitioner, to be successful, must be fairly conventional may explain the former rarity in medicine of that kind of man whom Sir Thomas Browne described as "complexionally propense to innovation". It was all very well for Isaac Ray (1873) to write, "In all philosophy there is no error more obstinate, or more fatal to true progress, than that so often witnessed – of believing that any conclusion, however defective, is better than none"; but, as A. N. Whitehead was later to observe, it is more important for a hypothesis to be useful than for it to be true. If the masturbatory hypothesis were to be shelved just because it might not be true, then there was nothing left from which the alienist could draw the comfort of having a rational approach to prevention and therapy.[39]

---

[39] As far as schizophrenia is concerned, the masturbatory hypothesis has not been replaced. When it had to be abandoned, the rational treatment based on it was replaced by a succession of empirical treatments which, being founded on practice rather than on theory, were perhaps a little more effective. The most striking advances in the management of schizophrenia, however, came when psychiatrists paid less attention to treatment (in the traditional sense) and more attention to care.

But it was not only alienists who were concerned with the validity of the masturbatory hypothesis, nor was insanity the only consequence to be feared from masturbation. There were more subtle dangers. It was believed that every youth who masturbated endangered the vitality of his future children; and for 200 years the horrid phantom of racial decay terrified the physicians and educators of the western world. From Tissot to Sachs, physicians saw themselves as the guardians of civilization;[40] they proclaimed it the duty of parents and teachers to prevent by all means the habit of masturbation in the young; and they believed that whereas in adolescence an appeal to reason or the picture of future disease might suffice, in children the most satisfactory method of prevention was the threat of an immediate and alarming punishment.[41] In this respect, the masturbatory hypothesis was like Pascal's religious hypothesis. One doubted it as one's peril or at the peril of one's race; and, with so much at stake and in the absence of definite disproof, the reasonable man was prepared to act on the assumption that it was true.

3. A wide variety of clinical observations were believed to support the masturbatory hypothesis, but we can now see that these beliefs were founded on a number of fallacies of reasoning. We may point first to the fallacy of the biased sample. This arises from the fact that doctors tend to study only sick people. They make the correct observation that a sizeable proportion of their patients masturbate (or have unconscious conflicts, or experience 'stress') and, in jumping to the conclusion that the association is a causal one, forget that the supposedly harmful event may occur with equal frequency among healthy people.[42]

A second fallacy lay in the argument from false analogy. The effects of masturbation were compared with those of alcohol. No one doubted that alcohol, taken in excess for a long time, could cause mental disorder, and it was also evident that not all alcoholics became mentally disordered. Add to this the facts that the immediate effects appeared more severe in young persons, that many of the patients improved when they stopped taking alcohol and that the physiological mechanism by which alcohol damaged the mind was by no means clear, and the analogy between the effects of alcohol and of

---

[40] Johann Frank, in his *Medizinischen Polizey* (1780), says that onanism has become so widespread in schools and colleges and its consequences are so dreadful, that the authorities "cannot take too much care to stamp out such a plague". Lallemand (1842, p. 479) feared that if masturbation became any commoner it would "menace the future of modern societies; therefore it is urgently necessary for us to try and extirpate this public calamity". Pouillet (1876) begins his treatise with the words: "Of all the vices and of all the misdeeds which may properly be called crimes against nature, which devour humanity, menace its physical vitality and tend to destroy its intellectual and moral faculties, one of the greatest and most widespread – no one will deny it – is masturbation."

[41] In the treatment of masturbation, says Bloch (1908, p. 427), the method of the older physicians, "who appeared before the child armed with great knives and scissors, and threatened a painful operation or even to cut off the genital organs", may often be found useful and may effect a radical cure. Huschka (1938) found that, of 320 problem children, 46 remembered being threatened with genital injury if they were caught masturbating. It is certain that during the latter half of the 19th century little boys (and little girls too) commonly suffered the threat of genital amputation, and we may deduce that the frequency with which Freud's early patients remembered this threat reflected the fashionable belief of their parents in the importance of preventing masturbation. Viewed from this perspective, Freud's universal 'castration complex' is seen to be no more substantial than Tissot's ghost.

[42] The fallacy is not confined to medicine. As Wootton (1959) has noted, the same fallacy inheres in a facile acceptance of the belief that the association between juvenile delinquency and broken homes is a causal one.

masturbation seemed fairly close. But, as we can now see, the analogy was deficient in two important respects. In all individuals, a sufficiently large dose of alcohol is followed by a temporary mental disturbance; and the mental disorders accompanying chronic alcoholic intoxication are (as Burrows – 1828, p. 94 – observed) very generally associated with demonstrable and characteristic pathological changes in the bodily organs. It is the one-to-one correspondence of the association in the first of these respects, and the objective and characteristic nature of the changes in the second, that form the real basis of our belief in the causal effects of alcohol in mental disorder.

Sound reasoning about the masturbatory hypothesis was further inhibited by causal nomenclature. It was a considerable achievement for Skae to isolate the syndrome of adolescent psychosis, but by naming it 'masturbatory insanity' he shut the door on further enquiry into its cause. Again, some of the character traits of a particular type of constitution (which we now recognize as the schizoid type) came to be collectively labelled signs of the masturbator; and the fact that young people who showed these signs often went on to develop masturbatory insanity was taken as additional evidence of the correctness of the nomenclature.

Another source of error, widespread in medicine, may be termed the therapeutic fallacy, A causal hypothesis of disease commonly suggests a rational method of treatment. If such treatment is given and is associated with an improvement in a patient's condition, there is a tendency to conclude that the improvement is due to the treatment and that therefore the causal hypothesis is substantiated. To jump to such a conclusion is fallacious for at least two reasons: the improvement, though contemporaneous with the treatment, may have been due to other factors; or, if the improvement was due to the treatment, this may have been for reasons other than those postulated by the hypothesis. The second circumstance is illustrated by the discovery of the use of bromide in epilepsy. Sir Charles Locock (1857) believed that "a great number of cases of epilepsy, both in girls and boys, arose from the practice of onanism. This cause was very frequently overlooked and might account for the great increase in the disease of late years". Having read an account "of some experiments performed by a German on himself with bromide of potassium" which led to temporary impotency, Sir Charles concluded that the drug, by causing impotence and so preventing masturbation, ought to be of value in epilepsy. He tried it, and "out of 14 or 15 cases treated by this medicine, only one remained uncured".[43] Much more common, however, is the fallacy of attributing to treatment an improvement which has occurred spontaneously. Many mental illnesses remit spontaneously or run a phasic course, so that the administration of any form of treatment, particularly if long-continued, must often coincide with the beginning of a remission.[44]

---

[43] The difficulties of believing that masturbation is a cause of epilepsy were summarized by Gowers (1881). Yet he concluded, "I am inclined to think that it [masturbation] is much less frequently the cause of true epilepsy than of untypical attacks, sometimes hysteroid, sometimes of characters intermediate between hysteroid and epileptoid forms. I have so frequently in boys met with this form of attack in association with the practice that I can scarcely doubt their etiological connection".

[44] It is becoming generally accepted that, if continued long enough, the psychotherapy of depressive states is almost certain to be attended with success.

We may examine one other source of fallacy. The influence of a prediction upon the event which it predicts has been termed by Karl Popper (1957) the 'oedipus effect'. The same phenomenon was referred to by William James in his phrase, "the belief creates the fact", and by Florence Nightingale (1861) when she said, "Patients do what they are expected to do". It was because masturbation was widely believed to be both sinful and harmful that patients suffering from depressive illness were so ready to attribute their troubles to this habit. For the same reason, patients whose illness did not induce a tendency to self-blame were apt to deny masturbation. No doubt, too, the reluctance of healthy people to discuss the subject was one of the reasons why prevalence surveys were not made until towards the end of the 19th century, when moral standards were becoming less severe. But the reluctance to be frank remained strong,[45] and the prevalence surveys, especially among women, were often incomplete and led to differing conclusions. Thus, of 10 000 university graduates and club women approached by Davis (1925), only 1203 replied to her questionnaire on sexual topics; and although the 40% of these who admitted masturbating at some time were sexually no less well adjusted in their marriages than the rest, yet a physician who believed that masturbation led to frigidity or aversion to coitus could reasonably have discounted this conclusion on the ground that the sample was not representative. Estimates of the prevalence of masturbation among patients were apt to be even more unsatisfactory. Zilboorg, for example, in a series of patients with puerperal psychosis, found that all but one were chronic masturbators; while among a similar series of patients studied by Anderson (1933), only six out of fifty admitted masturbating.

Conclusion

Progress in the application of scientific method to medicine enables us to see more clearly than did our predecessors the best way of assessing the validity of a causal hypothesis. We see now that the problem presented by the masturbatory hypothesis is the problem of assessing whether an association is a causal one. Confronted with this hypothesis today, a psychiatrist would begin – as very few in the 18th and 19th centuries began – by defining his terms so that his readers would know precisely what he intended by the words 'masturbation' and 'mental disorder'. Next he would consider by what methods the fact of masturbation could be ascertained, and with what degree of reliability. Then he would proceed to determine how often the habit of masturbation (practised with stated frequency and over stated periods of time) was present in patients suffering from various types of mental disorder and in healthy persons; and how the prevalence in these groups varied with sex, age, social class and cultural background. He would search, too, for an association between masturbation and pathological changes in bodily systems. Finally, he would investigate

---

[45] "For the older generation of males of every social level it is simpler to get a record of pre-marital intercourse than to get a record of masturbation. With many females it is simpler to get a record of homosexuality than a record of masturbatory activity" (Kinsey et al., 1948, p. 48).

whether there were practicable methods of preventing masturbation among patients and, if so, he would determine by a controlled trial whether its prevention had any significant effect on the course of the disorder. In short, he would recognize that, in the absence of any clearly related anatomical or physiological changes susceptible to quantitative assay, the causal effect of masturbation in mental disorder could only be gauged in terms of the closeness of the association. There is no way of disproving the masturbatory hypothesis – or, indeed, any causal hypothesis in psychiatry where there is no associated objective and measurable change in the patient; all we can say, from the evidence, is that the association between masturbation and mental disorder is weak and inconstant and that therefore, if masturbation is a causal factor, it is probably not a very important one.

We can see today with some clarity how the masturbatory hypothesis should have been examined. Its history, dealing with times "not long enough past to be romantic, but full of instruction and warning", as Greenwood writes in *Some British Pioneers of Social Medicine* (London, 1948), shows how in fact it was examined. The contrast ought to be a measure of our progress; it may at least lead us to consider how far, in attempting to establish new causal hypotheses in psychiatry, we have been able to avoid the errors of the past.

References

Allnatt RH. (1843) Case of Atrophy of the Testicle From Excessive Masturbation. *Lancet* ii: 654.

Anderson EW. (1933) A Study of the Sexual Life in Psychoses associated with Childbirth. *J Ment Sci* **79**: 137.

Asher R. (1959) Making Sense. *Lancet* ii: 359.

Barrus C. (1896) Insanity in Young Women. *J Nerv Ment Dis* **21**: 365.

Bell L and Ray I. (1844) *Annual Report of the McLean Asylum*. (Quoted by Bucknill and Tuke, 1874.)

Berne E. (1944) The Problem of Masturbation. *Dis Nerv Syst* **5**: 301.

Bianchi L. (1906) *A Textbook of Psychiatry*. Transl Macdonald JH. London, p. 696.

Blandford GF. (1871) *Insanity and its Treatment*. Edinburgh, p. 59.

Bleuler E. (1911) *Dementia Praecox*. Transl. Zinkin J (1950), New York, p. 343.

Bloch I. (1908) *The Sexual Life of our Time*. Transl Paul ME from 6th German edn (1908) London.

Boerhaave H. (1708) *Institutes of Medicine*, para 776. Translation of Vol. V (1746), London, p. 456.

Brown W. (1934) *Psychology and Psychotherapy* (3rd edn). London, p. 118.

Bucknill JC and Tuke DH. (1874) *A Manual of Psychological Medicine* (3rd edn). London.

Burrows GM. (1828) *Commentaries on the Causes, etc., of Insanity*. London.

Christian J. (1881) Article on 'Onanisme'. In: *Dictionnaire Encyclopédique des Sciences Médicales*. Paris.

Clark AC and Clark HE. (1899) Neurectomy, a Preventive of Masturbation. *Lancet* ii: 838.

Clouston TS. (1883) *Clinical Lectures on Mental Disease*. London.

Clouston TS. (1904) *Clinical Lectures on Mental Disease* (6th edn). London.

Clouston TS. (1888) Presidential Address to the Medico-Psychological Association. *J Ment Sci* **34**: 325.

Copland J. (1844) *A Dictionary of Practical Medicine*. London.

Davis KB. (1925) A Study of Certain Auto-erotic Practices. *Ment Hyg* **9**: 28.

Dukes –. (1884) *The Preservation of Health* (Quoted by Ellis, 1901).

Ellinger –. (1845) *Zeit f Psychiat* **2**: 22 (Quoted by Morel, 1860).

Ellis H. (1901) *Studies in the Psychology of Sex*, Vol. I, Part 1. Page references to the 1936 edition, New York.

Ellis WC. (1839) *Treatise on Insanity*, London.

Esquirol E. (1816) Article on 'Folie'. In: *Dictionnaire des Sciences Médicales*. Paris.
Esquirol E. (1822) Article on 'Manie'. In: *Dictionnaire des Sciences Médicales*. Paris.
Esquirol E. (1838) *Des Maladies Mentales*. Paris.
Eyer A. (1894) Clitoridectomy for the Cure of Masturbation in Girls. *Int Med Mag* 3: 259.
Field MJ. (1955) Witchcraft as a primitive interpretation of Mental Disorder. *J Ment Sci* 101: 826.
Flemming GF. (1838) Uber das Causal-Verhältniss der Selbstbefleckung zur Geistesverwirrung. *Zeit f d Beurtheilung u Heilung der krankhaften Seelenzustände* 1: 205.
Fournier –. and Régis –. (1819) Article on 'Masturbation'. In: *Dictionnaire des Sciences Médicales*. Paris.
Frank JP. (1780) *System einer vollständigen medizinischen Polizey* Vol. II, Mannheim, p. 599.
Gall FJ. (1825) *Fonctions du Cerveau* Vol. III. p. 337 (Quoted by Ellis, 1901).
Gowers WR. (1881) *Epilepsy and other Chronic Convulsive Diseases*. London, p. 31
Griesinger W. (1861) *Mental Pathology and Therapeutics* (2nd edn). Transl Robertson CL and Rutherford J (1867), London.
Grieves J. (1756) Translation of Celsus' *De Medicina*. London.
Guislain J. (1852) *Leçons Orales sur les Phrénopathies* Vol. 2. Ghent, p. 61.
Hagenbach AW. (1879) Masturbation as a Cause of Insanity. *J Nerv Ment Dis* 6: 603.
Haire N. (ed) (1952) *Encyclopaedia of Sexual Knowledge* (2nd edn). London, p. 80.
Hall S. (1904) *Adolescence* Vol. I. New York.
Haslam J. (1809) *Observations on Madness and Melancholy* (2nd edn). London.
Henderson DK and Gillespie RD. (1936) *A Textbook of Psychiatry* (4th edn). Oxford, p. 200.
Huhner M. (1944) Masturbation in both Sexes. *Med Times* 72: 188, 220.
Hunter J. (1786) *A Treatise on the Venereal Disease*. London, p. 200.
Huschka M. (1938) The Incidence and Character of Masturbatory Threats in a Group of Problem Children. *Psychoanalyt Quart* 7: 338.
Hutchinson J. (1891) On Circumcision as Preventive of Masturbation. *Arch Surg* 2: 267.
Jeffreys MDW. (1951) Onanism, an Anthropological Survey. *Int J Sexology* 5: 61.
Jones E. (1918) *Papers on Psychoanalysis* (2nd edn). pp 388, 559.
Kinsey AC, Pomeroy WB and Martin CE. (1948) *Sexual Behaviour in the Human Male*. London.
Kinsey AC and Gebhard PH. (1953) *Sexual Behaviour in the Human Female*. London.
Kraepelin E. (1896) *Psychiatrie* (5th edn). Leipzig, p. 51.
Lallemand CF. (1838–1842) *Des Pertes Séminales Involontaires* (3 vols). Paris.
Lancet (1866) Letters on Clitoridectomy ii: 495, 561.
Locock C. (1857) *Lancet* i: 528.
McClanahan AC. (1897) An Investigation into the Effects of Masturbation. *NY Med J* 66: 499.
Malamud W and Palmer G. (1932) The Role played by masturbation in the Causation of Mental Disturbances. *J Nerv Ment Dis* 76: 220, 366.
Maudsley H. (1867) *The Physiology and Pathology of Mind*. London.
Maudsley H. (1868) Illustrations of a Variety of Insanity. *J Ment Sci* 14: 149.
Maudsley H. (1879) *The Pathology of Mind*. London.
Maudsley H. (1895) *The Pathology of Mind* (2nd edn). London.
Meagher JFW. (1923) Quackery de Luxe. *NY Med J and Med Record* 117: 224.
Meagher JFW. (1924) *A Study of Masturbation and its Reputed Sequelae*. London.
Meagher JFW. (1936) *A Study of Masturbation and its Reputed Sequelae* (3rd edn). London.
Medical Times and Gazette (1873) Obituary notice of Isaac Baker Brown.
Menzies K. (1919) *Autoerotic Phenomena in Adolescence*. London.
Moragia –. (1897) *Zeit f Criminal-Anthropologie*. p. 487 (Quoted by Ellis, 1901).
Morel BA. (1860) *Traité des Maladies Mentales*. Paris, p. 178.
Nightingale F. (1861) *Notes on Nursing* (1952 edn). London, p. 120.
Onania, or The Heinous Sin of Self-Pollution, and all its Frightful Consequences, in both Sexes, etc. (?1726) (4th edn). London.
Onania, or The Heinous Sin of Self-Pollution, and all its Frightful Consequences, in both Sexes, etc. (1730) (15th edn). London.
Paget J. (1879) *Clinical Lectures and Essays* (2nd edn). London, p. 275.
'Philo-Castitatus' (1723) *Onania Examined, and Detected, etc.* London.

Pinel P. (1809) *Traité Médico-philosophique sur l'Aliénation Mentale* (2nd edn). Paris.

Popper KR. (1957) *The Poverty of Historicism*. London, p. 13.

Pouillet T. (1876) *Essai Médico-Philosophique sur les Formes, les Causes, les Signes, les Conséquences et le Traitement de l'Onanisme chez la Femme*. Paris.

Prichard JC. (1835) *A Treatise on Insanity*. London, p. 205.

Ray I. (1873) *Contributions to Mental Pathology*. Boston, p. 36.

Robertson, A. (1869) Notes on a Visit to American Asylums. *J Ment Sci* **17**: 516.

Robinson N. (1729) *A New System of the Spleen, Vapours and Hypochondriack Melancholy, etc.* London, p. 191.

Rohleder H. (1899) *Die Masturbation*, Berlin (Quoted by Ellis, 1901).

Rosanoff AJ. (1938) *Manual of Psychiatry and Mental Hygiene* (7th edn). London, p. 153.

Rush B. (1812) *Medical Inquiries and Observations upon the Diseases of the Mind*. Philadelphia, pp 33, 347.

Sankey WHO. (1866) *Lectures on Mental Diseases*. London, p. 248.

Sankey WHO. (1884) *Lectures on Mental Diseases* (2nd edn). London, p. 223.

Savage GH and Goodall E. (1907) *Insanity and Allied Neuroses* (4th edn). London, p. 68.

Schroeder van der Kolk JLC. (1870) *Pathology and Therapeutics of Mental Diseases*. Transl Rudall JT, London.

Schwartz A. (1815) *Dissertation sur les Dangers de l'Onanisme et les Maladies qui en Résultent*. Strasbourg.

Skae D. (1868) A Rational and Practical Classification of Insanity. *J Ment Sci* **14**: 149.

Skae D. (1874) The Morrisonian Lectures on Insanity for 1873. *J Ment Sci* **19**: 491.

Spitz, RA. (1952) Authority and Masturbation. *Psychoanalyst Quart* **21**: 490.

Spitzka EC. (1887) Cases of Masturbation (Masturbatic Insanity). *J Ment Sci* **33**: 57, 238; (1888) **34**: 58, 216.

Spratling EJ. (1895) Masturbation in the Adult. *Med Record* **48**: 442.

Stekel W. (1951) *Auto-erotism, A Psychiatric Study of Masturbation and Neurosis*. Transl Teslaar JS van, London.

Stern A. (1930) Masturbation, its Role in the Neuroses. *Amer J Psychiat* **9**(ii): 1081.

Tissot S-AAD. (1766) *Onania, or a Treatise upon the Disorders produced by Masturbation; or the Dangerous Effects of Secret and Excessive Venery*. Transl by Hume A, London.

Voltaire FA. (1784) Article on 'Onan, Onanisme'. In: *Oeuvres Completes*. Vol. 42 *Dictionnaire Philosophique*. Paris.

Wootton B. (1959) *Social Science and Social Pathology*. London.

Yellowlees D. (1876) *J Ment Sci* **22**: 336.

Yellowlees D. (1892) Article on 'Masturbation' in Hack Tuke's *Dictionary of Psychological Medicine*. London.

Index